Allen Guw

12

Allen Guw

# Dental

# Biochemistry

# Dental Biochemistry

EUGENE P. LAZZARI, Ph.D., EDITOR

*Assistant Professor, Department of Biochemistry*

*University of Texas Dental Branch at Houston, Texas*

ILLUSTRATED

Lea & Febiger · *Philadelphia* · *1968*

# *Preface*

"You ask me one question," cried the old man; "let
me answer by asking another: Which is the most
durable, a hard thing or a soft thing; that which resists,
or that which makes no resistance?"

"A hard thing, to be sure," replied the mandarin.

"There you are wrong," returned Shingfu. "I am
now four score years old; and, if you look in my mouth,
you will find that I have lost all my teeth, but not a bit
of my tongue."

Goldsmith, Oliver: *The Citizen of the World* (1762), reprinted J. Dent. Educ., *28*, 378, (1964).

After years of giving "tongue" to these topics in our teaching and research, it was decided the biochemical time had come to make a permanent record for ourselves and others. That decision resulted in this book.

Because there are many good textbooks on elementary biochemistry, this book was designed to be used as a supplement to those already existing and is intended for use in the second quarter or semester of a course. Therefore, it has been written on the supposition that the reader has or is willing to obtain the appropriate background.

As editor, I must be held responsible for the selection of chapter headings and to some extent, albeit slight, for the emphasis and level of the material selected for inclusion. Unfortunately, I cannot take credit for the style, knowledge, and authority of presentation which each chapter exhibits, but I do gain satisfaction and comfort in the fact that I selected the contributors. To them, my deepest gratitude. My gratitude also goes to Mrs. Eleanor Edmonds for her indispensable aid in proofreading and to our secretary, Mrs. Martha Ennis who spent many long hours typing the manuscript.

It is to be hoped that this book will prove useful to teachers and students interested in the biochemical processes of tissues of the oral cavity. Not all that is known has been presented here; for instance, there has been little or nothing said of the biochemistry of taste, muscle mechanism, nerve action, or bone metabolism. However, it is my wish that this small spring of truths, near truths, and hoped-for truths will prove refreshing to the thirsty pilgrim already on his journey and that it will stay potable and sweet for the wayfarers yet to come.

EUGENE P. LAZZARI
*Houston, Texas*

# Contributors

ERNEST BEERSTECHER, JR., PH.D., Chairman, Department of Biochemistry, The University of Texas Dental Branch, Houston, Texas

NICOLA DI FERRANTE, M.D., PH.D., Department of Biochemistry, Baylor University College of Medicine, Houson, Texas

SAMUEL DREIZEN, D.D.S., M.D., The University of Texas Dental Science Institute, Houston, Texas

J. P. KENNEDY, PH.D., Department of Anatomy, The University of Texas Dental Branch, Houston, Texas

JAMES M. KLINKHAMER, D.M.D., The University of Texas Dental Science Institute, Houston, Texas

EUGENE P. LAZZARI, PH.D., Department of Biochemistry, University of Texas Dental Branch, Houston, Texas

MARTIN D. LIDSKY, M.D., Department of Medicine, Veterans Administration Hospital and Baylor University College of Medicine, Houston, Texas

KENNETH O. MADSEN, PH.D., Department of Biochemistry and Nutrition, The University of Texas Dental Branch, Houston, Texas

JAMES J. VOGEL, PH.D., The University of Texas Dental Science Institute, Houston, Texas

STUART ZIMMERMAN, PH.D., Department of Biomathematics, The University of Texas, M.D. Anderson Hospital and Tumor Institute, Houston, Texas

# Contents

# Chapter 1

## Chemical Composition of Teeth

### Eugene P. Lazzari, Ph.D.

Introduction
Sample Preparation
Hardness
Inorganic Constituents
Organic Constituents
Acquired Pellicle

## INTRODUCTION

Vertebrate tooth-like projections and jaws first appeared in the fossil record about 405 million years ago in a class of bony Paleozoic fishes called the Placodermi.

All vertebrates, except the Agnatha, jawless fishes, either possess teeth or have evolved from toothed ancestors. There also exist many deceptively tooth-like structures such as the horny tubercles of the lamprey, the serrations on the beaks of some turtles and the enamel-coated, bony ridges on the jaws of Sphenodon, or Tuatara, a primitive reptile living on Madagascar.

The primitive ancestors of the vertebrates were polyodont, many toothed, as would be expected since teeth originated from numerous, small dermal denticles. The general trend in all vertebrates has been toward fewer teeth, oligodonty, larger in size and with firmer attachment. Man has but eight teeth on each side of his jaw (Fig. 1–1) and has not become as extreme in oligodonty as some mammals such as the female norwhal, a type of toothless whale. The male norwhal is only slightly better provided in that he has a single large left incisor protruding tusk-like forward from his head. The dentition of man, like that of most mammals, is heterodont, having two or more types or tooth forms. Because he has an incomplete set of deciduous teeth and a secondary permanent set he is also a hemidiphyodont.

True teeth (Fig. 1–2) can be defined as individual structures consisting of an outer thin layer of enamel derived from ectoderm, a thicker middle layer of dentine derived from mesoderm and an inner pulp.

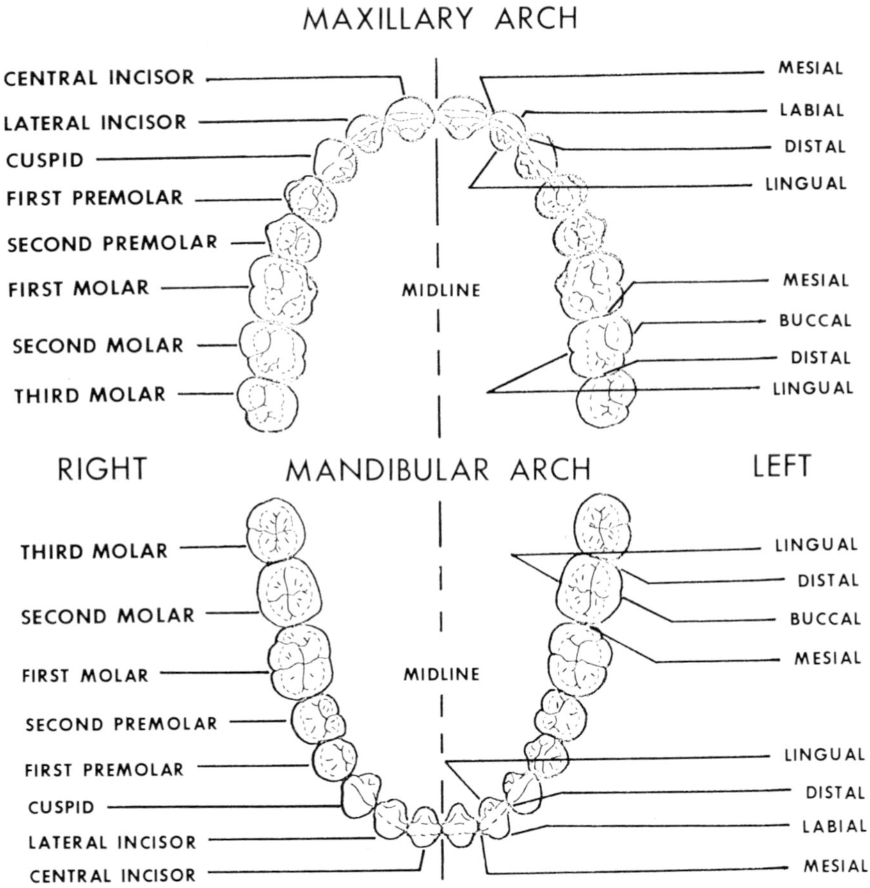

## MAXILLARY ARCH

CENTRAL INCISOR

LATERAL INCISOR

CUSPID

FIRST PREMOLAR

SECOND PREMOLAR

FIRST MOLAR

SECOND MOLAR

THIRD MOLAR

MESIAL

LABIAL

DISTAL

LINGUAL

MIDLINE

MESIAL

BUCCAL

DISTAL

LINGUAL

RIGHT          MANDIBULAR ARCH          LEFT

THIRD MOLAR

SECOND MOLAR

FIRST MOLAR

SECOND PREMOLAR

FIRST PREMOLAR

CUSPID

LATERAL INCISOR

CENTRAL INCISOR

LINGUAL

DISTAL

BUCCAL

MESIAL

MIDLINE

LINGUAL

DISTAL

LABIAL

MESIAL

FIG. 1–1. A diagram of the permanent human dentition. Buccal (toward cheeks), Distal (away from midline), Labial (toward lips), Lingual (toward tongue), Mesial (toward midline). (Drawn by Gary W. Johnston.)

Enamel is a non-living, exceedingly hard, almost totally inorganic material. Dentine is very bone-like in inorganic and organic composition and contains fine protoplasmic strands of living matter originating from the odontoblasts. Odontoblasts lie in a layer near the inner wall of the dentine in the pulp cavity which also contains connective tissue, blood vessels, and nerves.

## SAMPLE PREPARATION

Due to the anatomy of the tooth it is difficult to obtain dentine-free enamel for exact chemical analysis. In attempts to overcome this sampling problem three methods and/or combinations of these methods have evolved which, although still not perfect, are the best presently available.

### Mechanical

A blunt dental chisel can be used to remove the enamel or dentine. This is a tedious and painstaking procedure.

A diamond saw or cutting disc is usually used to obtain layers of enamel or dentine or thin sections of longitudinal or horizonal planes for use as slides in light microscopy or electron probe analysis.

Larger amounts of dentine or enamel material are usually prepared by using a diamond grinding wheel with great care to avoid contaminating the desired material. It is possible that the heat generated from the grinding and the material lost from the wheel may cause some undesirable changes through pyrolysis or contamination in the samples being prepared.

### Flotation Technique of Manly and Hodge

Once the tooth has been pulverized, the more dense enamel particles can be separated from the dentine by using a flotation or centrifuge-flotation technique. The particles are introduced into a solution of acetone-bromoform having a specific gravity of 2.70. Enamel having a density of $2.92 \pm 0.1$ settles during centrifugation or flotation, while the lighter dentine with a

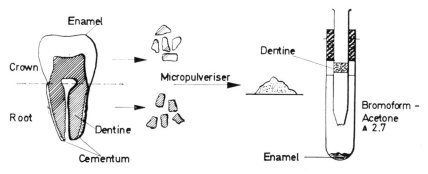

FIG. 1–3. Procedure involved in the separation methods of the dental tissues. (Courtesy of W. C. Armstrong.)

density of about 2.40 floats on the surface permitting either fraction to be readily collected (Fig. 1–3). A single separation gives enamel and dentine of 99% purity as determined by a refractive index method. Cementum, density 2.03, can also be separated by this technique.

### Chemical

Acids have been used to etch away successive layers of enamel and dentine to give either solutions of the desired soluble material or pure residues of wanted material. By adjusting the strength of the acid and the etching time, any thickness from as low as 10 microns may be achieved.

## HARDNESS

The Knoop hardness numbers on sections of mature, freshly-extracted, human, noncarious teeth gave an over-all average of $343 \pm 23$ Kg/mm$^2$ for enamel and $68 \pm 3$ for dentine. These would be comparable to the mineral magnesia, MgO, or periclase (a good refractory material), and metallic silver respectively. No definite trend was detected in the hardness of the enamel from the dentino-enamel junction to the outer surface or from the crown to the cervical margin. The dentine showed no change in hardness from one area to another.

## CHEMICAL COMPOSITION

A tooth, unlike a shaker full of recrystallized salt, has no single, constant chemical stoichiometry. It has been constituted and shaped by a unique genetic and biochemical individual and therefore can be as varied as nature will permit. On reporting the composition of a tooth one must constantly keep in mind the effects of diet, position in the mouth, geographical locality, age, condition of the tooth and medical history of the contributing individual. In the instances where those facts and their effects are known, they will be noted.

## INORGANIC CONSTITUENTS

Analytical chemists in the middle of the 19th century knew that the tooth consisted mainly of "phosphate of lime" with lesser amounts of "phosphate of magnesium, carbonate of lime, soda, salts, water and organic matter." By the end of the century, Tomes reported an average of 72.5% lime salts in dentine. Carious teeth had 1% fewer lime salts, and molars and bicuspids were more highly calcified than incisors and canines, 73.2 versus 71.5%. More recent studies show that incisors possess about 30% enamel with the percentage increasing gradually from the canines to the molars which contain about 40% enamel. By 1906, a complete and accurate analysis of the inorganic and organic elemental composition of the enamel and dentine of pooled teeth was reported.

After the first quarter of this century, Armstrong and others decided that a comprehensive study of the analysis of enamel and dentine by "modern methods" was necessary to understand the calcification process. They concluded that the mineral phase of enamel and dentine were not identical, that carious and sound teeth do not differ in the elements determined, that no correlation of enamel composition with susceptibility to decay or with an eruption age existed and that variations in enamel composition are as great in the teeth of one person as in teeth from several individuals.

Contrary to Armstrong, in the following year French and her co-workers found that the average calcium to phosphorus ratio (Ca/P) for dentine was the same as for enamel and the mineral, hydroxyapatite. They concluded that the dentine and enamel consisted principally of "particles of hydroxyapatite with occluded, absorbed or interstitially crystallized carbonates and other salts."

## Tooth Analysis

In 1957, Lefevre and Hodge reported the values in Table 1-1 for the chemical analysis of teeth. Their data permitted the following conclusions: (1) deciduous teeth have more moisture, less inorganic residue, Ca and P, and about the same carbonate content as permanent teeth, (2) there is little difference, except in moisture content, between sound and carious teeth, (3) age causes no change in the chemical constitution of teeth, (4) there is little chemical difference between teeth from male and female patients, (5) increasing severity of pyorrhea may cause a decrease in the carbonate content of teeth, and (6) the composition of tooth substance is remarkably constant.

## Calcium and Phosphorus

The latest studies show that Ca, P and Ca/P ratio are slightly lower in carious than in sound enamel (Table 1-1). Sound enamel from age groups beyond 30 years have a lower Ca/P ratio (1.97) than sound enamel from the younger age group (2.07).

Electron probe microanalysis of sound human dental enamel shows that the concentration of Ca and P slightly increases from the dentino-enamel junction (DEJ) towards the enamel surface.

As can be seen in Table 1-1, the Ca/P ratio of enamel and dentine lies between that of octacalcium phosphate, $Ca_8H_2(PO_4)_6+_5H_2O$, 1.72, and hydroxyapatite, $Ca_{10}(PO_4)_6(OH)_2$, 2.15. Possible intermediate compounds include hydrated tricalcium phosphate. Two theories have been formulated to explain the continuous series of apatitic calcium phosphate:
1. The absorption theory, in which acid phosphate groups absorb to microcrystalline hydroxyapatite.
2. The defect theory, which proposes that hydrogen ions in hydroxyapatite are substituted for Ca ions.

Table 1-1.  Inorganic Composition of Human Teeth, Enamel, Dentine, Cementum, Calculus and Bone

| Chemical | Teeth % | Enamel, Dry Wt.% Sound | Enamel, Dry Wt.% Carious | Dentine, Dry Wt.% Sound and Carious | Cementum Dry Wt.% | Calculus Dry Wt.% | Bone Mean % Fat-Free, Dry |
|---|---|---|---|---|---|---|---|
| Mineral Cont. | | 95 | | 70 | 72 | 76.4 ± 5.0 | 57.1 |
| $H_2O$ | 8.98 ± 2.23 | 2.02 ± 0.04 | 3.07 ± 0.05 | 3.57 ± 0.103 | | | |
| Ca | 35.2 ± 0.76 | 36.75 ± 0.17 | 35.95 ± 0.21 | 28.2 ± 1.2 | 26.2 | 26.0 ± 4.2 | 22.5 |
| P | 16.8 ± 0.36 | 17.4 ± 0.04 | 17.01 ± 0.06 | 13.5 ± 2.8 | 12.2 | 11.6 ± 3.6 | 10.3 |
| Mg | 0.32 ± 0.25 | 0.54 ± 0.01 | 0.40 ± 0.01 | 0.83 ± 0.083 | | 0.84 ± 0.42 | 0.26 |
| $CO_2$ | 3.45 ± 0.26 | 2.42 ± 0.02 | 1.56 ± 0.03 | 3.57 ± 0.103 | | 1.92 ± 0.56 | 3.5 |
| Ca/P | 2.10 ± 0.03 | 2.09 ± 0.02 | 2.08 ± 0.03 | 2.05 | 2.08 | 1.44 ± 1.74 | 2.18 |
| | | | LESSER ELEMENTS IN % OR PPM ASH WEIGHT | | | | |
| F | 90–310* | | 490–580* | 0.02% | | 0.136 ± 0.005 | 0.054% |

| Element | | | | | |
|---|---|---|---|---|---|
| Pb | 60* | 93* | | | 0.006% |
| Sn | <3* | 24* | | | |
| Mn | <0.4* | <1* | 0.19 ± 0.06* | | |
| Fe | 25* | 52* | | 2.3 ± 1.1* | 0.014% |
| Al | 32* | 93* | | | |
| Sr | 94* | 99* | 69.8 ±18.0* | 34.3 ± 3.2* | |
| Na | 0.65 ± 0.3% | | 0.75 ± 0.21* | 1.56 ± 0.6% | 0.01 % |
| Cl | Reported | | 0.39 ± 0.11% | 0.9 ± 0.2% | 0.52 % |
| Zn | | Reported | 199 ± 78.1* | 255 ± 109* | 0.11 % |
| Br | | | 4.0 ± 2.0* | 12.1 ± 2.8* | Reported |
| W | | | 2.6 ± 1.1* | 0.11 ± 0.04* | |
| Cu | Reported | | 0.21 ± 0.1* | 3.9 ± 1.0* | 0.0025% |
| Au | | | 0.03 ± 0.01* | 0.01 ± 0.003* | |
| Ag | Reported | Reported | | | Reported |
| Cr | Reported | Reported | | | |
| Si | Reported | Reported | | | Reported |

* PPM

A recent study by Winand involving the physicochemical techniques of infrared spectroscopy, x-ray diffraction, differential thermal analysis, thermogravimetry, and chemical analysis resulted in the derivation of a general formula for the apatitic calcium phosphate series: $Ca_{10-X}H_X(PO_4)_6$-$(OH)_{2-X}$ where x can vary between 0 and 2. In this calcium defect concept it was suggested that adjacent orthophosphate groups of the apatitic lattice are linked by hydrogen bonds. In this dynamic crystalline system, magnesium can substitute for calcium and carbonate can replace the phosphate radical to a limited extent.

## Water

Brudevold and his co-workers believe that sound enamel contains about 4% by weight of free water, that is, water which fills the free spaces in the crystal lattice and organic matrix. Others believe it to be closer to 2% by weight. The density of dry normal enamel is very close to 3.0 and water, as defined, is 1.0; therefore water makes up approximately 6 to 12% of the volume of human enamel. About 10% of this extremely hard, seemingly impervious substance consists of easily penetrable space. There probably also exists "bound" water either associated with the organic matrix or as water of crystallization as well as the "loosely bound" or free water.

Altered enamel increases 150% in water by weight indicating a loss of inorganic crystals and a replacement by water, a procedure believed to be the reverse of the mineralization phenomenon. Older enamel appears to have a lesser amount of water than that under 30 years of age.

The use of nuclear magnetic resonance techniques revealed that heating to $200°C$ was insufficient to dehydrate dental enamel. Bone, dentine, synthetic mixtures of hydroxy and fluorapatite with casein and apatite mineral did not display this phenomenon. In addition, enamel water does not show signs of freezing until $-40°C$ and over a 3-hour period only 10% of the water exchanges with $D_2O$.

## Carbonate

Carbon dioxide (carbonate), unlike materials such as zinc, lead or fluoride, has a reverse distribution pattern. The content in the outer enamel surface is about 1.5 weight % and increases in a smooth rising (concave upward) curve to about 2.9 weight % at the dentino-enamel junction. Carbonate concentrations in the external enamel tend to decrease with age, while no changes are observed in the body of the enamel. That and the decreased $CO_2$ in carious enamel may be due to a selective loss during demineralization.

## Magnesium

Brudevold and his co-workers showed that the surface enamel has a lower Mg content than the body of intact enamel, 30 to 60 versus 60 to 74 $\mu M$

per gm. Unlike bone, there is no apparent effect on the magnesium composition of enamel related to the presence of fluoride, carbonate, or citrate. Johansen postulates that the reduced content of carbonate and magnesium in carious enamel might reflect a low concentration of these substances in the lesion environment during recrystallization and/or a preferential loss of the substances during demineralization.

## Fluoride

Most investigators agree that the caries-inhibiting effect of fluoride is due to its relatively high concentration in the surface layer of the enamel. Brudevold and his co-workers reported their extensive study of this distribution in 1956 (Fig. 1–4). The continuous drinking of water containing 0.1 to 0.5 ppm of fluoride by persons under 20 years of age caused the level of surface enamel fluoride to rise from 419 to 3,370 ppm. A high degree of caries protection occurs when one hydroxyl group of hydroxyapatite ions is replaced by a fluoride per surface unit cell. The rate of fluoride uptake in teeth is much greater preeruptively and accessible tooth surfaces take up more fluoride than inaccessible tooth surfaces posteruptively. This latter fact limits the effectiveness of fluoride exposure on caries reduction since the

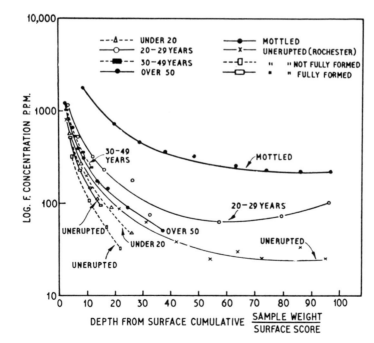

FIG. 1–4. Layer samples pooled from groups of 20 or more unerupted teeth in different stages of development, and of erupted teeth from persons under 20, 20–29, 30–49 and over 50 years of age. All the teeth except the mottled group came from a low fluoride area. (Brudevold, Gardner and Smith: J. Dent. Res., 35: 420, 1956.)

inaccessible tooth areas are most caries susceptible.  Unlike bone, there appears to be no relationship between enamel fluoride and carbonate, citrate or magnesium.  Therefore, the inhibition of caries found in fluoride areas is due to the presence of fluoride alone and not to changes in other enamel components.

Fluoride concentration follows a similar pattern in deciduous teeth as in permanent teeth although the levels in the enamel surface to approximately 30 microns in depth are lower than in the permanent teeth.

Fluoride concentration shows a consistent increase from the dentino-enamel junction to the pulp.  Junction dentine contains 3 or 4 times more fluoride than junction enamel and crown dentine near the pulp shows a marked increase with age, while the remainder shows no change.

The distribution of fluoride in the roots is high in the cementum, decreasing to a minimum in the mid-root regions and again increasing near the pulp to a level equaling the cementum.

## Chloride

Chloride is capable of exchanging with the hydroxyl group of hydroxy-apatite but is not fixed in calcified tissues.  The distribution profile of chloride concentration obtained by electron probe microanalysis shows a gradual decrease from the enamel surface to the DEJ.  The surface area showed levels of 0.6% decreasing to 0.1% in the deepest enamel.  The distribution of chloride is similar in the enamel of erupted and unerupted teeth.  It does not appear to be associated with the water spaces nor does it follow sodium, which is evenly distributed in enamel.

## Strontium

The uptake of strontium occurs prior to eruption, probably during tooth formation, since there is no change in concentration with age.  The level of concentration, 90 to 150 ppm, is about constant in surface and subsurface enamel; however, different geographical areas show considerable variation in concentration which is paralleled by the level of strontium found in the bone of the individual.

## Trace Elements (Table 1–1)

Hardwick and Martin, in 1967, reporting on the results of a pilot study using mass spectrometry stated that, "trace elements can be divided into three categories:

(1) Those which appear to have no biological role and which are present in tissues only as adventitious contaminants from the environment.

(2) Those elements which appear to be essential to the enzymatic processes of living cells (*e.g.* Fe, Zn, Cu, Mo, I, Co, Mn, Se).

(3) Elements which are probably essential nutrients but whose metabolic action is not clear (*e.g.* F, Br, Ba, Sr)."

## ORGANIC CONSTITUENTS

### Citrate

Citrate occurs in greater concentration in the surface and junction enamel than in the body of the enamel going from values of 3.5 $\mu$M/gm to 1.1 and back to about 4.4 $\mu$M/gm. Whether the distribution varies with age has not yet been determined.

Citrate, which has been found in all mineralized tissues, may be (1) an accidental coprecipitation component of calcium phosphates, (2) in a citrate containing-arginine rich peptide, (3) and/or in the form of phospho- or pyrophosphoric-citrate. The foregoing speculations, based on incomplete evidence, indicate that citrate may be an intimate part of the mineralized structure.

### Lactate

Lactate follows almost the same distribution and content as citrate and it is possible that both are located primarily in the water in the enamel since a comparison shows similar curves. Lactate, unlike citrate, does not coprecipitate with apatite at physiological pH and its role in mineralized tissue is even more conjectural than that of citrate.

### Nitrogen

The amount of nitrogen can be used as a measure of the concentration of organic material in areas of the tooth . Brudevold and his co-workers found that there is no change with age in the N concentration in enamel except that occurring in the last decades of life when measured on a weight basis. There is no theoretical basis to expect that the organic material in a tooth should change with age. Possible alterations may occur from external sources through cracks and voids which would be more numerous in the older tooth due to wear and tear. Teeth over 50 years old differ from younger teeth by having: (1) greater N concentrations in the surface enamel, 0.15% versus 0.1%; (2) greater N concentration at the dentino-enamel junction, 0.2% versus ca. 0.12%, and (3) lower N concentration in the body of the enamel for a greater depth, ca. 0.04% versus ca. 0.07% N.

Dentine has a nitrogen content between 3.4 and 3.5% which is about 1% less than that reported for human femur (Table 1–2).

### Protein

The presence of protein in enamel and dentine has been known for about 100 years. However, the amino acid content of those proteins has been reported only in the last 10 years.

Although much thought and care has been given to overcoming the problem of obtaining pure samples of enamel or dentine, it becomes critically

Table 1–2.  Organic Constituents of Human Sound and Carious Enamel, Dentine and Bone

| | Enamel Dry % | | Dentine Dry % | Bone |
|---|---|---|---|---|
| | Sound | Carious | Sound and Carious | Dry % |
| Lactic | 0.01 –0.03 | | | |
| Citrate | 0.10 | | 0.8 – 0.9 | 0.82–1.25 |
| Total Organic | 1.53 –3.80 | 3.65–6.98 | 19–21 | 24–27 |
| N | 0.073–0.077 | | 3.4 – 3.5 | 4.15–4.97 |
| Protein | 0.194–0.275 | 0.64–1.89 | 22.24 | 15–27 |
| Collagen | 0.09 | | 17–18 | 23 |
| Insoluble Protein | All | | 0.2 | 1–2 |
| Carbohydrate | 0.015$\pm$0.005 | 0.18 | 0.2 – 0.6* | 0.04 |
| Mucopoly-saccharide | 0.1 | | 0.2 | 0.24–0.4 |
| Lipid | 0.6 | 0.04–0.18 | 0.2 | 0.1 |

* In carious dentine this value is 4%

important when discussing the organic composition of the tooth and its separate areas.  Since the dentine has about 22% protein which is 100 times that found in enamel, an enamel sample contaminated with just 1% dentine, or 99% pure enamel, will have equal amounts of dentinal as well as enamel protein.  Any quantitative value reported on such a sample would be the result of a pooling of dentinal and enamel material.

As can be seen in Table 1–3, the soluble protein isolated from human enamel does not resemble ichthyocol, a collagen derived from carp swim bladder, in amino acid composition.  The differences are clearly seen in the hydroxyproline, glycine, cysteine and histidine content as well as others.  Since it also does not resemble keratin, the protein found in hair, it has been called eukeratin, an unfortunate term of no descriptional meaning.  The enamel material shall be referred to henceforth as enamel protein.

The amino acid composition of carious dentine (Table 1–4) differs from sound dentine in that there are lesser amounts of the basic amino acids, Group I, than in sound dentine, whereas the reverse is true of most of the neutral and acidic amino acids (Chapter 10, p. 154).  It is doubtful that the differences observed are due to leaching of the tooth matrix nor could such large changes, as in phenylalanine and tyrosine content for example, be

Table 1–3.   Amino Acid Composition of Tooth Protein and Collagen in Residues/1000 AA Residues

| AA | Human dentine collagen | Human enamel soluble | Ichthyocol |
|---|---|---|---|
| CYSO₄H | 0 | 12 | 0 |
| HYPRO (HYP) | 99 | 0 | 67 |
| ASP | 46 | 83 | 46 |
| THR | 17 | 58 | 18 |
| SER | 33 | 76 | 16 |
| GLU | 74 | 144 | 70 |
| PRO | 116 | 146 | 131 |
| GLY | 329 | 97 | 356 |
| ALA | 112 | 56 | 124 |
| CYS | 0 | 0 | — |
| VAL | 25 | 45 | 19 |
| MET | 5.3 | 21 | 12 |
| ILEU | 9.3 | 30 | 11 |
| LEU | 24 | 96 | 21 |
| TYR | 6.4 | 0 | 4 |
| PHE | 16 | 51 | 7 |
| HYLYS (HYL) | 9.6 | 3.4 | 29 |
| LYS | 22 | 21 | 29 |
| HIS | 4.7 | 30 | 5 |
| ARG | 52 | 31 | 50 |
| TRY | 0 | — | — |

due to the penetration of proteins into the tooth from the oral environment. The enamel of carious teeth is reported (Table 1–2) to have 5 to 10 times the amount of protein as sound teeth enamel.

Whether the changes in the amount and composition of the protein between sound and carious teeth are a cause of the demineralization process or result after the carious lesion is formed is unknown. The lesion can easily provide a pathway for the entrance of foreign proteinaceous material or for the removal of native protein, peptide and amino acids or substances containing those moieties.

## Carbohydrate

An analysis of the carbohydrates found in human enamel gave the results reported in Table 1–5. Bovine enamel treated in the same way gave similar results. It could not be determined conclusively which or if glucuronic and galacturonic acids were present. Clear-cut evidence for the presence of the

Table 1-4. Amino Acid Analyses of Sound and Carious Human Dentine

| Amino Acid | Sound dentine* | Carious dentine* |
|---|---|---|
| GROUP I | | |
| Hydroxylysine . . . . | 0.99 | 0.87 |
| Histidine . . . . . | 1.07 | 0.88 |
| Lysine . . . . . . | 3.31 | 3.28 |
| Arginine . . . . . | 7.90 | 5.76 |
| Proline . . . . . . | 13.17 | 9.01 |
| Hydroxyproline . . . | 11.79 | 9.01 |
| GROUP II | | |
| Aspartic . . . . . | 6.85 | 8.64 |
| Threonine . . . . . | 2.08 | 3.00 |
| Serine . . . . . . | 3.00 | 4.06 |
| Glutamic . . . . . | 10.29 | 11.47 |
| Glycine . . . . . | 17.54 | 19.52 |
| Alanine . . . . . | 8.41 | 10.81 |
| Valine . . . . . . | 2.49 | 3.57 |
| Methionine . . . . | 0.71 | 1.12 |
| Isoleucine . . . . . | 1.34 | 1.92 |
| Leucine . . . . . | 3.17 | 4.38 |
| Tyrosine . . . . . | 0.54 | 1.54 |
| Phenylalanine . . . . | 1.82 | 3.57 |
| | 96.45 | 102.65 |

* Results calculated as grams amino acid residue per 100 gm dentine matrix.

hexosamines, galactosamine and glucosamine could not be obtained in the reported study. The insoluble enamel organic fraction contained over 80% protein revealing that the aldoses must be part of a carbohydrate-protein complex. The carbohydrate and protein moieties of the soluble organic fraction could not be separated by electrophoresis indicating the presence of protein-bound aldose sugars or mucopolysaccharide.

Armstrong determined the carbohydrate content in sound and carious dentine hydrolysates prepared by an EDTA demineralization and partial formic or sulfuric acid hydrolysis. The carbohydrate content was arbitrarily expressed in "glucose" units using the α-naphthol, anthrone and cysteine methods. The hexosamine content was expressed in "glucosamine" units of color developed with Ehrlich's reagent. The results are shown in Table 1-6.

Table 1-5. Approximate Concentration of Aldose Sugars in Human Enamel

| | Galactose | Glucose | Mannose | Fucose | Xylose | Rhamnose | Total Aldose |
|---|---|---|---|---|---|---|---|
| Mg Sugar per 100 gm Enamel | 0.83 | 0.63 | 0.23 | 0.04 | 0.05 | trace | 1.78 |
| % of total Aldose Sugar | 46.8 | 32.4 | 15.1 | 3.2 | 2.5 | — | 100 |

Table 1-6. Carbohydrate Determination of Sound and Carious Dentine

| Dentine Sample | Percentage | | | |
|---|---|---|---|---|
| | α-Naphthol | Anthrone | Cysteine | Hexosamine |
| Sound . . . . . | 0.05 | 0.4 | 0.3 | 0.3 |
| Carious . . . . | 1.8 | 4.0 | 3.7 | 2.0 |

[ 15 ]

Attempts to separate and identify the possible hexosamines by paper chromatography were unsuccessful.

The carbohydrate material in carious dentine may be due to contaminants absorbed from the environment, bacterial polysaccharides, salivary mucopolysaccharides or other external sources.

A study in 1965 on the dentine-cementum and enamel of human teeth used similar colorimetric procedures. The total hexosamine content of dentine-cementum and enamel is 0.08 and 0.03% respectively. The enamel contained 10 times the amount of chondroitin 4- and/or 6- sulfate than hyaluronic acid, whereas the dentine-cementum had 20 times the amount. However, these accounted for about one-half of the hexosamines and the remainder most probably have a glycoprotein rather than a glycosaminoglycan source.

An unidentified component separated from the dentine-cementum hydrolysate by a strong cation exchange column made up 15% of the total hexosamine. The unknown hexosamine, present in dentine-cementum but not in enamel, is thought to be 20 to 30% of the total hexosamine in sheep wool and human hair.

It was concluded that the dentine-cementum and enamel contain chondroitin 4-sulfate and/or chondroitin 6-sulfate as the major glycosaminoglycan in human teeth.

Carious dentine and enamel are reported to have a carbohydrate content of 10 to 12 times the sound material. Whether the carbohydrate increase is an important cause or an unfortunate consequence of the carious process is unknown. It is believed that carbohydrates are lost during calcification; the possibility exists that a reverse process may occur during demineralization.

Glycogen has a wide distribution in the developing tooth and is believed to play a part in the production of mineralized tissue. It has been suggested that the glycogen stored in the ameloblasts and the stratum intermedium is the initial source of hexosephosphate which is hydrolyzed by alkaline phosphatase. The phosphate released may be utilized in bone salt formation or utilized in the synthesis of the mucopolysaccharide component of hard tissue. The absence of glycogen from the odontoblasts may be due to the adequate supply of hexosephosphate from the ameloblasts making an accumulation of glycogen by the odontoblasts unnecessary.

### Lipids

Of a total lipid content, other than cholesterol, of 0.6% in enamel, the phospholipid content is 0.075% and the cholesterol content is 0.008%.

Histological stains have shown that various granules observed in the cytoplasm and peripheral dentinal extensions of odontoblasts contain mostly lipids and probably small amounts of mucopolysaccharide. Dirksen has used paper chromatography to show a qualitative difference in the lipid

Table 1–7.  A Comparison of the Lipid Content of Sound Dentine
Prepared by Two Extraction Procedures

| | I† | II‡ |
|---|---|---|
| Total Lipid Wt. . . . . . | 40.9* | 176.6 |
| Cholesterol Esters . . . . . | 2.89 | 4.14 |
| Free Cholesterol . . . . . | 3.42 | 6.53 |
| Triglycerides . . . . . . | 1.59 | 1.61 |
| Diglycerides . . . . . . | 0.75 | 1.15 |
| Monoglycerides . . . . . | 0.45 | 0.80 |
| Phospholipids . . . . . . | 0.45 | 4.94 |

* All values based on mg per 100 gm of dried dentine.
† A chloroform-methanol extraction.
‡ An EDTA decalcification.

composition of sound and carious dentine.  He demonstrated the presence of cholesterol esters, triglycerides, fatty acids, cholesterol, diglycerides, possibly monoglycerides, various phospholipids, inositol phosphatide, sphingomyelin, lecithin, phosphatidyl-ethanolamine, lysocephalin and three unidentified phosphatides that may be polyglycerol phosphatides and/or phosphatic acids.  Carious dentine also contained phosphatidyl serine and other phosphatides in various degrees of degradation.

Dirksen later used silicic acid column chromatography to determine quantitatively the sound dentine lipids obtained by two extraction procedures.  The results are given in Table 1–7.

Other workers have reported higher values of 0.024% total cholesterol, 0.36% total lipids in excess of cholesterol and 0.014% phospholipids.

## ACQUIRED PELLICLE

The human enamel acquires an acellular integumental mixture termed "acquired pellicle" after eruption.  Analysis of the pellicle hydrolysate shows 45 to 50% amino acids, about 3% hexosamine and a minimal total carbohydrate measure of 10 to 15%.  Absence and incorrect ratios of certain amino acids eliminated the possibility that the protein was a collagenous, keratinous or hemoglobin type.  The analytical results suggest that the "acquired pellicle" may be a complex of salivary mucoprotein and embedded bacterial material which may also be similar or identical to plaque or plaque-like matter.

## SELECTED REFERENCES

ARMSTRONG, W. G.:  Modifications of the Properties and Composition of the Dentine Matrix Caused by Dental Caries, Adv. Oral Biol., 7, 309, 1964.

BRUDEVOLD, F., McCANN, H. G., and GRØN, P.: Caries Resistance as Related to the Chemistry of the Enamel in Caries-Resistant Teeth, CIBA Foundation Symposium, Wolststenholme, G. E. W., and O'Connor, Maeve, Editors, Little, Brown and Company, Boston, 1965.

BRUDEVOLD, F., STEADMAN, L. T., and SMITH, F. A.: Inorganic and Organic Components of Tooth Structure, Ann. N.Y. Acad. Sci., 85, 110, 1960.

DIRKSEN, T. R. and IKELS, K. G.: Quantitative Determination of Some Constituent Lipids in Human Dentine, J. Dent. Res., 43, 246, 1964.

FRENCH, E. L., WELCH, E. A., SIMMONS, E. J., LEFEVRE, M. L., and HODGE, H. C.: Calcium, Phosphorus and Carbon Dioxide Determinations of All the Dentine from Sound and Carious Teeth, J. Dent. Res., 77, 401, 1938.

GRØN, P. and VAN CAMPEN, G. J.: Mineral Composition of Human Dental Calculus, Hel. Odont. Acta, 77, 71–74, April, 1967.

JENKINS, G. N.: The Physiology of the Mouth, F. A. Davis Co., Phila., Pa., 3rd Ed. 1966.

JOHANSEN, E.: Comparison of the Ulta Structure and Chemical Composition of Sound and Carious Enamel from Human Permanent Teeth in Tooth Enamel, Stack, M. V., and Fearnhead, R. W., Editors, Williams and Wilkins Co., Baltimore, 1965, p. 177.

LEFEVRE, M. L. and HODGE, H. G.: Chemical Analyses of Tooth Samples Composed of Enamel, Dentine and Cementum, II, J. Dent. Res., 16, 279, 1937.

MILES, A. G. W., Editor: Structural and Chemical Organization of Teeth, Academic Press, New York, 1967, Vol. I and II.

STEWART, J. M., CLAIBOURNE, P. A., and LUIKART, C. A.: A Histologic and Histochemical Study of Lipids in Human Odontoblasts, J. Dent. Res., 44, 608, 1965.

SMITH, H. M.: Evolution of Chordate Structure, Holt, Rinehart and Winston, Inc., New York, 1960, p. 265–278.

ZIPKIN, I.: The Science of Nutrition and Its Application in Clinical Dentistry, Nizel, A. E., Editor, W. B. Saunders Co., Philadelphia, Pa. 1966, p. 281.

*Chapter 2*

# Proteins in Teeth

## Martin D. Lidsky, M.D.

## INTRODUCTION

Recent development of more sophisticated techniques in protein chemistry has permitted more intensive study of the proteins of teeth. In spite of this, our knowledge is limited principally because of the difficulty in obtaining sufficient quantities of pure material. The proteins of the teeth reside in a highly mineralized environment and their investigation requires careful separation and demineralization of the three calcified layers of the solid tooth—enamel, dentine, and cementum.

### Isolation of Cementum

Cementum is the calcified layer which covers the submerged root of the tooth and, in at least one species (bovine), extends over the crown. Cementum has been separated by differential density flotation or removed mechanically either by revolving steel burrs or by a rotating carborundum disc under a jet of water. Recently, Glimcher dissected cementum from the underlying layers following partial demineralization of the whole tooth.

### Separation of Enamel and Dentine

Mature enamel is the most highly mineralized vertebrate tissue and in the human tooth, contains about 0.3 to 0.4% protein. Dentine interdigitates with enamel, making it difficult to obtain clean separation between the two.

Two major approaches have been utilized to effect separation and purification of enamel and dentine: differential density flotation and mechanical separation under the dissecting microscope utilizing the dentino-enamel junction as a landmark.

## AMINO ACID COMPOSITION

As a step in the study of the intact native proteins, investigation of the amino acid composition of the enamel, dentine, and cementum has been carried out.

Amino acids are the fundamental structural units of proteins and are sequentially linked together through peptide bonds, thereby constituting the primary structure of the protein. Hydrolysis of the linkages allows identification and quantitation of the resulting free amino acids.

### Preparation of Sample

The calcified tissue usually is demineralized prior to hydrolysis of the peptide bonds to avoid possible excessive destruction of the constituent amino acids during hydrolysis and to avoid inferior resolution during the subsequent analysis. Demineralization is achieved at physiological pH with the chelating agent, ethylenediaminetetraacetic acid (EDTA). The demineralized sample then is hydrolyzed. The common method of hydrolysis involves heating the sample at 100 to 110° C for 20 to 24 hours in a sealed tube containing excess 6N hydrochloric acid (HCl) in a low oxygen environment. After removal of HCl, the protein hydrolysate is dissolved in a sodium citrate buffer (pH 2.2) and further analyzed for amino acid content by ion exchange column chromatography.

### Amino Acid Analysis

Ion exchange column chromatography generally has superseded the gravimetric and microbiologic methods of amino acid analysis. Sulfonated polystyrene, a synthetic cation exchange resin bearing many sulfonic acid groups ($-SO_3H$), is employed for quantitative separation of the amino acids. The resin is placed in a column and is converted to the sodium salt ($-SO_3^-Na^+$). Amino acids in the cationic form (pH ~2) are introduced at the top of the column. The cationic amino acid molecule is attracted to the resin principally through ionic forces and displaces $Na^+$. Each amino acid moves down the column in an individual and independent zone depending on the strength of the forces between the amino acid and the resin. A colorimetric method using ninhydrin reagent is employed for the detection and quantitation of the amino acids in the effluent from the column. Under controlled conditions, the position of emergence from the column and the color response are constant for each amino acid. The method has been automated.

## ENAMEL PROTEINS

The organic matrix of enamel is synthesized by cells (ameloblasts) derived from the stratified epithelium of the primitive oral cavity. In discussing the enamel proteins, attention must be given to the age of the tooth because of major differences observed in the developing (immature) and the mature tooth. These differences include: (1) total protein content, (2) solubility, and (3) amino acid composition.

The total protein content of human enamel diminishes from approximately 15 to 20% in the developing tooth to about 0.3 to 0.4% at maturity. A similar large decrease in the enamel protein content of the maturing bovine tooth has been observed. An absolute loss of 90% in the weight of enamel protein during maturation has been demonstrated. The process responsible for the loss is unknown.

In the erupted mature human and bovine tooth, the major portion of the enamel protein is soluble in ethylenediaminetetraacetic acid (EDTA) and is dialysable. Eastoe found that 85% of human fetal enamel was insoluble in water and in EDTA.

Detailed analysis of the structure of enamel proteins has been hampered by the great difficulty in obtaining sufficient quantities of purified material. Several studies on the amino acid composition of enamel organic matrix have been reported, but even in this type of study, the purity of the sample has not been uniform. The principal problem involves preventing contamination of the isolated enamel protein sample with collagenous proteins which reside in the contiguous dentinal and cemental layers. Many analyses of mature enamel have revealed varying but significant amounts of hydroxyproline, an amino acid which, in vertebrates, has been found only in collagen.

The most recent careful isolation techniques have been carried out by Glimcher and his colleagues using mature bovine teeth. They separated mature enamel from the overlying coronal cemental collagen and from the underlying dentinal collagen. Analysis of the mature bovine enamel revealed an amino acid composition different from that of collagen. It was characterized by a relatively high content of serine, glutamic acid, and glycine (Table 2-1). Furthermore, several fractions with differing amino acid compositions were isolated, suggesting heterogeneity of enamel proteins.

Studies on mature human enamel with similar careful isolation techniques have not been reported. Previous analyses of mature human enamel were

## Table 2–1. Amino Acid Composition of Some Enamel Proteins

| Amino Acid | Mature Enamel | Developing Enamel | | | | | |
|---|---|---|---|---|---|---|---|
| | Bovine[1] | Bovine[2] | Human[3] | Rhesus[4] Monkey | Horse[4] | Canine[4] | Pig[4] |
| | | residues of amino acids/1000 residues | | | | | |
| 3-Hydroxyproline . . . | 0 | trace | 0 | — | — | — | — |
| 4-Hydroxyproline . . . | 0 | trace | 0 | trace | — | — | — |
| Aspartic acid . . . | 94 | 37 | 30 | 28 | 40 | 58 | 39 |
| Threonine . . . | 48 | 29 | 38 | 42 | 30 | 32 | 39 |
| Serine . . . | 102 | 63 | 62 | 50 | 63 | 58 | 50 |
| Proline . . . | 90 | 213 | 251 | 264 | 221 | 221 | 218 |
| Glutamic acid . . . | 128 | 156 | 142 | 156 | 153 | 153 | 152 |
| Glycine . . . | 195 | 70 | 65 | 55 | 61 | 61 | 69 |

| Amino acid | | | | | | | |
|---|---|---|---|---|---|---|---|
| Alanine | 59 | 22 | 20 | 21 | 20 | 32 | 24 |
| Valine | 36 | 37 | 40 | 42 | 36 | 41 | 35 |
| Half-cystine | 11 | 1 | 2 | — | — | — | — |
| Methionine | 5 | 49 | 42 | 51 | 44 | 47 | 54 |
| Isoleucine | 28 | 30 | 33 | 25 | 38 | 36 | 38 |
| Leucine | 67 | 96 | 91 | 92 | 103 | 83 | 95 |
| Tyrosine | 7 | 49 | 53 | 52 | 58 | 43 | 51 |
| Phenylalanine | 39 | 36 | 23 | 16 | 25 | 24 | 25 |
| Hydroxylysine | 21 | 2.5 | 0 | — | trace | — | — |
| Lysine | 35 | 19 | 18 | 17 | 17 | 26 | 16 |
| Histidine | 26 | 62 | 65 | 66 | 56 | 69 | 71 |
| Arginine | 29 | 27 | 23 | 16 | 18 | 18 | 20 |

[1] From Glimcher, M. J. and Levine, P. T., Biochem. J., 93, 202, 1964.
[2] From Glimcher, M. J., Mechanic, G. L. and Friberg, U. A., Biochem. J., 93, 198, 1964.
[3] From Eastoe, J. E., Arch. Oral Biol., 8, 633, 1963.
[4] From Levine, P. T., Seyer, J., Huddleston, J. and Glimcher, M. J., Arch. Oral Biol., 12, 407, 1967.

3

performed on samples most likely vitiated by collagen as indicated by the quantity of hydroxyproline. Nevertheless, these analyses did reveal serine in higher quantity than found in collagen. The amino acid composition of purified mature human enamel probably is similar to that of purified bovine enamel.

The higher protein content of enamel from developing teeth has permitted more extensive studies. X-ray diffraction analysis of enamel isolated from developing bovine teeth revealed a pattern (cross-$\beta$ configuration) distinct from the characteristic one produced by the triple helical fibrous collagen, thereby establishing the fact that enamel protein is not a collagen.

Analysis of enamel isolated from human fetal central incisors revealed an amino acid composition different from that of mature enamel protein (Table 2–1). Noteworthy was the high content of the amino acid proline, accounting for about one-quarter of the total number of amino acid residues. This respresents the highest proline content thus far reported for any vertebrate protein. Additional important features included the high content of glutamic acid, leucine and histidine. Similar analyses have been carried out on the enamel of developing teeth from 15 different species and a clear pattern has emerged. All the analyses revealed high contents of proline and relatively high contents of glutamic acid, leucine, and histidine. These 4 amino acids constituted approximately 60% of the total amino acid residues in 14 of the 15 species. Such data suggest the presence of a distinct class of enamel proteins in the developing tooth.

The proteins of both developing and mature bovine enamel have been shown to contain relatively large amounts of phosphate which appears to be covalently linked to the amino acid residue, serine. The possible role of protein-bound serine phosphate in initiating nucleation of the inorganic crystals of enamel has been proposed.

Few studies on the biosynthesis of enamel proteins have been reported.

## PROTEIN MATRIX OF DENTINE AND CEMENTUM

The decalcified matrix of human and bovine dentine is composed essentially of collagen. Dentinal protein possesses the distinctive wide-angle x-ray diffraction pattern and amino acid composition of collagen (Table 2–2). No significant difference in amino acid composition of dentine is observed as the tooth matures. Demineralized bovine dentine contains covalently bound phosphate which is at least partially linked to serine. The function of the phosphopeptide is unknown.

Collagen also constitutes the major portion of the demineralized organic matrix of cementum (Table 2–2). Glimcher has presented evidence indicating the existence of a layer of cementum covering the crown of the erupted bovine tooth. The coronal cemental layer has both the x-ray diffraction pattern and amino acid composition of collagen and is continuous with cementum surrounding the root of the tooth.

Table 2–2.  Amino Acid Composition of Some Collagens

| Amino Acid | Dentine Human[1] | Dentine Bovine[2] | Cementum Bovine[3] | Tendon Bovine[4] |
|---|---|---|---|---|
| | RESIDUES OF AMINO ACIDS/1000 RESIDUES | | | |
| 3-Hydroxyproline | — | | 1 | 2 |
| 4-Hydroxyproline | 99 | 99 | 105 | 90 |
| Aspartic acid | 46 | 50 | 50 | 47 |
| Theonine | 17 | 17 | 19 | 17 |
| Serine | 33 | 38 | 39 | 34 |
| Proline | 116 | 118 | 124 | 120 |
| Glutamic acid | 74 | 71 | 80 | 74 |
| Glycine | 329 | 326 | 307 | 331 |
| Alanine | 112 | 125 | 115 | 112 |
| Valine | 25 | 21 | 21 | 23 |
| Half-cystine | 0 | 0 | $<0.5$ | 0 |
| Methionine | 5 | 4 | 3 | 5 |
| Isoleucine | 9 | 11 | 12 | 12 |
| Leucine | 24 | 25 | 27 | 27 |
| Tyrosine | 6 | 4 | 3 | 5 |
| Phenylalanine | 16 | 12 | 14 | 14 |
| Hydroxylysine | 10 | 9 | 11 | 9 |
| Lysine | 22 | 19 | 25 | 22 |
| Histidine | 5 | 5 | | 5 |
| Arginine | 52 | 47 | 51 | 51 |

[1] From Piez, K. A., Science, 134, 841, 1961.
[2] From Veis, A. and Schleuter, R. J.: Biochemistry, 3, 1650, 1964.
[3] From Glimcher, M. J., Friberg, U. A., and Levine, P. T.: J. Ultrastruct. Res., 10, 76, 1964.
[4] From Lidsky, M. D., Sharp, J. T., and Rudee, M. L. Arch. Biochem., 121, 496, 1967.

## COLLAGEN

### Physicochemical Properties

Quantitatively, collagen is the major protein in teeth and is the most abundant protein in the body, comprising about one-third of the total protein.  Phylogenetically, collagen is a ubiquitous protein found in all vertebrates and in invertebrate species down to the most primitive multi-cellular organisms.  Functionally, it is a structural protein serving principally as the prime mechanical support of tissue.

From the standpoint of protein structure, collagen is a unique molecule. Its most distinctive feature, the wide-angle x-ray diffraction pattern obtained

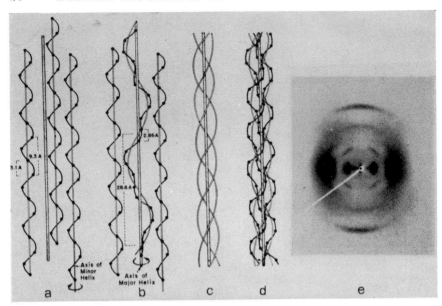

FIG. 2–1. Diagram of the coiled-coil structure of the collagen macromolecule with its wide-angle x-ray diffraction pattern. (*a*) Each of the three polypeptide chains is wound around its own axis in a left-handed threefold screw fashion. Axes are parallel. The screw repeat for polyglycine is 9.3 Å and the amino acid residues (black dots) are 3.1 Å apart. (*b*) In the center, deformation of the axis of one polypeptide chain in order to coil the chain around the axis of the major helix. The amino acid residues are 2.86 Å apart and the screw repeat of the major helix is 28.6 Å. (*c*) and (*d*). Deformation of the axis of the three chains to give the right-handed major helix. (*e*) Wide-angle x-ray diffraction pattern. (Adapted from Rich and Crick, 1955.)

in the solid state, is accepted as the fundamental defining criterion for collagen. The x-ray pattern represents a unique polypeptide configuration believed to consist of three chains arranged linearly in a helix (Fig. 2–1). Chemically, collagen possesses some remarkable features. One-third of the amino acid residues are glycine, while the amino acids proline and hydroxyproline account for about one-fourth of the total. Thus far, collagen is the only vertebrate protein in which the hydroxyamino acids, hydroxyproline and hydroxylysine, are known to coexist. Half-cystine residues are notably not found in vertebrate collagens but have been detected in invertebrate collagens. Collagens are further characterized by the low content of tyrosine and phenylalanine.

Morphologically, when viewed with the electron microscope, collagen from mesenchymal tissue is composed of fibrils having a repeated pattern of cross-striations, termed the 640 Å (700 Å in the hydrated form) repeating period (Fig. 2–2). However, certain vertebrate and invertebrate proteins showing the characteristic wide-angle x-ray diffraction pattern of collagen do not appear to manifest the typical 640 Å periodicity.

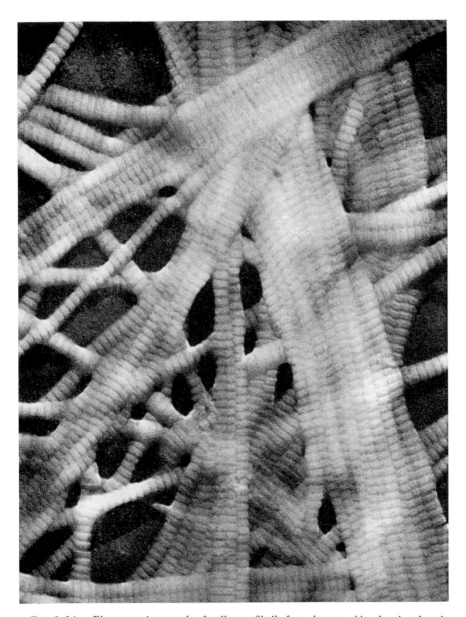

Fig. 2–2A. Electron micrograph of collagen fibrils from human skin showing bands spaced about 700 Å apart. 42,000 ×. (From J. Gross, Scientific American, May, 1961.)

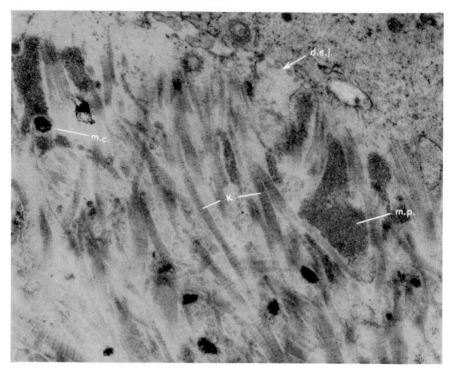

Fig. 2–2B. Electron micrograph illustrating the collagen fibrils in dentin. ×36,000. (From Bevelander, G., and Nakahara, H.: Formation and mineralization of dentin. Anat. Rec., *156*, 303, 1966.)

Another property characteristic of collagen is its heat induced transition to gelatin. The transition, resulting in the loss of many of the native properties of collagen, can be observed by various methods. Heat denaturation of the insoluble fiber produces a sharp contraction (thermal shrinkage) of the fiber, while prolonged heating at neutral pH yields a soluble preparation called gelatin. The amino acid composition of gelatin is identical to that of the native, insoluble collagen.

### Structure

In the native state, most collagen is insoluble. An important discovery was the finding that native soluble collagen can be obtained *in vitro* under certain conditions. Extraction of soft-tissue collagens of very young, rapidly growing animals with either cold neutral salt solution or dilute acetic acid or citrate buffer yields a solution of the monomer or fundamental unit of collagen, termed *tropocollagen* (from the Greek meaning "turning into collagen"). The tropocollagen molecule is highly asymmetric, being 2,800 Å long and 14 Å wide and has a molecular weight of about 300,000.

Fig. 2–3. Block of collagen (*right*) forms when a cold neutral salt solution of collagen (*left*) is warmed to body temperature for 10 minutes.   Gel redissolves if cooled promptly. (From J. Gross, Sc. American, May, 1961.)

Radioisotope labeling studies have indicated that cold neutral salt extracts of soluble collagen represent the most recently synthesized extracellular collagen.   The more rapidly the animal grows, the larger is the amount of collagen that can be extracted.   Presumably, the collagen is still soluble because it has not yet formed cross-linkages with adjacent tropocollagen units. Warming the tropocollagen solution to body temperature results in a gel composed of the typical banded collagen fibrils.   Rapid cooling of the gel redissolves the fibrils but if the gel remains at 37 to 40° C for 24 hours, it no longer dissolves on cooling (Fig. 2–3).

Tropocollagen consists of three polypeptide chains, each chain being twisted into a left-handed helix.   The three helices are wrapped around each other to form a right-handed super or major helix (Fig. 2–1).   The triple helical structure is possible only because of the high incidence (one-third) of glycine.   The pitch of the helix is determined by the frequent proline and hydroxyproline residues which do not permit the more common helical arrangements.

Denaturation of tropocollagen results in the appearance of three molecular components, termed $\alpha$, $\beta$, and $\gamma$ components.   When a solution of native collagen (tropocollagen) is denatured by heating or by the action of urea, thiocyanate, or guanidine, the three components can be detected by ultra-centrifugation, ion exchange chromatography, or gel electrophoresis (Fig.

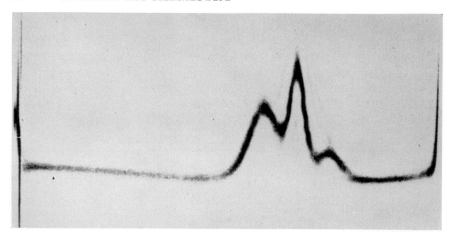

FIG. 2–4. Sedimentation velocity pattern of denatured dogfish skin collagen showing boundaries resulting from single ($\alpha$), double ($\beta$) and triple chain($\gamma$) components in order of increasing sedimentation rate (left to right). (From The Characterization of Collagen from the Skin of the Dogfish Shark, Squalus Acanthias, J. Biol. Chem., *239*, 3336, 1964 by Lewis, M. S. and Piez, K. A. Reproduced by courtesy of The American Society of Biological Chemists, Inc.)

2–4). The molecular weight of the $\alpha$ component is about 100,000 or one-third the molecular weight of tropocollagen. The $\alpha$ component is considered to represent any single chain of which there are three in the collagen molecule. By chromatographic means, the $\alpha$ component is separable into at least two distinct units, designated $\alpha_1$ and $\alpha_2$, which have approximately the same molecular weight (100,000) and are present in a ratio of 2 : 1. It is postulated that the tropocollagen molecule is built of two chains of the $\alpha_1$ type and one of the $\alpha_2$. This is consistent with the different amino acid composition of $\alpha_1$ and $\alpha_2$ and with the amino acid composition of native collagen.

Piez has further separated the $\alpha_1$ chain of codfish skin collagen into two peaks present in equal amounts and designated $\alpha_1$ and $\alpha_3$. Thus, the tropocollagen molecule of codfish skin contains three nonidentical $\alpha$ chains. Studies on the possible heterogeneity of the $\alpha_1$ chains in other species have not yet been reported.

The $\beta$ components have a molecular weight of 200,000 and an amino composition indicating they are dimers consisting of two $\alpha$ chains. These are formed by covalent cross-links between the $\alpha$ chains. For codfish skin collagen, the intramonomer $\beta$ components, $\beta_{12}$, $\beta_{13}$, and $\beta_{23}$, have been identified (Fig. 2–5).

The $\gamma$ components have the same amino acid composition as that of unfractionated tropocollagen and probably represent many possible combinations of trimers of covalently-linked $\alpha$ chains.

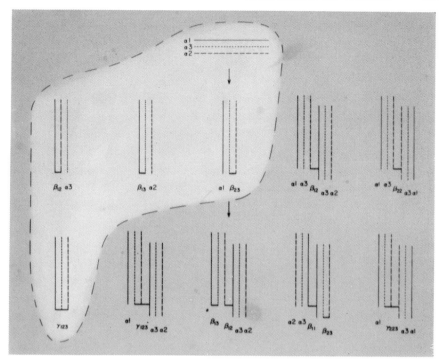

FIG. 2-5. Diagrammatic representation of the crosslinking of collagen. The molecule as synthesized (top) contains three nonidentical chains. Crosslinking proceeds intra– and intermolecularly by a single process to produce a variety of $\beta$ and $\gamma$ components and may continue giving rise to higher aggregates. Salt and acid extraction yield largely intramolecularly crosslinked components (within the dash line) while a denaturing agent such as 5M guanidine also extracts components derived from intermolecular crosslinks.

Maturation or fibrogenesis is conceived as involving the formation of both intramonomer bonds between the $\alpha$ chains and intermonomer bonds between adjacent tropocollagen units. In collagen fibrils showing the 640Å periodicity, the tropocollagen molecules are aligned in parallel array. The N-terminus of each tropocollagen molecule is displaced one-quarter length from the N-termini of the tropocollagen on either side (Fig. 2–6).

Highly purified collagens contain a small amount of carbohydrate, identified as hexoses, covalently bound to a polypeptide chain. The disaccharide unit, 2-0-$\alpha$-D-glucopyranosyl-D-galactose, has been isolated from several vertebrate collagens, including bovine collagens from skin, tendon, and glomerular basement membrane, guinea pig skin collagen, and ichthyocol. The evidence indicates the disaccharide is linked O-glycosidically to the hydroxyl group of a hydroxylysine residue in the peptide chain (Fig. 2–7).

As already mentioned, one important characteristic of native mature collagen is its insolubility. Recent evidence indicated that dentine collagen

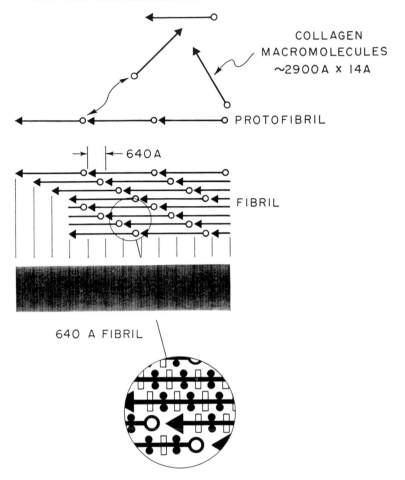

FIG. 2–6. A schematic showing the aggregation of tropocollagen to form collagen fibrils. The quarter-stagger array produces the typical 640 Å spacing. (From M. J. Glimcher, Calcification in Biological Systems, R. F. Sognnaes, Ed., Am. Assoc. Adv. Science, Washington, D.C., 1960, p. 437.)

is even more difficult to solubilize than collagen extracted from softer tissues such as skin and tendon. The insolubility of mature collagen in any aqueous or organic solvent that does not attack it chemically is considered indicative of a highly cross-linked system. The cross-links are conceived as occurring between polypeptide chains, both within the collagen monomer and between monomers. Such cross-links could consist of hydrogen bonds, hydrophobic bonds, electrostatic bonds, or covalent bonds. Available information indicates the cross-linking system in collagen consists of covalent bonds.

The nature of the covalent cross-links remains to be established, but some pertinent data have accumulated. The absence of half-cystine residues in

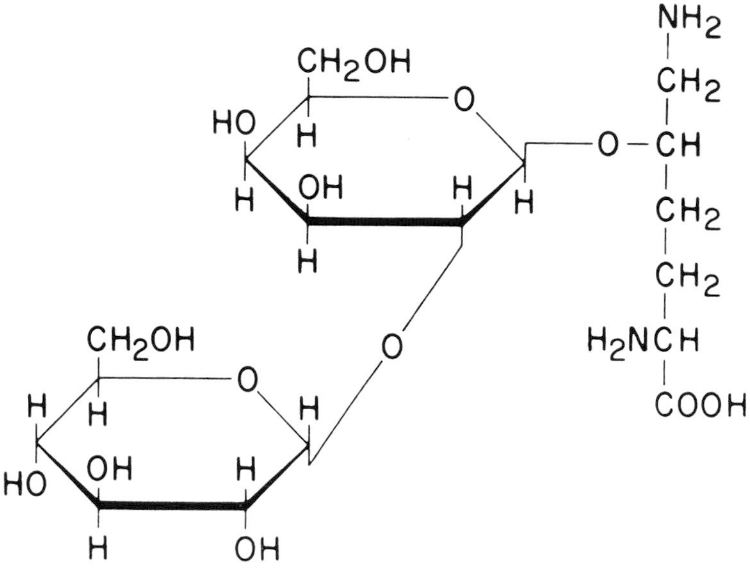

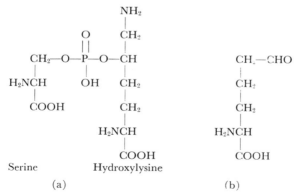

FIG. 2–7.   2-0-a-D-glucopyranosyl-0-β-D-galactopyranosylhydroxylysine

vertebrate collagen excludes cystine disulfide bridges from significant participation in cross-linking.   Grassman and Gallop have provided evidence for
the existence of ester linkages in collagen and these have been implicated in
the cross-linking system.   Recently, Harada *et al.* reported the presence of a
considerably larger quantity of ester-type linkages (22 moles/$10^5$ grams of
protein) in sound human dentine collagen than found in bovine skin collagen
(2 moles/$10^5$ grams of protein).   The specific chemical nature of the ester
linkages is unknown.   Veis has reported data suggesting the presence of a
phosphodiester bond between serine and hydroxylysine in bovine dentine
collagen (Fig. 2–8).

FIG 2–8.   (a) Phosphodiester bond between the amino acid residues, serine and hydroxylysine
(b) Lysyl-derived δ-semialdehyde of a-aminoadipic acid

Aldehyde links also have been proposed as participating in the collagen interchain cross-linking system. The presence of a few aldehyde groups in collagen has been demonstrated. Bornstein and Piez have isolated a residue of the lysyl-derived δ-semialdehyde of α-aminoadipic acid from a single α chain in soluble rat skin collagen (Fig. 2–8). The proposal has been made that a intramonomer interchain cross-link emerges from an aldol-type condensation of the two lysyl-derived aldehydes on adjacent chains.

At present, extensive studies are being carried out on the amino acid sequence of the α chains and on the nature and number of cross-links and their distribution in the collagen molecule.

## Biosynthesis

In recent years, the biosynthesis of collagen has received increased attention by several investigators, notably M. R. Stetten, Van Slyke, Robertson, Meister, Undenfriend, Prockop, Lukens, and Manner.

Most collagens are synthesized by the fibroblast, such synthesis having been directly observed in tissue culture. There is evidence that certain collagens may be produced by cells of epidermal origin.

Many of the details of collagen biosynthesis have been established by utilizing guinea pig granulomas as well as intact cell and cell-free systems from chick embryos. It is clear that the early steps of collagen synthesis are similar to the steps involved in the biosynthesis of other proteins. A proline-rich polypeptide is synthesized by components residing in the microsomal and soluble fractions of the cell. The polypeptide is assembled on aggregates of ribosomes (polyribosome or polysome) through the interaction of: (1) messenger ribonucleic acid (mRNA), (2) soluble or transfer RNA (tRNA), (3) soluble enzymes required for the formation of amino acyl-tRNA complexes and for the transfer of these complexes to mRNA on the polysome, (4) energy source (adenosine triphosphate-generating system), (5) $Mg^{++}$ and (6) guanosine triphosphate. Available evidence suggests that the molecular weight of the polypeptide assembled on the polysome is approximately 100,000, thereby being similar to the molecular weight of the α chains of tropocollagen. The specific mRNA for collagen has not been identified. The size of the polysome and the number of ribosomes comprising the polysome remain uncertain.

The formation of collagen involves at least one distinct aspect, the biosynthesis of 4- and 3- hydroxyprolines and hydroxylysine. Neither free hydroxyproline $-^{14}C$ nor free hydroxylysine $-^{14}C$ can serve as precursors for the respective $^{14}C-$ labeled hydroxyamino acids in newly formed collagen. Collagen hydroxyproline and hydroxylysine are derived from free proline and free lysine.

The conversion of free proline to free hydroxyproline and of free lysine to free hydroxylysine has never been demonstrated. Studies have established that hydroxylation of proline and lysine occur after these amino acids are incorporated into a proline-rich polypeptide. (Although small amounts of hydroxyprolyl-tRNA may exist, there is no evidence that this complex plays any significant role in the formation of hydroxyproline-bound polypeptide or protein.) The proline-rich polypeptide serves as the substrate for the hydroxylating enzyme system found in the microsomal fraction of the cell (Fig. 2–9). For hydroxylation, collagen proline hydroxylase requires: (1) a polypeptide substrate with a molecular weight of at least 1300 and a sequence of glycine-proline-proline (the second proline is hydroxylated); the enzyme cannot hydroxylate the tripeptide, glycyl-L-prolyl-L-proline, (2) atmospheric oxygen, (3) $Fe^{2+}$, (4) ascorbate, and (5) α-ketoglutarate. The requirement of ascorbic acid as a cofactor appears to represent at least a partial explanation of the connective tissue defects observed in the scorbutic animal. Most likely, the steps involved in the hydroxylation of lysine are similar but fewer studies have been reported.

Finally, additional investigations are needed to elucidate the mechanism of delivery of collagen to the extracellular space.

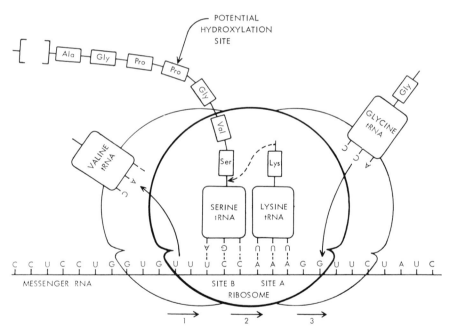

FIG. 2–9. Collagen is synthesized by ribosomes according to coded instructions of messenger ribonucleic acid (mRNA). The code letters of mRNA are four bases: adenine (A), guanine (G), cytosine (C), and uracil (U). A sequence of three bases, called a codon, is required to specify each amino acid, except hydroxyproline and hydroxylysine. Each amino acid (again, except hydroxyproline and hydroxylysine) is carried to the ribosome by a particular form of RNA called transfer RNA (tRNA) which carries an anticodon (three bases) that forms a temporary bond with one of the codons in mRNA. The ribosome is shown moving along the chain of mRNA. Two binding sites for tRNA appear to exist on the ribosome: one site (A) for a newly arrived tRNA molecule and another (B) for holding the growing polypeptide chain. Hydroxylation of proline and lysine occurs after these amino acids are incorporated into the growing polypeptide chain.

## SELECTED REFERENCES

EASTOE, J. E.: The amino acid composition of proteins from the oral tissues—II, Arch. Oral Biol., *8*, 633–652, 1963.

GLIMCHER, M. J., BONAR, L. C., and DANIEL, E. J.: The molecular structure of the protein matrix of bovine dental enamel, J. Mol. Biol., *3*, 541–546, 1961.

GLIMCHER, M. J., FRIBERG, U. A., and LEVINE, P. T.: The isolation and amino acid composition of the enamel proteins of erupted bovine teeth, Biochem. J., *93*, 202–210, 1964.

————: The identification and characterization of a calcified layer of coronal cementum in erupted bovine teeth, J. Ultrastuct. Res., *10*, 76–88, 1964.

GLIMCHER, M. J., LEVINE, P. T., and MECHANIC, G. L.: Studies on the source of hydroxyproline in bovine enamel, Biochim. Biophys. Acta, *136*, 36–44, 1967.

GROSS, J.: Studies on the formation of collagen, J. Exp. Med., *107*, 247–263, 1958.

————: Collagen, Scientific American, *204*, 120–128, 1961.

HARRINGTON, W. F. and VON HIPPEL, P. H.: The structure of collagen and gelatin, Advan. Protein Chem., *16*, 1–138, 1961.

LEVINE, P. T., SEYER, J., HUDDLESTON, J., and GLIMCHER, M. J.: The comparative biochemistry of the organic matrix proteins of developing enamel—I, Arch. Oral Biol., *12*, 407–410, 1967.

PIEZ, K. A.: Amino acid composition of some calcified proteins, Science, *134*, 841–842, 1961.

————: Crosslinking of collagen, birth defects, Original Articles Series, *2*, 5–9, 1966. (Published by the National Foundation-March of Dimes, N.Y.)

PIEZ, K. A., EIGNER, E. A., and LEWIS, M. S.: The chromatographic separation and amino acid composition of the subunits of several collagens, Biochemistry, *2*, 58–66, 1963.

UNDENFRIEND, S.: Formation of hydroxyproline in collagen, Science, *152*, 1335–1340, 1966.

VEIS, A. and SCHLEUTER, R. J.: The macromolecular organization of dentine matrix collagen, Biochemistry, *3*, 1650–1657, 1964.

# Chapter 3

# Carbohydrate Components of Teeth

## Nicola Di Ferrante, M.D., Ph.D.

Introduction
Carbohydrate Components
  Dental Pulp
  Cementum, Dentine, Enamel, and Their Cells
  Structure and Function of Hyaluronic Acid
    Chondroitin-4-Sulfate and Chondroitin-6-Sulfate
Metabolism of Mucopolysaccharides and of Protein-
    Mucopolysaccharide Complexes

## INTRODUCTION

The carbohydrate components of teeth have been studied with histochemical and analytical procedures. Both approaches have specific advantages and inherent limitation.

The histochemical methods, which consist of staining a tissue section with various dyes specific for different types of natural compounds, are essentially qualitative and are subject to great variability due to differences in purity of various batches of dye, minor variations in the technique employed, and, last but not least, the subjective interpretation of the investigator. Moreover, they suffer from a limited specificity, as they usually fail to differentiate among compounds belonging to the same class and are frequently hindered by steric factors, which do not allow the dye to reach and stain its substrates. These steric factors may also prevent the action of various enzymes specific for substrates possibly present in the histological sections. The latter limitation is particularly evident in mineralized tissues where specific staining may take place only after demineralization. Unfortunately, during demineralization, organic components may easily be removed along with inorganic ones.

Despite these limitations, the histochemical methods offer the paramount advantage of showing the relationship among the different compounds in a given section and frequently reveal zonal, tissual, temporal, or species heterogeneities which may be of physiopathological relevance.

The analytical methods consist of suitable extraction procedures, followed by purification and separation steps dictated by the chemical specificity of the compounds to be isolated. The final products, analyzed with highly specific chemical or enzymatic tests, provide a quantitative measurement of the various tissue components which were extracted and carried through the procedure. The analytical methods usually involve large scale preparative procedures to obtain sufficient amounts of material for analyses; only seldom a quantitative recovery of the various compounds originally present in the tissue is emphasized. Thus, frequently, the results represent an average of the molecular species retained through the various procedural steps but not necessarily of those originally present in the tissue. The analytical methods involve homogenization of the original material, and this unavoidably leads to a disruption of the structural relationship among the various tissue components, as well as to a disappearance of any structural or functional heterogeneity of the sample.

These considerations indicate that histochemical and analytical methods are complementary rather than exclusive of one another. Therefore, it is with a great deal of expectation that the biologist looks upon some recently described methods utilizing adjacent sections of the same specimen for histochemistry and microanalytical determinations, thus providing an excellent correlation between chemical and morphological structure of a given tissue.

## CARBOHYDRATE COMPONENTS

### Dental Pulp

Histochemically, the extracellular matrix of human dental pulp is characterized by the presence of glycoproteins, acid mucopolysaccharides, and proteins containing appreciable amounts of $\epsilon$-amino groups (collagen). The structure of the glycoproteins is not known. Some seem to contain sialic acid as suggested by a decrease of specific staining after treatment with sialidase. As indicated by the study of the chemical and immunological properties of glycoproteins of various organs or tissues, it is possible that the glycoproteins of dental pulp possess a specific structure different from that of similar compounds occurring elsewhere. The basement membrane of the blood vessels of the dental pulp is particularly rich in glycoproteins.

The macromolecules of the dental pulp have amphoteric properties. At a physiological pH, the carboxyl groups of collagen, the glycoproteins, and the acid mucopolysaccharides confer a negative charge to the extracellular matrix. This has been considered to be responsible for the binding not only of specific dyes, but also of cations of physiological importance.

The extracellular matrix of the dental pulp consists of two fractions, one readily soluble in water and saline and the other insoluble and resistant to extraction with neutral or acidic buffers. These two phases are considered to be in equilibrium, and their relative amounts vary in physiological and pathological conditions. Some of these changes occur with age; for instance, the collagen increases and replaces the ground substance, the matrix itself becomes more resistant to proteolytic enzymes and less soluble, while its water content decreases. These changes suggest that in old dental pulp, as in old connective tissue present elsewhere in the body, there is an increase of cross-linked collagen at the expense of glycoproteins and mucopolysaccharides. These changes may be responsible for modification in the distribution of electrolytes and for the high incidence of calcification in aged dental pulp.

## Cementum, Dentine, Enamel, and Their Cells

Histochemically, the cytoplasm of cementoblasts and cementocytes is variably basophilic. Cementum itself, when demineralized, reacts strongly with periodic acid-Schiff's reagent (PAS) and with Hale's colloidal iron reagent. It is also metachromatic, especially around lacunae, cementocytes, Sharpey's fibers, and the interlamellar regions. The cytoplasm of odontoblasts is intensively stained with PAS; since the stainable component is not removed by a previous treatment with diastase, it is not glycogen.

Demineralized dentine stains readily with PAS, while nondemineralized dentine fails to do so. Sections of demineralized dentine from normal, fully formed but unerupted teeth stain strongly with alcian blue and show metachromasia (to indicate the presence of acid mucopolysaccharides), while predentine does not stain. In nondemineralized sections, however, predentine stains metachromatically but dentine remains unstained. Sections of formalin-fixed, demineralized dentine from infants are intensely metachromatic; with increasing age, the metachromasia is replaced by a moderate basophilia which, in turn, decreases gradually with further aging. The basophilia surrounding dentine tubules remains longest.

Engle, Wislocki, and Sognnaes have demonstrated that glycogen is present in large amounts in the oral epithelium, dental lamina, outer enamel epithelium, and stellate reticulum of fetal teeth. Perceptible reactions for glycogen were also recorded in the stratum intermedium, ameloblasts, odontoblasts, and dental papillae of a human fetus 130 mm long. Although histochemical methods failed to show glycogen in adult teeth, Egyedi claims to have demonstrated chemically its presence in the insoluble portion of the organic matrix of enamel and, to a lesser extent, in dentine. The presence of carbohydrate-protein complexes in the dentine and enamel matrices of rat teeth and of glycoprotein granules in the cytoplasm of odontoblasts and ameloblasts has been reported. PAS positive material has been described as occurring in the interstitial matrix of nondecalcified ground sections of dentine from human and monkey teeth, but these findings have not been confirmed. The periphery of dentinal tubules has a substance that is not only metachromatic, but also strongly basophilic at pH 2 to 3. This material surrounds the odontoblastic processes.

4

The calcifying enamel in the interprismatic regions and the cross striation of the prisms are strongly metachromatic.

In summary, various histochemical contributions suggest that glycogen is present in osteogenic and odontogenic cells before the onset of calcification, and carbohydrate-protein complexes are present within the cytoplasm of active osteoblasts, cementoblasts, odontoblasts, and ameloblasts and in the ground substance surrounding them. The ground substance of the stellate reticulum of the enamel organ and the interprismatic regions of calcifying enamel prisms seems to be rich in acid mucopolysaccharides, as indicated by metachromasia and basophilia. The same reactions for mucopolysaccharides are evident in the ground substance of the dental papilla, in the peripheral regions of the dentinal tubules, in the ground substance of the dental sac, and around the Sharpey's fibers of cementum.

Various attempts have been made to extract and characterize the carbohydrate-containing components of teeth. In 1950, Pincus extracted a mucopolysaccharide from dentine which, on the basis of qualitative tests, was considered akin to chondroitin sulfate. Defatted human dentine powder was extracted with calcium chloride, and the extract was deproteinized with a chloroform amyl alcohol mixture. The final product, obtained by precipitation with ethanol and glacial acetic acid, when analyzed revealed an excess of nitrogen and low hexosamine and hexuronic acid values. This led Pincus to believe that chondroitin sulfate existed in dentine as a protein complex. It is also conceivable, however, that the material isolated was contaminated by protein not covalently linked to chondroitin sulfate.

In 1952 Hess and Lee extracted powdered dentine from normal human molars with a solution of potassium chloride-potassium carbonate, according to the method of Einbinder and Schubert. Concurrently, they extracted dry bovine tracheal cartilage with the same method to obtain a reference sample of chondroitin sulfate and dry dentine powder with the method previously used by Pincus. The percentage of chondroitin sulfate extracted from dentine with Einbinder and Schubert's and Pincus' methods was 0.64 and

Table 3–1. Mucopolysaccharide Extracted from Dentine

| Sample source | Hexosamine % | Hexuronic acid % | Nitrogen % |
|---|---|---|---|
| Bovine tracheae | 28.07 | 29.20 | 2.13 |
| Dentine (Einbinder & Schubert) | 27.78 | 25.08 | 2.63 |
| Dentine (Pincus) | 15.3 | 14 | |
| Theory for $C_{14}H_{19}NSO_4.4H_2O$ | 29.49 | 31.96 | 2.31 |

(From Hess, W. C. and Lee, C.: J. Dent. Res. *31*, 793–797, 1952.)

0.75 respectively. The analytical data of the two products, however, were quite different, as the one prepared with the Pincus method was associated with a discrete amount of protein (Table 3–1).

More recently, Clark, Smith, and Davidson have measured the total amount and distribution of hexosamine in enamel and dentine-cementum. Moreover, they have isolated and identified various acid mucopolysaccharides present in the same material. Whole human teeth were cleaned, dried, crushed, and ground. The fine powder was treated with a mixture of 91% bromoform and 9% acetone, of specific gravity 2.7 to separate enamel from dentine-cementum. Dried aliquots of the two fractions were decalcified with 5% EDTA at pH 6.0 and dialyzed. The nondialyzable material was incubated with proteolytic enzymes, and the remnant protein was precipitated with trichloroacetic acid. The supernatant, dialyzed and concentrated, was precipitated with cetylpyridinium chloride, and the insoluble product was solubilized with increasing concentrations of sodium chloride (0.4M, 1.20M, and 2.1M). After removing the precipitant, the dialyzed solutions were analyzed with the orcinol and carbazole reactions for hexuronic acids and with the Elson-Morgan reaction for total hexosamine. Individual amino sugars were identified by column chromatography on cation exchange resins and by paper chromatography of the degradation products obtained by oxidative deamination performed with ninhydrin. It was found that the dentine-cementum and enamel fractions of human teeth contain, respectively, 0.08 and 0.03% total hexosamine. Of this, glucosamine represents 42 and 47% of the total respectively in dentine-cementum and enamel, while galactosamine represents 43 and 54%. Dentine-cementum also contained a third compound (accounting for 15% of total hexosamine) which reacted with the Elson-Morgan reagent but behaved differently from glucosamine and galactosamine on column chromatography. A similar component, hitherto unidentified in its structure, has been described in sheep wool, human hair, and epidermis. The acid mucopolysaccharides isolated from dentine-cementum were hyaluronic acid, chondroitin-4-sulfate, and chondroitin-6-sulfate, the latter ones being differentiated by infrared spectroscopy, paper chromatography, and optical rotation. The ratio between sulfated and nonsulfated mucopolysaccharides in dentine-cementum was 20:1. The same acid mucopolysaccharides were isolated from enamel, the ratio between the sulfated and nonsulfated ones being 10:1.

Assuming that the extraction and recovery of the acid mucopolysaccharides was quantitative, they accounted for 45% of the total hexosamine present in dentine-cementum and for 9% of that present in enamel, the balance being probably represented by glycoproteins which were degraded by the proteolytic enzymes to products eliminated during dialysis. To this extent, it is pertinent to mention that sialic acid, a component of many glycoproteins, has been isolated from dentine.

### Structure and Function of Hyaluronic Acid, Chondroitin-4-Sulfate, and Chondroitin-6-Sulfate

These components of connective tissue are high molecular weight hetero-polysaccharides containing aminosugars. Referred to as "acid mucopoly-saccharides" or "glycosaminoglycans," they may be conveniently represented by a "repeating unit," which by polymerization, produces chains of different length. Eight different acid mucopolysaccharides have been isolated and characterized on the basis of (1) the structure of the repeating unit, (2) optical rotation, (3) solubility in alcoholic solutions, and (4) enzymatic degradation. The acidic character of these compounds is due to the presence of three different functional groups: carboxylic ($-COOH$), ester sulfate ($-O-SO_3H$), and sulfoamide ($-N-SO_3H$). Figure 3–1 shows the repeating units of several acid mucopolysaccharides, and Table 3–2 summarizes some of their properties.

Hyaluronic acid is a linear polysaccharide composed of equimolar amounts of D-glucuronic acid and D-acetylglucosamine, linked by alternating $\beta$ 1–3 and $\beta$ 1–4 glycosidic linkages (Fig. 3–1, formula 1). It has been isolated from various sources such as vitreous humor, umbilical cord, rooster comb, embryonic pig skin, human serum, Rous sarcoma, synovial fluid, brain and spinal cord, platelets, electric organ of the eel, and several bacteria. It is rapidly depolymerized by bacterial, testicular, and leech hyaluronidase, the latter being specific for this substrate.

Hyaluronic acid isolated from vitreous humor consists of several fractions of different molecular weight (from 77,000 to 1,500,000). These fractions contain a small protein component which seems to be an integral part of the polymer. It has been demonstrated that oxidation-reduction processes may remove most of the protein moiety and depolymerize the carbohydrate

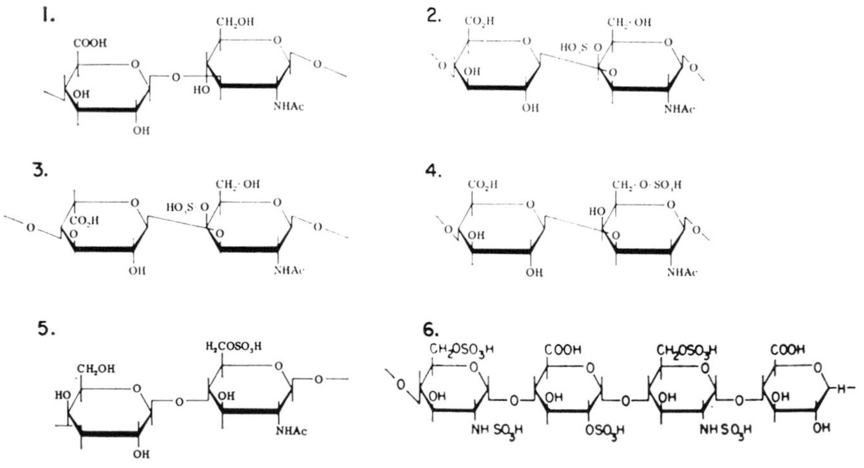

FIG. 3–1. The structure of acid mucopolysaccharides (1) Hyaluronic acid; (2) chondroitin sulfate A; (3) chondroitin sulfate B; (4) chondroitin sulfate C; (5) keratan sulfate; (6) heparin.

chain. The hyaluronic acid-protein complex of synovial fluid behaves like a semi-rigid coil with a molecular weight of approximately 4 million. In solution, these macromolecules resist compression and limit the flow of solvent and the diffusion of other solutes, either small or large. In fact, when in solution, hyaluronic acid secludes the volume of solvent necessary for its solubilization, preventing its function as a solvent for other molecules or its free flow in the intercellular space. This effect, quite different from that shown by salts or protein in solution, is referred to as "excluded volume" to indicate the dominating influence of the solute over the solvent. This property of hyaluronic acid in solution explains the absence of plasma proteins in normal synovial fluid and their presence in those pathological fluids in which the degree of polymerization of hyaluronic acid may be reduced. Moreover, the recent demonstration that in the joints the hyaline cartilage is covered by a thin layer of hyaluronic acid seems to support the theory that water layers may be interposed between the articular surfaces, serving as a lubricating and shock-absorbing device.

Chondroitin-4-sulfate and chondroitin-6-sulfate (previously referred to as chondroitin sulfate A and C) are very similar linear polymers found in various connective tissue areas and mainly in cartilage, bone, cornea, vascular walls, chordoma, and chondrosarcoma.

Composed of equimolar amounts of D-glucuronic acid and D-acetyl-galactosamine, linked by alternating $\beta$ 1–3 and $\beta$ 1–4 glycosidic linkages (Fig. 3–1, formulas 2 and 4), they are both depolymerized by testicular hyaluronidase and resistant to bacterial hyaluronidase. They differ in optical rotation (Table 3–2) and in the position of the sulfate groups which are located in position 4 of the acetylgalactosamine in chondroitin sulfate A and in position 6 in chondroitin sulfate C (Fig. 3–1). This structural difference may be demonstrated with colorimetric determinations or with infrared analyses.

Chondroitin sulfate occurs in nature covalently bound to a protein different from collagen. With mild methods of extraction, it is possible to obtain a fraction containing 15% protein and another containing 50% protein; from these, chondroitin sulfate and small mounts of keratan sulfate may be obtained either by alkali degradation or by treatment with proteolytic enzymes. In the zone of linkage between the chondroitin sulfate chains and the protein, the last glucuronic acid residue is followed by two units of galactose and one of xylose, this being joined by a glucosidic linkage to the hydroxyl group of a serine which is part of the protein structure. Approximately 50 to 60 chains of chondroitin sulfate are present in each macromolecule.

Different types of chondroitin sulfate present in a given tissue may stimulate or inhibit the phase of "nucleation"* or "growth" of the collagen

---

* Nucleation refers to the aggregation of the triple helix collagen macromolecules (tropocollagen) which act as seeds. These nuclei grow by accretion of the soluble tropocollagen to form larger collagen fibers. This process is not to be confused with the seeding out of hydroxyapatite as in calcification or mineralization.

Table 3-2.  Isolated Acid Mucopolysaccharides

| | Hyaluronic Acid | Chondroitin | Chondroitin Sulfate A (4-sulfate) | Chondroitin Sulfate B (dermatan sulfate) | Chondroitin Sulfate C (6-sulfate) | Keratan Sulfate | Heparin | Heparitin Sulfate (heparan sulfate) |
|---|---|---|---|---|---|---|---|---|
| Optical Rotation $[\alpha]_D$ | $-70°, -80°$ | $-21°$ | $-28°, -32°$ | $-55°, -63°$ | $-16°, -22°$ | $-13°, +5°$ | $+44°$ | $+39°, +50°$ |
| Ethanol concentration precipitating Ca salts | | | 30–40% | 18–25% | 40–50% | | | |
| Sensitivity to hyaluronidase: | | | | | | | | |
| testicular | + | + | + | | + | — | — | — |
| bacterial | + | + | — | | — | — | — | — |
| leech | + | — | — | | — | — | — | — |
| Aminosugar | acetylglucosamine | acetylgalactosamine | acetylgalactosamine | acetylgalactosamine | acetylgalactosamine | acetylglucosamine | glucosamine-N-sulfate | acetylglucosamine and glucosamine-N-sulfate |
| Hexuronic acid | glucuronic | glucuronic | glucuronic | iduronic | glucuronic | absent | glucuronic | glucuronic |
| Anionic groups | carboxylic | carboxylic | carboxylic + sulfate esters | carboxylic + sulfate esters | carboxylic + sulfate esters | sulfate esters | carboxylic, sulfate esters, and amides | carboxylic, sulfate esters, and amides |
| S% | — | 0–2% | 6–7% | 6–7% | 6–7% | 6–9% | 11–12% | 6% |
| Anticoagulant activity | — | — | — | — | — | — | + | — |

fibers, thus influencing the types of fibers eventually appearing in the tissue.

In solution, the protein-chondroitin sulfate complex behaves like the hyaluronic acid-protein complex; the stiffness of the glycosidic chains and the repulsion of the various anionic groups cause each macromolecule to spread and to cover a vast domain, thus subtracting a large volume of solvent for the transit of other solutes.

The protein-polysaccharide complexes seem to play a role of paramount importance in the process of calcification. Small amounts of these complexes added to an aqueous suspension of calcium phosphate prevent the sedimentation of the salt. However, if the complex is treated with proteolytic enzymes or with testicular hyaluronidase, its degradation allows the immediate sedimentation of the calcium salt as if it were in aqueous suspension. The calcium phosphate present in the plasma and in the extracellular fluid is in supersaturated, metastable solution, and the presence of protein-polysaccharide complexes in tissues may represent one of the factors preventing its precipitation. It is relevant to mention that proteases capable of degrading the protein part of the complex have been described in cartilage, and this may account for the reduction in the amount of this protein immediately prior to the onset of calcification.

## METABOLISM OF MUCOPOLYSACCHARIDES AND OF PROTEIN-POLYSACCHARIDE COMPLEXES

Acid mucopolysaccharides are the products of the biosynthetic activities of fibroblasts, and the Golgi apparatus seems to be the site involved in their synthesis and extracellular transfer. Heparin, however, is synthesized and stored in the mast cells. According to one investigator, the latter cells are also responsible for the synthesis of hyaluronic acid.

D-glucose is the precursor of both components of hyaluronic acid. In the hemolytic streptococcus, glucosamine is synthesized from fructose-6-phosphate (F-6-P) and the amide group of glutamine. This irreversible reaction has a great functional importance because at its level acts one of the most efficient control mechanisms for the synthesis of mucopolysaccharides. In some tissues, the synthesis of glucosamine requires not glutamine but ammonia, as indicated by the following reaction:

$$NH_3 + \text{fructose-6-phosphate} \rightleftharpoons \text{glucosamine-6-phosphate} + H_2O.$$

Acetylation of the glucosamine-6-phosphate by coenzyme A and an appropriate enzyme pulls the reversible reaction to the right. As soon as N-acetylglucosamine-6-phosphate is transformed by a mutase to N-acetylglucosamine-1-phosphate, the latter reacts with uridine triphosphate (UTP) to produce uridine diphospho-N-acetylglucosamine (UDP-NAcGlu) and pyrophosphate.

The second component of hyaluronic acid, glucuronic acid, is produced from oxidation of the nucleotide uridine-diphosphoglucose (UDPG) by a specific dehydrogenase and the coenzyme nicotinamide-adenosine dinucleotide (NAD). The uridine diphosphoglucuronic acid (UDPGA) thus

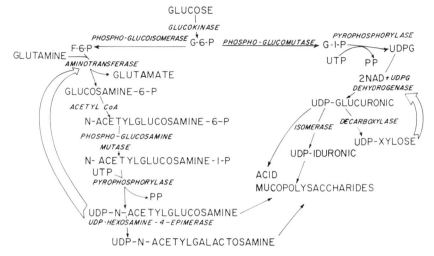

FIG. 3–2. The synthesis of acid mucopolysaccharides. The large arrows indicate feedback inhibition of the synthetic pathway.

formed is ready for the reaction with the uridine diphospho-N-acetylglucosamine. It seems that there are two different enzymes (synthetases), each specific for one of the two nucleotides, capable of adding their substrates to the growing glycosidic chain while the nucleotide uridine diphosphate is set free (Fig. 3–2). The mechanism instrumental for the termination of the synthesis is not known.

The synthesis of chondroitin sulfate requires, in addition to the enzymes already mentioned, an epimerase which transforms uridine diphospho-N-acetylglucosamine to uridine diphospho-N-acetylgalactosamine (UDP-NAcGal). The synthesis of the ester sulfates (and that of the sulfoamido groups of heparin and heparitin sulfate) requires he presence of "active sulfate" or adenosine-3-phosphate-5-phosphosulfate or PAPS. This nucleotide is formed in two steps (Fig. 3–3) by enzymes widely distributed in various organs. First, adenosine-5-phosphosulfate is formed by a sulfurylase which eliminates pyrophosphate from ATP and substitutes it with sulfate. Then, a phosphokinase transfers the terminal phosphate of another ATP to position 3 of adenosine-5-phosphosulfate thus producing the "active sulfate." A series of specific sulfotransferases transfers the sulfate groups of "active sulfate" to various substrates like phenolic compounds, steroids and mucopolysaccharides.

It is not quite clear whether the synthesis of sulfate esters takes place at the monosaccharide or oligosaccharide level or after the glycosidic chain has been formed. Some investigators believe that the sulfate esters are introduced after completion of the polymer. This would be synthesized from UDP-NAcGal and UDPGA by two synthetases capable of alternate addition of their substrates to the growing chain. The transfer of ester sulfates to the last residue of N-acetylgalactosamine present in the polymer would prevent the additional incorporation of glucuronic acid thus ending the synthetic process.

The synthesis of the protein-chondroitin sulfate complex may be summarized as follows: the protein moiety is synthesized on the ribosomes. A specific enzyme is responsible for the establishment of the linkage between uridine diphosphoxylose (UDPXyl) and serine. Uridine diphosphoxylose is the product of enzymatic decarboxylation of uridine diphosphoglucuronic acid; subsequently, another enzyme acts on uridine diphosphogalactose, introducing two galactose residues after the xylose already attached to the serine. A residue of glucuronic acid follows and then the alternate incorporation of acetylgalactosamine and glucuronic acid. Puromycin inhibits protein synthesis and also the subsequent synthesis of chondroitin sulfate; however, it is not clear whether the xylose-serine linkage takes place after completion of the protein synthesis or if the glycosidic chain starts to be synthesized as soon as such linkage is established, independently from the completion of the protein structure.

Besides the stimulating or inhibiting effect of hormones, vitamins, and drugs on the synthesis of mucopolysaccharides, particularly interesting is the regulatory activity performed by some intermediates of the synthetic process itself (feedback inhibition). For instance, uridine diphosphoxylose inhibits the dehydrogenase which produces uridine diphosphoglucuronic acid from uridine diphosphoglucose (Fig. 3–2). Thus, when the utilization of uridine diphosphoxylose is slow, its accumulation produces a secondary accumulation of uridine diphosphoglucose. This, in turn, may cause specific enzymes to direct glucose-1-phosphate toward different metabolic pathways (toward the glycolytic pathway, for instance, after glucose-1-phosphate has been transformed to glucose-6-phosphate). Similarly, when uridine diphospho-N-acetylglucosamine accumulates, the aminotransferase responsible for transferring the amino group of glutamine to fructose-6-phosphate becomes specifically inhibited, causing a decreased production of the nucleotide temporarily not utilized and a shunt of fructose-6-phosphate toward different pathways.

The catabolism of acid mucopolysaccharides takes place in the tissues where these compounds are found. Ubiquitous lysosomal proteases degrade the protein moieties; as a result, the carbohydrate moieties become very soluble and available to the depolymerizing action of lysosomal hydrolases (hyaluronidase-like enzymes). While some of the partially depolymerized material appears in the urine, the major part of it is completely degraded by a variety of tissue enzymes and is utilized either as a source of energy or for new synthetic reactions.

Although various experimental data indicate that mammalian organisms are capable of removing the sulfate groups from the ester and amido groups of acid mucopolysaccharides, the existence of glycosulfatases or other enzymes responsible for these reactions has not been demonstrated.

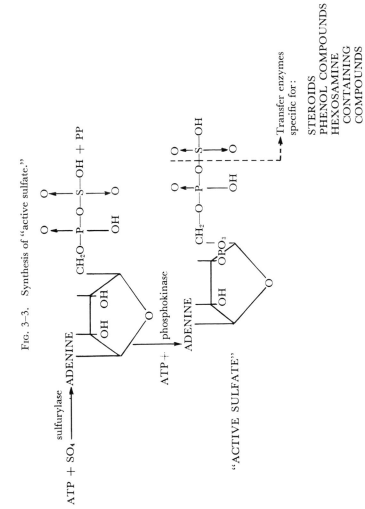

FIG. 3-3.  Synthesis of "active sulfate."

## SELECTED REFERENCES

BRIMACOMBE, J. S. and WEBBER, J. M.: *Mucopolysaccharides*, London, Elsevier Publishing Co., 1964.

CLARK, R. D., SMITH, G. J., JR., and DAVIDSON, E. A.: Hexosamine and acid glycosaminoglycans in human teeth, Biochim. Biophys. Acta, *101*, 267–272, 1965.

SOGNNAES, R. F.: Microstructure and histochemical characteristics of the mineralized tissues, Ann. N.Y. Acad. Sci., *60*, 545–574, 1955.

STACK, M. V.: The chemical nature of the organic matrix of bone, dentine and enamel, Ann. N.Y. Acad. Sci., *60*, 585–595, 1955.

SZIRMAI, J. A., VAN BOVEN-DE Tyssonsk, E., and GARDELL, S.: Microchemical analysis of glycosaminoglycans, collagen, total protein and water in histological layers of nasal septum cartilage, Biochim. Biophys. Acta, *136*, 331–350, 1967.

# Chapter 4

# Histochemistry of Developing Teeth

## J. P. Kennedy, Ph.D.

Introduction
Histogenesis
Histochemistry
Dentinogenesis
Amelogenesis
Cementogenesis

## INTRODUCTION

The development of human teeth is a complex, dynamic physicochemical process that begins about the sixth or seventh week of intrauterine life. Each tooth develops from a tooth germ which is derived from two embryonic tissues, ectoderm and mesoderm. The tooth germs of either deciduous or permanent teeth undergo similar structural and chemical transformations. Morphodifferentiation of tooth germs specific for premolars is different from that of tooth germs that give rise to incisors. This is a brief discussion of certain histochemical changes in the development of a tooth from initiation through the formation of hard dental tissues which begins about the twentieth week of intrauterine life.

Human enamel is formed from the epithelial dental organ or enamel organ which is derived from part of the ectodermal epithelium that lines the oral cavity. Dentine and pulp are formed from the dental papilla which is derived from the mesenchyme that condenses and lies partly within the inverted cup-like epithelial dental organ. Mesenchyme is a loosely arranged, unspecialized embryonic tissue that is the source of all connective tissue. Cells, fibers, tissue fluid, and ground substance are the components of connective tissue. The epithelial dental organ and its subjacent dental papilla are invested by a connective tissue follicle, the dental sac. Cementum, peridental ligament, and part of the alveolar bone are derived from the dental sac. Thus, the epithelial dental organ, dental papilla, and the dental sac produce all components of teeth exclusive of the nerve and vascular supply (Table 4-1).

Table 4–1.  Schema of Tooth Development

| ectodermal epithelium | dental lamina | epithelial dental organ | outer dental epithelium stellate reticulum stratum intermedium inner dental epithelium (ameloblasts) | enamel Nasmyth's membrane Hertwig's epithelial sheath |
|---|---|---|---|---|
| mesoderm | | dental papilla | odontoblasts Korff's fibers blood vessels | dentine pulp |
| | | dental sac | osteoblasts fibroblasts cementoblasts | alveolus peridental membrane cementum |

Oral tissues contain several chemical constituents which reflect their epithelial and connective tissue origin and structure.  These chemical substances include mucopolysaccharides, glycoproteins, mucins and certain enzymes.

## HISTOGENESIS

The derivation and development of dental tissues may be considered in the physiological and histogenetic phases of (1) initiation, (2) proliferation, (3) histodifferentiation and morphodifferentiation, and (4) apposition.  The life cycle of a tooth is depicted in Figure 4–1.

Continuity and interrelationships in the histogenesis of dental tissues have been described in general, but much additional critical study is needed before a precise and coherent understanding is possible.  Even with information obtained from studies using techniques such as historadiography, autoradiography, electron microscopy, special histochemical procedures, and others, the histogenesis and histochemistry of dental tissues remains controversial and inadequately known.  Methods of histology and cytology are described by Bloom and Fawcett, histochemistry by Pearse and instrumental or physical techniques by Newman in their respective publications.  A simple and fundamental account of the developing tooth germ follows.

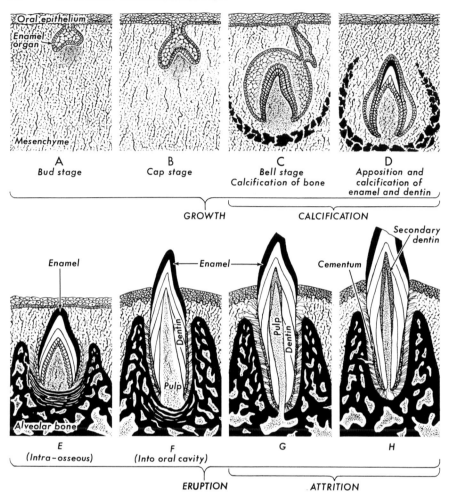

Fig. 4–1.  Diagram of the life cycle of a human deciduous incisor.  (Bloom and Fawcett, *A Textbook of Histology*, courtesy of W. B. Saunders Co.)

Initiation or the beginning of tooth development is a brief but significant process that occurs in human embryos of about 11 mm in length.  Initiation is clearly indicated by the appearance of the dental lamina, a local thickening of the ectodermal epithelium which outlines the future dental arches. Mitotic cells of epithelium and mesenchyme are present.  Glycogen is evident in the cytoplasm.  By subsequent ingrowth the dental lamina presents a continuous band-like ridge into the mesenchyme.  At points indicative of specific deciduous teeth, small epithelial buds appear from the dental lamina.  These bud-like structures with pertinent underlying mesenchyme are the developing tooth germs.

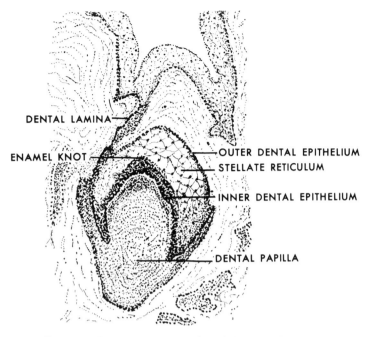

DENTAL LAMINA

ENAMEL KNOT

OUTER DENTAL EPITHELIUM

STELLATE RETICULUM

INNER DENTAL EPITHELIUM

DENTAL PAPILLA

FIG. 4–2.   Intermediate stage of epithelial dental organ.
(Redrawn and modified from Bevelander.)

Proliferation or cell multiplication and growth continues at a rapid but unequal rate until the epithelial tooth germ caps a condensing mass of mesenchyme, the dental papilla.   The cap-like epithelial tooth germ continues to proliferate and begins to histodifferentiate into a bell-shaped structure, the epithelial dental organ, which partially encloses the dental papilla.   At this early stage of development the epithelial dental organ (Fig. 4–2) consists of an outer dental epithelium separated from the inner dental epithelium by a fluid filled cellular network, the stellate reticulum. Metachromatic properties of the stellate reticulum ground substance suggest the presence of acid mucopolysaccharides.   At a later stage an additional layer is seen between the stellate reticulum and the inner dental epithelium. It is the stratum intermedium which may be derived from some of the subjacent cells of the inner dental epithelium.   The cuboidal cells of the stratum intermedium may be pertinent to the formation of the future epithelial attachment of the cervix of the tooth to the oral mucosa.   The cuboidal cells of the outer dental epithelium are arranged radially; the low columnar cells of the inner dental epithelium appear regular and increase in height to form the ameloblasts.

Functions of the stellate reticulum and the stratum intermedium are problematical.   It is doubtful that they serve solely as a cushion to be replaced by hard tissue.   The presence and similar commencement of enzymatic activity in the stellate reticulum and the stratum intermedium suggest a metabolic function. Dehydrogenase activity in these two layers has been reported.

After the disintegration of the epithelial remnant that connected the epithelial dental organ to the oral epithelium, the tooth germ is completely invested by the dental sac. Within the dental sac a small epithelial strand projects from the lingual surface of the epithelial dental organ. It is the dental lamina or successional lamina of the permanent tooth. Molars that are not preceded by deciduous teeth develop from the extension of the dental lamina posterior to the position of the second deciduous molar.

The epithelial dental organ is important in the formation of human enamel. It also influences the elaboration of dentine and the shape of the tooth root through the formation of Hertwig's epithelial sheath. Hertwig's sheath consists of the inner and outer dental epithelium that extends inward about the apical region of the tooth apparently to function as a diaphragm during root formation. Nasmyth's membrane or cuticle covers the enamel of the erupting tooth. It is derived from the stratum intermedium. The cuticle is resistant to certain acids and may be protective.

## HISTOCHEMISTRY

Histochemical properties of the developing dental papilla may be summarized before discussing the elaboration of dentine and enamel. The ground substance of the dental papilla contains an acid mucopolysaccharide as inferred by metachromasia with toluidine blue. Cells of the dental papilla show cytoplasmic processes and are at first undifferentiated. These cells contain or are closely associated with a carbohydrate-protein complex as suggested by a positive periodic acid Schiff (PAS) reaction. Enzymatic activity seems first detectable in the dense mesenchyme that accompanies the developing blood vessels. Alkaline phosphatase activity is intense in the dental papilla.

The dental papilla is separated from the developing ameloblasts by a thin membrane-like structure, the membrana preformativa, which suggests the future dentino-enamel junction. Histochemical investigations of the membrana preformativa indicate that it (1) contains glycoprotein, (2) is metachromatic with toluidine blue, and (3) is periodic acid Schiff (PAS) positive. Reactivity of the membrana preformativa to PAS is greatest before the formation of predentine.

## DENTINOGENESIS

The precise role of the odontoblasts in dentinogenesis is not clear. Some believe they form dentine, others believe they provide its nourishment. Although their precise contribution to dentine formation is questionable, it is clear that these cells are necessary for dentine formation. Impending dentinogenesis is predictable when the odontoblasts and fibers of von Korff congregate near the membrana preformativa so as to obscure the previous cell-sparse zone of Weil. Odontoblasts function in protein synthesis as indicated by their active Golgi complex and the appreciable amount of cytoplasmic RNA. Just before the formation of dentine the odontoblasts develop glycoprotein which may be related to the ground substance.

The fibers of von Korff course between the odontoblasts to spread fan-like against the membrana preformativa. These fibers are precollagenous as indicated by argyrophilic staining and electron micrographs which depict the cross-banding pattern suggestive of collagen. Some believe the fibers of von Korff form collagen for the dentinal matrix. This is not certain. The course of these fibers into the developing dentine (Fig. 4–3) and their close association with the odontoblasts suggest their pertinence to matrix formation. There is evidence that the odontoblasts produce collagen for the dentinal matrix. When methionine labeled with methyl $^{14}$C and methyl $^{3}$H as well as with sulfate $^{35}$S was injected into adult mice, a similar uptake and distribution of methionine was observed in the incisors regardless of the labeled form of methionine that was used. At first a weak band of radioactivity was detectable at 30 minutes in odontoblasts and predentine. Later the reactivity decreased in the odontoblasts, increased in the predentine, and subsequently was present in dentine. Comparable studies with tritium-labeled glycine indicate a similar distribution in these tissues and support the premise that the odontoblasts function in the formation of protocollagen which, when extracellular, forms some collagen fibrils of the dentine.

It is generally believed that collagen or reticular fibers form the fibrous part of the dentinal matrix. The genesis of these fibers is controversial, but a dual origin is not unreasonable. Small width, randomly arranged fibers that are located near the odontoblast process apparently result from odontoblast activity. The larger fibers of von Korff probably originate from the pulp. Interestingly, regardless of their size all show staining and structural characteristics indicative of collagen.

Numerous histochemical investigations, mostly of rodent teeth, report the presence of various and diverse compounds in the developing odontoblastic layer and subjacent pulp. These compounds include glycogen, mucopolysaccharides, acid polysaccharides, alkaline phosphatase, acid phosphatase, 5-nucleic acid, lipid (sudanophilic droplets), sulfydryl and disulfide groups and ascorbic acid. The odontoblasts show dehydrogenase activity which may be related to citric acid and pentose cycles. Histochemical techniques have indicated the presence of succinic, malic, isocitric, glutamic, lactic, $\beta$-hydroxybutyrate, $\alpha$-glycerophosphate, glucose-6-phosphate and 6-phosphogluconate dehydrogenases and DPN and TPN diaphorases in the teeth of 5-day-old rats. In general enzymatic activity precedes the microscopic evidence of dentine and enamel; activity of dehydrogenases is seemingly related to the differentiation and function of the odontoblasts. This inventory of compounds in developing teeth, particularly in the odontoblastic layer and pulp, indicates a metabolic role of these tissues in dentinogenesis.

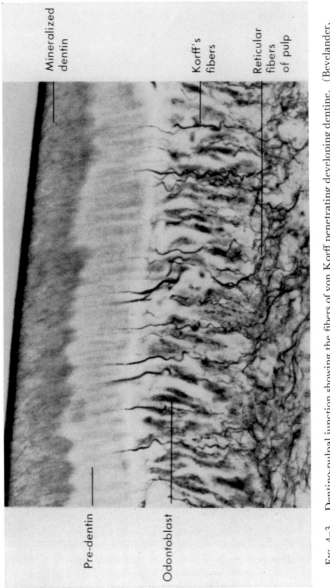

FIG. 4–3.   Dentino-pulpal junction showing the fibers of von Korff penetrating developing dentine.   (Bevelander, *Atlas of Oral Histology and Embryology*, courtesy of Lea & Febiger.)

Predentinal apposition always precedes the formation of dentine. Predentine appears near the developing occlusal surface of the tooth just before the formation of enamel. Concomitant with the deposition of predentine, changes are evident in the odontoblasts. The once columnar odontoblasts recede pulpward leaving cytoplasmic processes that course within small canals, the dentinal tubules, toward and sometimes slightly beyond the dentino-enamel junction. Thus, the formation of dentine consists first in the elaboration of a zone of predentine which contains fibers, a mucopolysaccharide ground substance and the vital odontoblast processes or Tomes dentinal fibrils, which do not calcify.

At thicknesses of about 10 to 20 microns mineralization of predentin begins, nearest the dentino-enamel junction. Dense granules of approximately 100 Å containing an acid mucopolysaccharide appear and may represent the first part of the matrix to undergo mineralization. Subsequently, small mineral crystals appear on the periodic 640 Å bands of the collagen fibers. These fibers appear to be coated with an acid mucopolysaccharide similar to that of the interfibrillar matrix. Development and coalescence mainly through crystal growth leads to the homogeneous mineralized matrix with mature apatite crystals.

Mineralization is usually at first intertubular and mineralization of this matrix is followed by the formation of peritubular dentine within the dentinal tubules. Peritubular dentine stains intensely and metachromatically with toluidine and methyl blue at pH 2.6 and 3.6 respectively. It stains deeply with alcian blue at pH 2.6. This indicates a high acid mucopolysaccharide content of peritubular dentine. Symons believes that the content of other polysaccharide is apparently low because of the failure to stain with the PAS method. It should be made clear that peritubular zone first begins to appear in the mineralized dentine within the dentinal tubule.

According to Bevelander and Nakahara the functional odontoblast elaborates an acid mucopolysaccharide which is probably chondroitin sulfate and is transported to the sites of mineralization. However, the mechanism that initiates crystal formation in the dentinal matrix is not fully understood (see Chapter 5). The acid mucopolysaccharide may serve to transport mineral from the cell to the dentinal matrix. Sulfated mucopolysaccharides may attract or bind positively charged metals such as calcium.

The process of predentine formation and its mineralization is repeated as long as dentine formation continues. As previously indicated, mineralization occurs first at the future dentino-enamel junction in the developing tooth and later at the dentine-predentine border after the first increment of dentine is formed. Hence dentine formation is by apposition of incremental zones. Estimates of the rate of daily dentine deposition in mammalian teeth, exclusive of the continuously growing teeth of rodents, range from about 2 to 16 microns.

## AMELOGENESIS

Amelogenesis may be considered as occurring in two conspicuous phases: (1) organic matrix formation and (2) maturation of enamel. After the initial formation of dentine, cells of the inner dental epithelium begin the formation of enamel and are referred to as ameloblasts. The formation of enamel and dentine is depicted in Figure 4–4.

On the basis of functional and cytological differences, two kinds of ameloblasts may be recognized. They are the tall ameloblasts which are synthesizing and secretory cells engaged in the initial elaboration of the enamel matrix, and the short or post-secretory ameloblasts which function in the maturation of enamel through the removal of organic material and possibly water from the enamel.

The tall ameloblasts are associated with a stratum intermedium in which enzymatic activity is seemingly intense. The close association of the stratum intermedium with blood vessels and its high alkaline phosphatase content suggest that this layer may serve as a barrier involved in the selective transport of certain material to the proximal or basal part of the ameloblasts, which is nearest the stratum intermedium. The precise role of alkaline

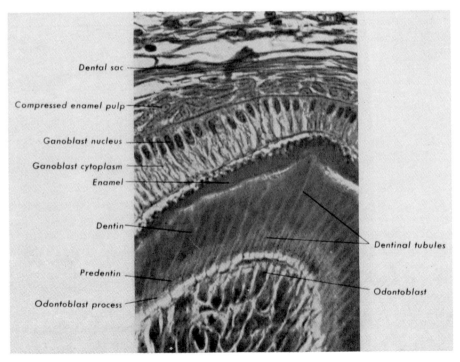

Dental sac

Compressed enamel pulp

Ganoblast nucleus

Ganoblast cytoplasm

Enamel

Dentin

Predentin

Odontoblast process

Dentinal tubules

Odontoblast

FIG. 4–4. Formation of enamel and dentine in the developing incisor of a 5 month human fetus. Mallory-azan stain. (Bloom and Fawcett, *A Textbook of Histology*, courtesy of W. B. Saunders Co.)

phosphatase is not known, but it can be associated with biological transport mechanisms. It has also been suggested that the stratum intermedium functions as a barrier and that alkaline phosphatase splits inhibitory organophosphates.

There is evidence that the formation of enamel involves an extracellular secretion rather than an intracellular transformation. Consideration of the enamel matrix as keratin or keratin-like is unjustified according to Reith and Butcher. Protein formation is intracellular, that is, the product of the proteinizing cell is retained. Nevertheless, protein has been considered an important structure in the formation of the enamel matrix. This conclusion has been supported by similarities in the staining properties of developing enamel and certain amino acids. It seems clear that enamel contains a protein with SH groups which stain intensely red with Mallory's trichrome stain. However, the sulfhydryl reaction is not specific for keratin and conclusions of the specific identity of this protein matrix must be made with caution. Other techniques suggest that the protein matrix has a cross-beta configuration in which polypeptide chains course transversely to the axis of the fibrils.

Tall secretory ameloblasts contain highly organized cisternae of granular endoplasmic reticulum. The demonstration of a plasma membrane between the cytoplasm of the secretory ameloblasts and the apparent product of these cells supports the premise that enamel is an extracellular product. This interpretation is at variance with the traditional view that the enamel matrix is a transformation of the apical cytoplasm or Tomes' process and that enamel prisms are essentially an intracellular elongation of the ameloblasts.

It is now believed that the ameloblasts elaborate enamel matrix which calcifies extracellularly. Calcification begins at the periphery of each prism. During maturation organic material and fluid are removed and calcium salts enter the developing enamel apparently by means of the epithelial dental organ. Inorganic crystallization begins after the initial deposition of the organic enamel matrix. Apatite crystal growth continues and subsequently mature apatite crystals appear. In mature enamel the organic material is almost entirely replaced by a calcified matrix.

## CEMENTOGENESIS

Cementogenesis consists of the formation of an uncalcified layer of cementoid and its subsequent transformation into calcified cementum. The process is suggestive of the formation of dentine and bone.

Dentine formation in the root is influenced by Hertwig's epithelial sheath which for a time separates dentine of the root from the surrounding dental sac. As the epithelial sheath degenerates, cells from the inner zone of the dental sac are observed near the root surface. These cells differentiate into cuboidal cells, the cementoblasts, which elaborate cementoid tissue. The formation of cementum is always preceded by the deposition of a thin layer of cementoid tissue.

The argyrophilic fibers of the dental sac apparently serve as a source of collagen for the formation of the collagen fibrils of the cementoid substance. Mucopolysaccharides from the connective tissue are transformed into the cementoid ground substance. Calcification involves a depolymerization of the ground substance, the incorporation of calcium phosphate and the deposition of apatite crystals along the collagen fibrils.

Fibers of the peridental ligament course into cementum and into alveolar bone where they are known as Sharpey's fibers. Cementum, peridental ligament, and alveolar bone form the suspensorium for a tooth. Interestingly, cells of the peripheral zone of the dental sac differentiate into osteoblasts of the periosteum of the alveolus. Cementum may be classified as cellular or acellular, but there is no functional difference.

## SELECTED REFERENCES

BLOOM, WILLIAM and FAWCETT, DON W.: *A Textbook of Histology*, 9th ed., Philadelphia, W. B. Saunders Co., 1968.

BEVELANDER, GERRIT: *Outline of Histology*, 6th ed., St. Louis, The C. V. Mosby Co., 1967.

BEVELANDER, GERRIT and NAKAHARA, HIROSHI: The formation and mineralization of dentine, Anat. Record, *156*(3): 303–323, 1966.

KRAUS, B. S. and JORDAN, R. E.: *The Human Dentition Before Birth*, Philadelphia, Lea & Febiger, 1965.

NEWMAN, DAVID N. (ed.): *Instrumental Methods of Experimental Biology*, New York, The Macmillan Co., 1964.

PEARSE, A. G. E.: *Histochemistry-Theoretical and Applied*, 2nd ed., Boston, Little, Brown & Co., 1960.

REITH, EDWARD J. and BUTCHER, EARL O.: Microanatomy and Histochemistry of Amelogenesis, p. 371–397. In A. E. W. Miles (ed.), *Structural and Chemical Organization of Teeth*. New York, Academic Press, Inc., 1967.

SICHER, HARRY (ed.): *Orban's Oral Histology and Embryology*, 5th ed., St. Louis, The C. V. Mosby Co., 1962.

SYMONS, N. B. B.: The Microanatomy and Histochemistry of Dentinogenesis, p. 285–324. In A. E. W. Miles (ed.), *Structural and Chemical Organization of Teeth*. New York, Academic Press, Inc., 1967.

# Chapter 5

# Mineralization of Bones and Teeth

James J. Vogel, Ph.D.

## INTRODUCTION

Certain biological tissues undergo a mineralization process commonly referred to as *calcification*. This process can be defined as a sequence of events where specific cells are induced to form an organic matrix within which insoluble calcium salts are deposited. The calcium salts can be either carbonates or phosphates depending upon the type of tissue and its environment. In mammalian calcified tissues (bones and teeth) and in certain bacteria, the major calcium salt is similar in composition to the mineral hydroxyapatite, $Ca_{10} (PO_4)_6 (OH)_2$. Calcification is a dynamic process with the formation and maintenance of the tissues controlled by cellular activity. In this chapter the mechanism of calcification and the formation of the oral calcified tissues enamel, dentine, cementum, and alveolar bone will be discussed.

## SOURCE OF CONSTITUENTS OF CALCIFIED TISSUES

The organic components of the calcified tissues are essentially of cellular origin. They are the protein matrix, the mucopolysaccharide ground substance and lipids. The inorganic constituents must come from external sources. The source for mammalian tissues is the blood. A dynamic equilibrium exists between inorganic ions in the blood and those in the tissues.

Since calcium and inorganic phosphate are the major constituents of calcified tissues, it is important to understand the relationship of these ions between the body fluids and the mineral phase of the tissues. At physiological pH calcium and phosphate exist essentially as $Ca^{2+}$ and $HPO_4^{2-}$. The normal level of total calcium in the blood serum is from 4.5 to 5.5 mEq/L. Approximately 50% of the total calcium is bound by serum protein and the remaining is either ionized or complexed with small anions such as citrate and phosphate. Both ionized calcium and calcium complexed with small anions are ultrafilterable through semipermeable membranes. Approximately 80% of the total phosphate in serum is $HPO_4^{2-}$ which would amount to 1.5 mEq/L.

The relationship of $Ca^{2+}$ and $HPO^{2-}$ between body fluids and the mineral phase of calcified tissues has been the subject of extensive investigation. The variable solubility of hydroxyapatite under physiological conditions has made the determination of a definite solubility product difficult. The general conclusion is that the product $Ca^{2+} \times HPO_4^{2-}$ in body fluids exceeds the experimentally determined solubility product for hydroxyapatite. Although the ion product is greater than the solubility product, spontaneous precipitation of hydroxyapatite does not occur provided the conditions are not changed. Thus in body fluids, a metastable state exists for calcium phosphate (Fig. 5–1).

Even though the concentration of calcium phosphate in the body fluid is in a state of supersaturation, it is unique in that only specific biological catalysts or crystal seeds of hydroxyapatite will induce the formation and growth of crystals. The relationship between calcium and phosphate in the body fluids and in the mineral phase is shown in Figure 5–2.

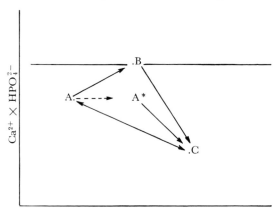

FIG. 5–1. The metastable state of $Ca^{2+} \times HPO_4^{2-}$ is at point A and the solid (Hydroxyapatite) state at point C. In order for hydroxyapatite to form, either the ionic product must be increased to point B at which spontaneous precipitation would occur or a catalyst must be introduced which would lower the energy required in forming apatite crystals. This is illustrated by the broken line, the catalyzed intermediate state A* and the line to C. Once hydroxyapatite is formed it is in physical and chemical equilibrium with the ion product of the fluid phase indicated by the double arrow between A and C. The nature of the catalyst will be discussed later in mechanism of calcification.

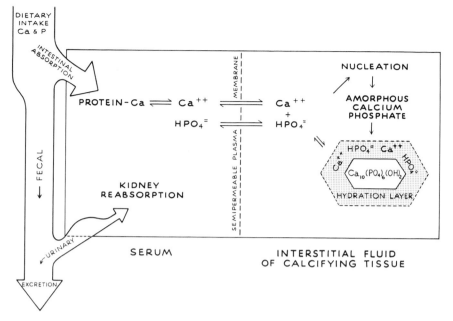

F$_{IG}$. 5–2.   Routes of calcium and phosphorus in
body fluids and calcified tissues.

The level of calcium in the blood is regulated by a homeostatic mechanism which requires the participation of skeletal tissues. Two hormones have important functions in serum calcium homeostasis. The parathyroid glands secrete a hormone, parathormone, which raises the level of blood calcium. Most investigations indicate that the effect of parathormone is to enhance bone resorption which in turn releases more calcium into the body fluids. It is not known whether the hormone does this by increasing osteoclastic activity or by affecting the cellular membrane transport of calcium. An indirect effect of the hormone is to increase renal excretion of phosphate which in turn lowers the serum phosphate concentration. The second hormone is produced by the thyroid glands and has been called thyrocalcitonin. It has the opposite effect of parathormone and lowers serum calcium by inhibiting bone resorption. It is not known whether calcitonin acts directly upon bone metabolism or whether it acts to regulate parathormone action. The homeostatic mechanism is influenced by the metabolic demands for calcium.

Other inorganic ions commonly present in the calcified tissues include sodium, potassium, magnesium, chloride, carbonate, and fluoride as well as trace amounts of iron, copper, manganese, and zinc. The calcified tissues, particularly bone, serve as a reservoir for most of these ions and the bulk of them are located in the hydration layer surrounding the surfaces of the apatite crystals. Certain amounts of $F^-$, $Cl^-$ and carbonate can be incorporated within the lattice of the apatite crystals as well. Certain ions have been shown to influence the formation and the solubility of hydroxyapatite. For example, fluoride enhances apatite formation and results in the formation of larger and more perfect crystals. The incorporation of carbonate into the lattice causes the crystals to be more soluble. Magnesium ions, if present in high enough concentration, can interfere with the formation of hydroxyapatite. Another function of the mineral phase of bone is to remove toxic or harmful ions such as lead and radiostrontium from the body fluids.

## THE MECHANISM OF CALCIFICATION

### Historical Aspects

In order to bring theories on the mechanism of calcification into a modern perspective, it is helpful to review briefly some of the historical background of research in this area. The fact that specific tissues undergo calcification while adjacent tissues within the same environment do not is one of the more intriguing phenomena of living organisms. Much effort has been directed toward attempting to understand the initial mechanisms responsible for the formation of bones and teeth.

The father of basic research on calcification was Franz Hofmeister who in 1910 proposed that the deposition of calcium phosphate in living animals was initiated by specific protein-metal ion binding reactions. Later investigators extended this concept to involve, as a repetitive process, the binding of calcium by protein followed by subsequent release to form insoluble calcium phosphate. A discovery by Robison in 1923 shifted the emphasis from calcium binding to the role of the enzyme alkaline phosphatase in the initiation of calcification. Robison observed that alkaline phosphatase was highly active in areas of bone undergoing active calcification. He proposed that the enzyme split sugar phosphate esters and produced a local concentration of phosphate ions sufficient to induce the spontaneous precipitation of calcium phosphate. After realizing that the calcifying tissues did not contain enough sugar phosphate esters, he suggested that an unknown secondary booster mechanism was also involved. When glycolysis was found to be active in calcifying tissues, it was suggested that glycogen breakdown could serve as the booster mechanism by providing sugar phosphate esters which were then hydrolyzed by the alkaline phosphatase. Because of its simplicity, the combination of glycolysis and alkaline phosphatase activity was cited for many years as being the initial mechanism in calcification. Although widely accepted, this concept was open to criticism. It was difficult to explain why other tissues high in alkaline phosphatase, such as intestinal mucosa, did not calcify. Even with the complete hydrolysis of the sugar phosphate esters produced by glycolysis, the concentration of inorganic phosphate did not reach the point where spontaneous precipitation could readily occur. Finally, careful histochemical studies indicated that both enzymatic activities were closely associated with cellular activity, whereas calcification occurred outside the cells.

Since the early 1950's because of the studies of Neumann and his co-workers, attention has turned from spontaneous precipitation to nucleation catalysis as being the initiating event in calcification. A "local factor" which could induce the formation of apatite crystals without requiring spontaneous precipitation was found to occur in tissues undergoing calcification. The conclusion was that this "local factor" catalyzed the formation of nuclei which in turn promoted crystal growth in a metastable solution. The exact nature of this nucleation catalysis is not known; however, various mechanisms have been suggested. One mechanism is that some component in the tissue matrix provides a template on which the apatite crystals can grow. Another is that the matrix contains a specific charged site which can form clusters of calcium and phosphate ions which then serve as nuclei for crystal growth. After the role of nucleation catalysis was generally accepted, attempts were made to define the nature of the catalyzing structure in the calcifying tissues. The roles of various constituents can be summarized as follows:

1. *The Role of Collagen.* Collagen has been the constituent most extensively studied in relation to the nucleation catalyst. Electron microscopic

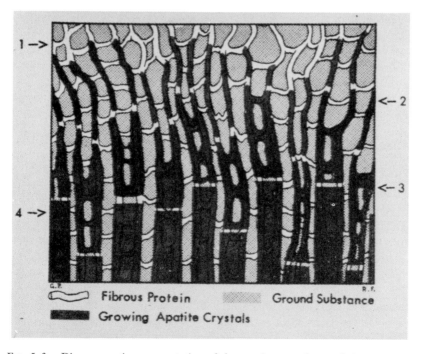

Fig. 5–3. Diagrammatic representation of the apatite crystal growth in rat enamel: (1) organic matrix formation; (2) beginning of calcification along the longitudinal fibrous protein; (3) partial fusion of adjacent calcifying fibrils; (4) young apatite crystals. (R. M. Frank, R. F. Sognnaes and R. Kern, Calcification and Enamel Ultrastructure in *Calcification in Biological Systems*, R. F. Sognnaes, Ed., Am. Assoc. Adv. Sci., Washington, D.C., 1960, p. 185.)

studies have demonstrated a close morphological relationship between collagen fibrils and the apatite crystals (Fig. 5–3). Also, reconstituted collagen fibrils have been shown to induce apatite crystal formation when placed in a metastable calcium phosphate solution. Only native type fibrils with the 640 Å banding pattern are able to act as a catalyst. The catalyzing effect of collagen has been attributed to the presence of specific sites within the molecules such as organically bound phosphate groups. The nucleating ability of collagen is not unique, since a variety of other proteins can also induce the formation of hydroxyapatite. Among these are the protein of enamel, elastin, and organic components of certain bacteria. One of the arguments against collagen is that it is present in tissues which do not calcify.

2. *The Role of Mucopolysaccharides.* Histological studies have shown that the synthesis of mucopolysaccharides in calcifying tissues is rapid just prior to the deposition of mineral. When the mucopolysaccharide was found to contain chondroitin sulfate, it was suggested that the acidic groups bound and localized calcium so that nucleation could occur. A demonstration that sulfate blocking groups inhibited *in vitro* calcification supported such a concept. Although the mucopolysaccharides are closely associated with calcification, their role in nucleation is not conclusive. Because they bind calcium so strongly, they have been postulated as being an inhibitor of calcification *in vivo*. As with collagen, other tissues which do not calcify contain large quantities of mucopolysaccharides.

3. *Role of Lipids.* A lipid substance has been found at the calcification front, that is, the area of tissue undergoing calcification. It has been shown to be acidic in nature but its role in the calcification mechanism has not been established. A lipid substance isolated from *Bacterionema matruchotii*, a microorganism which forms apatite intracellularly, has been found to bind calcium. It is unknown whether a lipid substance is involved in nucleation catalysis.

4. *The Role of Enzymes.* Marked synthesis of ATP has been observed in calcifying tissues. A phosphokinase has also been shown to be present and it has been suggested that this enzyme transfers phosphate groups from ATP into the collagen molecule. The phosphate which is organically bound then acts as the nucleation site for calcification. However, the phosphokinase is non-specific and can be found in connective tissues which normally do not calcify.

The other enzyme most frequently discussed in relation to calcification has been alkaline phosphatase. Its function in the spontaneous precipitation theory was discussed earlier. Another suggested function for alkaline phosphatase has been that it removes phosphate ester groups which block the site of active calcification in the organic matrix. Again the enzyme is not specific for the calcified tissues and is widely distributed in other non-calcifying tissues. Recently, certain sugar phosphate esters and inorganic pyrophosphate have been shown to interfere with calcification. The alkaline phosphatase in bone also has inorganic pyrophosphatase activity and the following mechanism for calcification has been proposed (Fig. 5–4). It in-

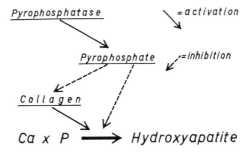

FIG. 5–4. Possible role of pyrophosphatase in calcification.

volves inhibition of calcification by pyrophosphate ions and removal of the inhibition by the pyrophosphatase activity.

One of the difficulties in evaluating the role of enzymes in nucleation catalysis is in separating those involved in the mechanism from those associated with cellular activity and matrix formation.

## CURRENT CONCEPTS CONCERNING CALCIFICATION

The heterogeneous nature of calcified tissues has made difficult the elucidation of the mechanism involved in initiating calcification. It is evident that some local factor is involved; however, most of the proposed mechanisms lack the specificity which would be required. It is possible that the process of calcification requires a sequence of specific steps. For example, a triphasic mechanism has been proposed. Calcium is bound to protein in the first step followed by phosphate ion association to form a protein-calcium-phosphate complex as the second step. The third and final step would be the formation of a geometric configuration of ions which could serve as a nucleation center. This requirement for a specific sequence of events might explain why some tissues, although similar in composition to bones and teeth, do not calcify.

## THE DEVELOPMENT AND MATURATION OF CALCIFICATION

Once nucleation has occurred, hydroxyapatite crystals form and grow within the framework defined by the organic matrix of the tissue. During maturation of the calcified tissues, there is an initial loss of some organic material (mainly protein), but the greatest change occurs with the loss of water and the accumulation of mineral. The process of calcification varies with each type of tissue.

## THE CALCIFICATION OF BONE

The cells responsible for mineralization of bone are the osteoblasts whose primary function is the formation of a calcifiable matrix. Electron micrographs of developing bone show that the osteoblasts are intimately associated with the process of mineral deposition. It is likely that the metabolism of these cells is a controlling factor in mineralization. As soon as the collagen fibrils are laid down by the cells, small dots of calcium phosphate appear on the fibrils. The dots eventually fuse into ribbons of electron dense material. This initial deposition of calcium phosphate is of an amorphous nature. Prior to extensive calcification collagen has a major 640 Å banding with periodicity at 100 Å as well. The earliest apatite crystals seem to be associated with the 100 Å periodicity. The apatite crystals are oriented with their long axis parallel to the axis of the collagen fibrils. In mature bone the crystals average $400 \times 200\text{--}300 \times 25\text{--}50$ Å in dimensions. Bone from an 80-year-old man was found to contain crystals up to 1500 Å in length. The morphological component of bone calcification is called the osteone and consists of cells, unmineralized matrix, and mineralized matrix.

## THE CALCIFICATION OF CEMENTUM AND DENTINE

The process of mineralization in cementum is similar to that of bone. The cells responsible are called cementoblasts and lie between the edge of the periodontal membrane and a thin layer of uncalcified precementum.

The formation of dentine occurs in two stages. First a collagenous matrix of predentine is laid down from the pulp. Then calcification occurs at a definite zone between predentine and dentine. The cells responsible for calcification of the predentine matrix are the odontoblasts. As with bone the initial calcium phosphate deposition is amorphous and begins in the matrix which is at the tip of the cusp. The matrix surrounding the odontoblastic process is referred to as the peritubular matrix and is altered just prior to mineral deposition. Small apatite crystals are oriented along the collagen fibers of the peritubular matrix. The crystals grow and fuse together until the entire matrix becomes calcified. The apatite crystals are smaller than in enamel and have been described as platelets up to 1000 Å in length.

## THE CALCIFICATION OF ENAMEL

Enamel is unique in comparison with the other oral calcified tissues. First, the organic matrix is not collagen but a different type protein. Secondly, the apatite crystals are much larger in size. The cells responsible for calcification of enamel are called ameloblasts. Significant amounts of calcium can be found in the matrix even in the earliest stages of formation. The initial apatite crystals are deposited next to dentine in juxtaposition to collagen fibrils. Some have the opinion that these collagen fibrils at the dentino-enamel junction are the nucleators for enamel calcification. The first apatite crystals are plates or ribbons about 15 Å thick and mature by increasing in width and length. The mature hexagonal crystals are 500 to 1200 Å in width and 3000 to 5000 Å in length. An average hydroxyapatite crystallite in enamel is $1600 \times 400 \times 170$ Å. In human enamel the crystallites are organized into a basic structural unit called a prism. The long axis of the crystallites is oriented in the same direction as the axis of the prisms. The junction between the ameloblasts and the prisms is called the Tomes' process and some investigators believe that each prism is formed by a single ameloblast. The enamel prisms are oriented in a cone-like fashion about the axis of the tooth. A non-oriented layer of sheath enamel is also present on the outer surface.

Unlike other calcified tissues, enamel contains virtually no detectable amorphous calcium phosphate. The apatite crystals appear to form rapidly as the organic matrix is formed by the cells.

## SELECTED REFERENCES

BACHRA, B. N.: Some molecular aspects of tissue calcification, Clinical Orthopaedics, *51*, 199–222, 1967.

McLEAN, F. C. and URIST, M. R.: *Bone, Dynamics of Calcification*, Chicago, University of Chicago, 1961.

MINER, R. W. (ed.): Recent advances in the study of the structure, composition and growth of mineralized tissues, Ann. N.Y. Acad. Sci., *60*, 54–806, 1955.

SOGNNAES, R. F. (ed.): *Calcification in Biological Systems*, Washington D.C., American Association for the Advancement of Science, pub. No. 64, 1960.

URIST, M. R.: Origins of current ideas about calcification, Clin. Orthopaedics, *44*, 13–39, 1966.

# Chapter 6

## Physicochemical Properties of Enamel and Dentine

### Stuart Zimmerman, Ph.D.

Introduction
Enamel Crystalline Structure
     Unit Cell
     Crystallite Size and Shape
     Chemical Substituents and Ca/P Ratio
     Possible Apatite Precursors
     Optical Properties
Enamel Solubility
     Variation in Depth of Chemical Components
Prism Structure
     Prism Dimensions
     Traditional Enamel Structure
     Recent Concept of Enamel Structure
Dentine
     Mineral Phase
     Dentinal Structure

## INTRODUCTION

Enamel and dentine, the two primary calcified tissues of the tooth have certain common features, but differ in other important respects. Therefore in the following discussion many of the physicochemical properties of the mineral phase will be discussed under enamel with exceptions noted where they are applicable to dentine.

## ENAMEL CRYSTALLINE STRUCTURE

### Unit Cell

The structural organization of the enamel has been extensively studied principally by means of ordinary microscopy, polarization microscopy, infrared spectrophotometry, x-ray diffraction, electron diffraction, and electron microscopy. Since the dimensions of crystallites comprising the enamel mineral phase are considerably smaller than the resolving power of the optical microscope, the latter three techniques have been the most informative. Only indirect evidence of the submicroscopic structure of enamel can be obtained by the optical techniques.

Early chemical analyses indicated that the mineral matter of enamel was a calcium phosphate salt. X-ray diffraction investigations confirmed that the mineral phase belongs to a class of compounds known as apatites. Specifically, hydroxyapatite is the particular apatite present in the enamel. More correctly it should be described as a carbonate apatite. The role of carbonate in enamel will be discussed later. Apatites are characterized by the preservation of a specific crystalline configuration, even under the influence of substitution of some of their chemical constituents. Pure hydroxyapatite can be stoichiometrically represented as $Ca_{10}(PO_4)_6(OH)_2$. However, magnesium, strontium, radium, and hydronium ions can substitute in the calcium position; fluoride can substitute in the hydroxyl position resulting in fluorapatite; and carbonate can substitute somewhere within the crystalline lattice. Naturally occurring geological apatites include francolite, dahllite (both carbonate containing apatites), and the aforementioned fluor-

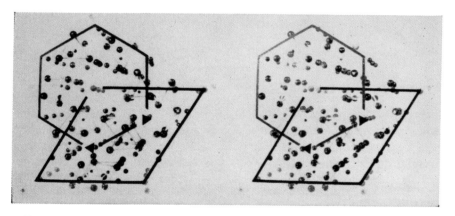

Fig. 6–1. Stereopicture of a model of apatite structure viewed parallel to the hexagonal axis down upon the basal plane. The hexagonal unit cell is outlined by the taped rhombus. The unit cell contains 10 Ca, 6 PO₄ (tetrahedra), 2 OH on the $c$-axes at the corners of the rhombus. The depth of the unit cell extends from the first to the third OH. The taped hexagon indicates the hexagonal symmetry around the $c$-axis. The PO₄ tetrahedra have one vertical and one horizontal edge and two vertical and two tilted faces. Two symmetry planes perpendicular to the $c$-axes pass through the horizontal edges of the PO₄ tetrahedra, and through the OH and the Ca ions not lying on the threefold rotation axes.

With a little practice one may succeed, without the use of a stereoscope, in seeing the stereoscopic picture in space. Place the well-illuminated pictures symmetrically before you. Align your eyes parallel by viewing "through the pictures" an imaginary distant spot. While the eyes accommodate to the closer distance of the pictures (25 to 30 cm) the two pictures fuse into a single three-dimensional view. A piece of cardboard placed vertically between the two pictures may be of help at the beginning. (This model was built by Dr. Edward Klein using data of Beevers and Mac-Intyre, 1946.) (A. E. W. Miles, courtesy of Academic Press, 1967.)

apatite. The crystal can be regarded as built-up of small units of parallel-epiped shape, the "unit cells." Repetition of unit cells in the direction of the three axes represents the entire crystal. The crystalline unit cell is shown in Figure 6–1.

The dimensions of the unit cell and the positions of ions within the cell have been determined by the employment of several experimental techniques, principally x-ray diffraction analysis. A discussion of the methodology can be found in Trautz's article. The lengths of the unit cell (horizontal) axes are $a_1 = a_2 = 9.42\text{Å}$, while the (vertical) c axes are 6.88Å. The spatial arrangement of ions composing the cell has been described by Trautz as: "The hexagonal unit cell, which is the smallest space unit of the structure containing all the crystallographic symmetry elements of the whole crystal, is a parallelepipedon whose edges are formed by the two horizontal 'a' axes, enclosing an angle of 120°, and by the vertical 'c' axes at right angles to the 'a' axes. The unit cell contains 10 $Ca^{2+}$, 6 $PO_4^{3-}$, and 2 $OH^-$ ions. The phosphate oxygens are arranged in tetrahedral groups enclosing the phosphorus and are tied more strongly to it than to the $Ca^{2+}$ ions, which are interspersed between the $PO_4^{3-}$ groups as such are built into the crystal. The two $OH^-$ ions sit on the hexagonal 'c' axes, each surrounded by three $Ca^{2+}$ ions at the same level. The other four $Ca^{2+}$ occupy positions on the two vertical triagonal axes which pass through the cell at one third and two thirds along the long cell diagonal." The symbolic representation for the apatite is $P6_3/M$. The P denotes a primitive cell, *i.e.* there is one unique arrangement of atoms consistent with the symmetry of the cell. The $6_3$ denotes the c axis is a sixfold screw axis. "This means that after rotating the structure about c through $2\pi/6 = 60°$, and simultaneously shifting along the c axes through c × 3/6, *i.e.* c/2, the appearance of the structure will be identical to what it was originally."

## Crystallite Size and Shape

The crystallites in enamel are considerably longer (up to a factor of 10) than those occurring in either bone, dentine, or cementum. Many naturally occurring apatite crystals grow in the form of hexagonal prisms. Developing enamel crystallites take the form of either rods or platelets, there being some disagreement about the magnitude of the crystallite width. Crystals ranging in length from 1200 to 2100 Å and width from 150 to 250 Å have been reported (Fig. 6–2).

Investigations of the crystallite shape in developing dentine by stereoscopic techniques provide a view of individual crystals at different angles. Crystals that gave a narrow dense profile in one orientation presented broad, less dense profiles after being tilted about their long axes. A needle-like structure would not behave in this manner, thus it was concluded that dentinal crystals are plate-like structures. As the enamel matures, the

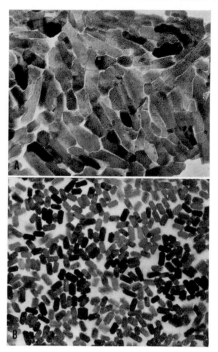

FIG. 6–2.   Electron micrograph of cross sectioned crystals from mature human (A) and immature rodent incisor enamel (B).   A central dark line (arrow) can be seen in some crystals in both types of enamel.   × 75,000.   (Nylen, Int. Dent. Journal, *17*, 719–733, 1967.)

crystallites become more densely packed.   Two arrangements of the crystallites in mature enamel are suggested in the electron microscopic study of Johansen.   In the first pattern (Fig. 6–3) the crystallites are oriented parallel to each other and appear as straight regular crystals.   The second pattern contains an irregular arrangement of crystallites of quite variable morphology (Fig. 6–4).

Quite a few of the crystallites deviate from parallelism to some extent with certain divergences reaching the maximum of 90°.   Those crystallites found in the irregular arrangement also vary widely in width and shape.   Both extensions and indentations are seen in Figure 6–4.   Many crystallites in this structural arrangement are formed such that the boundary of one crystallite is in complementary apposition to its neighbors.   It has been reasoned that the lateral enlargement of the crystallites during maturation would bring the originally sparsely spaced crystallites into approximation, with their final shape dependent upon the relative rate and direction of growth along with the remaining spatial configuration between adjacent crystallites.

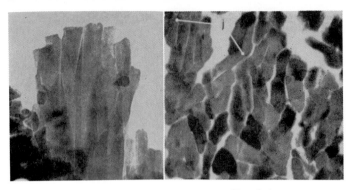

Fɪɢ. 6–3.          Fɪɢ. 6–4.

Fɪɢ. 6–3.  *1*, Crystallites of sound enamel in parallel and presumably natural arrangement.  Homogenate preparation.  ($\times$ approx. 91,300.)

Fɪɢ. 6–4.  Section of sound enamel illustrating irregular arrangement and varying morphology of crystallites.  Both parallel and diverging crystallites can be seen.  Individual crystallites show great variation in size and shape and junctions between terminal ends can be seen (j).  Note the structural arrangement whereby the boundary of one crystallite is in complementary apposition with those of adjacent crystallites.  ($\times$ approx. 113,400.)  (Johansen, E.: Comparison of the Ultrastructure and Chemical Composition of Sound and Carious Enamel from Human Permanent Teeth in *Tooth Enamel*, Stack, M. V. and Fearnhead, R. W. (Eds.), Bristol, John Wright & Sons, 1965, p. 177–181.)

Within the crystallites, the apatite unit cells are oriented with their c-axes almost parallel with the crystallite long axis, the maximum divergence encountered is about $2°$.  There is considerably more variation in the angle made between the long axis of the enamel crystallite and the long axis of the enamel prism.  This will be discussed further when the microanatomy of the enamel is presented.

The minute size of the apatite crystallites plays a decisive role in determining its variable chemical composition.  Since the enamel crystallites are only a few unit cells thick, a large fraction of the atoms are located at or near the surface.

### Chemical Substituents and the Ca/P Ratio

The large fraction of crystalline ionic sites at or near the crystal surface permit frequent homoionic exchange, *i.e.* exchange of like ions within the crystal lattice, as well as hetero-ionic exchange.  As mentioned earlier, lead, magnesium, manganese, strontium, and hydronium can substitute for the calcium in hydroxyapatite.  Arsenate or vanadate can substitute for phosphate and fluoride or chloride can substitute in the hydroxyl position.  In addition, ions can be adsorbed to the crystal surface by electrostatic attraction or retained in the strongly bound hydration layer associated with the crystal.

Under all these substitutions, the apatite crystals maintain essentially the same structural configuration. When the substituents do not appreciably change the size of the unit cell, *e.g.* fluorine resulting in fluorapatite, the two isomorphous apatites, such as fluor and hydroxyapatite, can mix in any proportion and form a continuous series of solid solutions. A dissimilarity of more than 10% in the cell dimensions of the two isomorphous crystals will limit the extent of substitution.

The chemical composition of the enamel mineral reflects the composition of the serum and calcifying fluid environment at the time of calcification. In this way, for example, $^{90}Sr$ removed from atmospheric fallout will be incorporated into teeth and bones following a period of nuclear testing. Whereas there is rapid exchange in developing enamel, as calcification progresses, ions both natural and foreign become "diffusion locked" due to the restricted intracrystalline space and electrostatic charge repulsion. The fluoride content of human enamel likewise increases with the fluoride content of the drinking water of a given area.

Pure synthetic hydroxyapatite has a Ca/P ratio of 1.67 on a molar basis or 2.15 on a weight basis. In actual analyses of dental enamel, Ca/P ratios of from 1.92 to 2.17 (by weight) have been reported in the literature. In nearly all cases, the ratio is below 2.15. Several explanations have been offered for this phenomenon. Adsorption of phosphate on the crystallites or the substitution of sodium, magnesium, or other ions has been proposed as a contributing factor. Specifically, a substitution of hydronium ion, $H_3O^+$ for 2 calcium ions has been suggested. More recently, the idea of a reduced Ca/P ratio arising from a defect in the crystalline structure has been postulated. One explanation offered is that calcium ions are missing in certain positions in the lattice. These calcium deficient apatites appear to be metastable with respect to hydroxyapatite towards which they slowly change by acquiring calcium ions from solution.

*Carbonate.* Carbonate, among the apatite substituents, has been the subject of many studies and deserves separate mention. The apatite present in dental enamel is not a pure hydroxyapatite, but rather a carbonate apatite with a carbonate content of 2 to 3%. For nearly 30 years there has been a controversy about the location of the carbonate in enamel, dentine, and bone.

One school of thought (Carlstrom, 1955) has maintained that the small fraction of carbonate present in the enamel existed in the form of a noncrystalline phase, adsorbed to the surface of hydroxyapatite crystallites. This carbonate phase, an amorphous calcium carbonate, would not be detectable by x-ray diffraction analysis as the non-crystalline material would not give rise to any lines in the diffractogram.

Another group of workers claim that the carbonate is actually incorporated in the apatite lattice. Most recent investigations support this point of view. There still exists some discussion as to the exact sites in the lattice that are occupied by the carbonate. The aforementioned investigations have analyzed naturally occurring carbonate apatites such as dahllite and francolite along with a series of synthetic carbonate apatites whose carbonate content varied from 0.4 to 22.5%. Crystallographic analysis of these carbonate apatites reveal that with increasing carbonate there is a decrease in the a axis dimension relative to hydroxyapatite. Also, chemical analyses show that a $PO_4$ decrease corresponds with a carbonate increase in these series. This evidence led them to propose a substitution of carbonate for phosphate in the lattice.

Other researchers employing infrared absorption spectroscopy report that only a fraction of the carbonate in the enamel is substituted within the lattice and that fraction appears in the hydroxyl position. Thus, while most recent investigators agree that carbonate appears to be substituting within the lattice rather than existing in an amorphous phase, there is still some disagreement as to the actual position of the carbonate.

The presence and location of carbonate in dental enamel may relate directly to the risk of carious attacks. Carbonate has been shown to be leached preferentially from early carious lesions. Further, carbonate content and susceptibility of teeth to dental caries have been correlated. Carbonate apatites have an increased acid solubility which most probably explains the increased caries susceptibility of high carbonate teeth.

*Fluoride.* Numerous clinical studies have shown that the addition of 1 ppm fluoride to public drinking water or the treatment of teeth with topically applied fluoride solution has been effective in reducing the occurrence of dental caries. Because of this caries inhibiting effect, fluoride has been studied quite extensively.

Two modes of fluoride interaction with hydroxyapatite dependent on the fluoride concentration are known. With high fluoride concentrations, around 5 to 10%, there is a surface reaction of the hydroxyapatite to form calcium fluoride, $CaF_2$. This reaction occurs to a certain extent as a result of topical application of sodium fluoride or stannous fluoride. The reaction may be represented by the equation:

$$Ca_{10}(PO_4)_6(OH)_2 + 20\ F^- \rightarrow 10\ CaF_2 + 6\ PO_4 + 2\ OH^-.$$

Calcium fluoride forms a precipitate because of its low solubility product $(K_{sp}3 \times 10^{-11})$. Its formation is associated with the dissolution of the apatite. While calcium fluoride has been found on powdered enamel and on intact enamel surfaces *in vitro* after fluoride topical treatment, there is uncertainty over the fate of calcium fluoride in the mouth. One possibility is that it may dissolve and provide fluoride for the formation of fluorapatite, although the kinetics of this reaction make it a very unlikely possibility.

When fluoride solution at a concentration 1 ppm is applied to hydroxyapatite, fluorapatite is formed by the reaction expressed in the following equation:

$$Ca_{10}(PO_4)_6(OH)_2 + 2\ F^- \rightarrow Ca_{10}(PO_4)_6F_2 + 2\ OH^-$$

Initially, fluoride is deposited in low concentrations, around 30 to 50 ppm, during the formation of the apatite crystals in the calcification phase of enamel development. After calcification is complete, more fluoride is taken up by the external enamel. Before eruption there is an increased uptake from tissue fluids; after eruption, the surface enamel continues to take up fluoride from the oral environment.

Fluoride increases the crystallinity of apatite, whereas bicarbonate reduces it. Octa-calcium phosphate instead of apatite forms when precipitation occurs from a solution of calcite and sodium phosphate under high partial pressures of carbon dioxide at almost neutral pH. However, addition of fluoride ions to the same solutions results in the formation of apatite. The fluoride increases the crystallinity of the formed apatite as measured by the broadening effects on the x-ray diffraction peaks. Legeros et al. also reported that apatites with a high carbonate content had a reduced crystallinity and smaller crystallite size, with increased surface area and solubility. These results are consistent with the caries inhibiting and caries potentiating effects of fluoride and carbonate respectively.

## Possible Apatite Precursors

*Octa-calcium Phosphate.* Walter E. Brown strongly advocated a mechanism of apatite formation in which octa-calcium phosphate appears as a precursor stage. Octa-calcium phosphate which is a hydrated calcium phosphate formula may be represented as $Ca_8H_2(PO_4)_6 \cdot 5H_2O$. In Brown's proposed mechanism, three stages occur in the growth of apatite crystals. The first is the formation of an incipient crystallization seed. In the second stage, the seed grows in two dimensions only, length and width, but not in thickness, resulting in a thin blade or ribbon-shaped crystallite. This blade is considered to be a single unit cell thickness of octa-calcium phosphate. The third and final stage results in the three-dimensional growth of the crystallite consists of two steps. The first is a precipitation of a single layer of octa-calcium phosphate, one unit cell in thickness, on the crystal followed by a hydrolysis of a unit cell thickness of octa-calcium phosphate to produce a layer of hydroxyapatite two unit cells thick. Fluoride ions would have a profound influence on this system since fluoride converts octa-calcium phosphate to an apatite, as mentioned earlier. Thus, fluoride's effectiveness in reducing dental caries is considered due to its initiation of hydrolysis and the elimination of accidental retention of the more soluble octa-calcium phosphate in the crystal. While octa-calcium phosphate is easily prepared synthetically and has occasionally been reported in studies on the mineralization of bone *in vitro*, no proof has been presented that octa-calcium phosphate is involved in the growth mechanism of enamel crystals or other biological apatitic crystals.

*Amorphous Calcium Phosphate.* Recent investigations have revealed that an amorphous calcium phosphate phase exists in bone along with the crystalline apatite phase. The presence of this phase and a quantitative evaluation of its percentage of the total bone mineral content has been determined by x-ray diffraction, infrared spectroscopy, and electron spin resonance techniques. In the femur or tibia of several day-old rats, it was discovered that approximately 35% of the bone mineral was in the crystalline apatite form, while approximately 65% was amorphous calcium phosphate. As the animal matured and reached 80 days of age, these percentages were essentially reversed with approximately 65% of bone mineral being crystalline apatite and only 35% being amorphous calcium phosphate. This latter composition was stable and seemed to represent the proportions of apatite and amorphous calcium phosphate in mature bone. Synthetic crystallization studies showed that an amorphous calcium phosphate was formed as a usual initial precipitate. This initial precipitate was metastable and would convert to hydroxyapatite. These two findings led to the conclusion that amorphous calcium phosphate is a predecessor of crystalline hydroxyapatite in bone growth. However, a considerable pool of amorphous calcium phosphate co-exists with the crystalline apatite in the mature bone. Analysis of human enamel indicated that it was 100% crystalline apatite. However, the mineral portion of the dentine was 65 to 70% crystalline, essentially similar in composition to compact bone. Magnesium and carbonate ions stabilize the amorphous calcium phosphate in synthetic preparations and prevent its conversion to the more stable apatite form. In bone and dentine stabilization could possibly be established by binding to an organic component.

## Optical Properties

Apatite is optically uniaxial and birefringent, *i.e.*, it has two refractive indices, one for the ordinary ray vibrating perpendicular to the c axis and another for the extraordinary ray vibrating parallel to c. The extent of birefringence, that is, the difference between these refractive indices, is weak and negative ($-0.004$). Because of this birefringent property of the enamel, it has been possible to study enamel structure by employing the polarization microscope. Microscopic spaces in the enamel will imbibe aqueous and non-aqueous fluids from solution. These spaces give rise to a positive form birefringence. The increase in submicroscopic spaces during the development of early enamel caries has been investigated by following the increase in form birefringence.

## ENAMEL SOLUBILITY

Because the acidogenic theory of enamel caries postulates that the enamel is attacked by organic acids arising from microbial metabolism, there has been considerable interest in the solubility of enamel and hydroxyapatite in acid solutions.

Some investigators have claimed from experimental evidence and theoretical reasoning that hydroxyapatite does not have a thermodynamically predictable solubility product constant based on the mass action law; *i.e.* it has an anomalous solubility behavior. More recently it has been reported that pure hydroxyapatite, when true equilibrium conditions have been reached, has a true solubility product constant $K_{sp}$ that is consistent with the law of mass action. It can be expressed as:

$$pK_{sp} = 10 \ pCa + 6 \ p(PO_4) + 2 \ p(OH).$$

Values of $pK_{sp}$ in the range of 114.4 to 116 have been determined.

In studies of the dissolution of dental enamel and synthetic hydroxyapatites in acid buffers, it has been observed that a relatively rapid equilibrium is reached where the extent of dissolution is governed by the solubility product for calcium monohydrogen phosphate. This has been interpreted as resulting from a thin layer of monohydrogen calcium phosphate dihydrate which forms on the apatite surface and determines the solubility. The reactions can be shown schematically as:

True Hydroxyapatite Equilibrium

$$Ca_{10}(PO_4)_6(OH)_2 \rightleftharpoons 10 \ Ca^{2+} + 6 \ PO_4^{3-} + 2 \ OH^-$$

In pH 4 to 6 Buffer solutions

$$Ca_{10}(PO_4)_6(OH)_2 + 8 \ H^+ \longrightarrow 10 \ Ca^{2+} + 6 \ HPO_4^{2-} + 2 \ H_2O$$

$$\Updownarrow \ H_2O$$

$$4 \ Ca^{2+} + 6 \ CaHPO_4 \cdot 2 \ H_2O$$

In kinetic studies of acid dissolution of apatite in acetate buffers, equilibrium is not usually reached. The net overall reaction can be expressed as:

$$Ca_{10}(PO_4)_6 (OH)_2 + 8 \ H^+ \longrightarrow 10 \ Ca^{2+} + 6 \ HPO_4^{2-} + 2 \ H_2O \ (\text{at pH 4 to 6})$$

Several theoretical formulations have been proposed that describe the kinetic rate of this reaction reasonably well.

## Variation in Depth of Chemical Components

Since mature enamel is exposed to an environment of saliva supersaturated with calcium and phosphate relative to hydroxyapatite and containing other ions with concentrations different from newly erupted enamel, it is not unusual to find that the composition of the surface enamel differs from that of interior enamel. In a series of papers primarily by Brudevold and co-workers, it has been reported that fluorine, zinc, and lead have a decreasing concentration gradient from the enamel surface toward the enamel junction, while carbonate and magnesium have a gradient in the opposite direction. Further, surface enamel is more mineralized than internal enamel and has a lower water content. The process of mineralization in the enamel involves the displacement of water by minerals. Therefore, the higher mineralization in the surface enamel is expected as a result of exposure to saliva, post-eruptively. Increased mineralization of the surface area results in a reduction of intercrystalline space. This space restriction, together with electrostatic charge repulsion from charges on the surface of crystallites, restricts ion movements as the intercrystalline spaces decrease from mineralization. Certain substituents such as strontium and copper are essentially uniformly distributed throughout enamel. These substances appear to be deposited at the time of enamel formation and are not subject to change subsequently. Substances such as carbonate and magnesium, which are found in an increasing gradient from the outer enamel surface towards the dentino-enamel junction, also appear to be deposited in the enamel at the time of formation. The gradient arises from surface loss of these components during exposure of the enamel to the oral environment.

## PRISM STRUCTURE

### Prism Dimensions

Anatomically mature enamel consists of a series of prisms or rods approximately 4 to 6 microns in diameter running from the dentino-enamel junction to the outer enamel surface. The prisms are composed of apatite crystallites in a hydrated organic matrix which is principally protein. The crystallites are aligned with their long axes approximately parallel to the long axis of the prism, although in certain regions they diverge quite significantly. During the past several years a new concept of prism architecture has been evolving. It appears to be supplanting the more traditional concept of enamel structure involving prisms, interprismatic substance, and prism sheaths. For the sake of completeness, both concepts of the enamel anatomy will be presented.

### Traditional Enamel Structure

The traditional picture of enamel microanatomy has been derived from optical microscopic studies, including polarization microscopy, supplemented by microradiography. Since enamel is a highly calcified tissue, most of the common histological stains will not stain undecalcified enamel. Decalcification of the enamel leaves only a delicate organic matrix which is difficult to retain. Even in those cases where the organic matrix can be preserved, without association with the corresponding mineral phase, it does not truly represent the enamel structure. Thus, most optical studies have been conducted with ground enamel sections of 30 microns in thickness or greater. This represents a width of at least 5 to 7 prisms and can result in optical artifacts and difficulties of interpretation. Only within the last several years have techniques for the convenient preparation of enamel sections of 4 to 8 microns in thickness been developed.

The typical appearance of enamel as seen in the optical microscope in both transverse and longitudinal sections is shown schematically in Figure 6–5. As mentioned earlier, the primary constituent of the enamel is the enamel prism. These prisms are sometimes roughly hexagonal in transverse section, but are often either round or arcade-shaped, the latter arrangement being similar to a pattern of fish scales. Each prism is surrounded by a prism sheath, a region with a higher concentration of organic material at the perimeter of the prism. The prisms do not lie immediately adjacent to each other, but are separated by the interprismatic substance. In certain regions of the enamel, no interprismatic substance can be demonstrated.

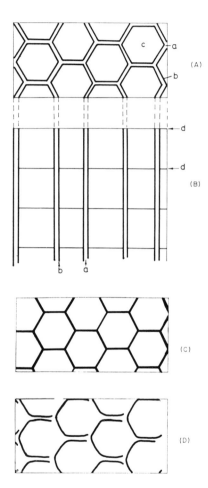

Fig. 6–5. Diagrammatic representation of prisms, prism sheaths and interprismatic substance. (A) Cross-cut prisms: *a*, interprismatic substance; *b*, prism sheaths; and *c*, prism core. (B) Longitudinally cut prisms. Between the cross-striations (*d*) are the prism segments. (C) Cross-cut prisms with no interprismatic substance. The prism sheaths are close to each other. (D) Cross-cut prisms with prism sheaths open on one side. Thus the interprismatic substance is in immediate contact with the prism core. The form of the prisms varies according to the relation of the axes of adjacent prisms or groups of prisms. The horseshoe form can therefore vary a great deal in details. (Gustafson and Gustafson: *Microanatomy and Histochemistry of Enamel in Structure and Chemical Organization of Teeth*, A. E. W. Miles (Ed.), New York, Academic Press, 1967, p. 83.)

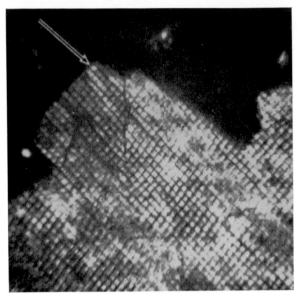

Fig. 6–6. Ground section of human enamel in polarized light (crossed polars). The prisms are divided into negatively birefringent square segments. Arrow indicates the direction of the prisms. × 420.

Prisms pursue a spiraling path from the dentino-enamel junction to the outer surface of the enamel. In a transverse section the spiraling course of the prisms results in the appearance of layers of the enamel formed in which all prisms run in the same direction. This gives rise to the appearance of the Hunter-Schreger bands which are found in the inner half of the enamel. In polarized light microscopy, enamel prisms appear to be segmented (Fig. 6–6). This segmentation has been called cross striation as the prisms appear to be divided by regular transverse lines into segments about 4 to 6 microns in length. Since this is about the same width as the prisms, the segments are practically box-like in appearance. The cross striations appear to be richer in organic material than the prism interior and less radiopaque. In many cases they seem to be mineralized to the same extent as the prism sheath with which they sometimes appear to be continuous. Some investigators believe that the prismatic segments or "boxes" represent periodic accretions from the Tomes' processes during the formation of the enamel matrix from the ameloblast.

Often throughout the enamel one finds a line of prism segments which is less calcified than neighboring prism segments (Fig. 6–7). These lines, often called striae of Retzius or Retzius' lines, represent variations in the degree of mineralization of the prism. Normal or incremental Retzius' lines represent essentially normal periodic variations in calcification. Pathological Retzius' lines, which are broader, result from disturbance in the mineralization. The neonatal line of birth is an example of this type of line. Retzius'

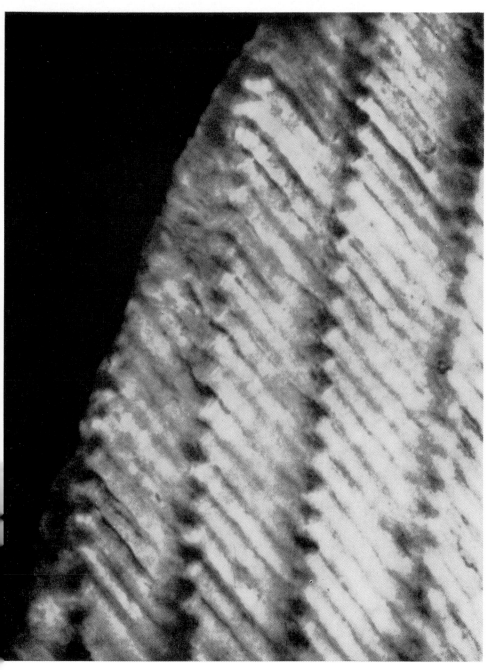

FIG. 6–7. Incremental Retzius lines ending on the surface of human enamel. The lines show a step-like appearance. The inner (right-hand) side of each line is demarcated sharply by lines transverse to the prism axes but on the other side towards the outer enamel surface the demarcation is much less sharp and less segmented. The lines are first isotropic and then slightly negatively birefringent. × 1100. (Gustafson & Gustafson: *Microanatomy and Histochemistry of Enamel in Structural and Chemical Organization of Teeth,* A. E. W. Miles (Ed.), New York, Academic Press, 1967, p. 91.)

[ 83 ]

lines rarely run transversely to the enamel prisms, but are usually at an oblique orientation. The Retzius' line is formed by a front or stage of ameloblastic activity where calcification was slightly disturbed. As the ameloblasts do not progress in the direction of the prisms, but at an angle to them, the Retzius' line represents a plane perpendicular to the direction of ameloblastic growth.

Retzius' lines are important in determining the progress of the carious lesion in the enamel since Darling has shown that caries tends to spread mainly along the striae of Retzius.

## Recent Concept of Enamel Structure

During the past few years, a new formulation of the microanatomy of dental enamel has arisen based largely on electron microscopy. A review of this work can be found in the paper by Nylen.

In the electron microscopic studies it was possible to distinguish enamel crystallites and it was observed that sudden changes in the orientation of the crystallites at the boundaries between prisms served to define the cross-sectional shape of the individual prisms. In cross section, the prisms have an appearance somewhat like keyholes. The prisms are approximately 5 microns in diameter at the round head, and about 9 microns from the top of the head to the extremity of the tail. The prisms are always oriented so that the head of the prism cross section points toward the occlusal surface of the tooth and the tail toward the cervical region of the tooth. Within a single prism, all crystallites are not parallel. In the head region of the prism, the long plate-like crystallites are oriented roughly with their long axes in the direction of the prism axis, but in the tail region the crystallites lie almost perpendicular to the prism long axis (Figs. 6–8, 6–9).

Meckel, Griebstein, and Neal (Fig. 6–10) have constructed a three-dimensional model of keyhole enamel prisms that shows the varying aspect of prisms for differing angles of the plane section. Essentially all these patterns corresponding to the three-dimensional construction were found in various electron microscopic investigations of actual enamel sections.

In this formulation there is no requirement for an interprismatic substance and no evidence that such a substance exists. The tail extension of one prism between adjacent prisms in the next row would be interpreted as an interprismatic substance in optical microscopy. The prism sheath between the prisms is actually a region of abrupt discontinuity in crystallite orientation. This can be seen clearly in Figure 6–11.

Recent work provides an explanation of the varying crystallite orientation within the prism. Previous workers had generally accepted the concept of a 1-to-1 ratio between the number of prisms and the number of ameloblasts. It had further been accepted that during development one ameloblast formed one prism. New studies reveal that in human enamel each prism is the result of the secretory activity of four ameloblasts. Under this proposal crystallite orientation in enamel is controlled by two major factors: (1)

FIG. 6–8. Electron micrograph of a section cut from a human deciduous molar. The plane or sectioning was perpendicular to the long axis of the enamel prisms. × 5000. (Meckel, A. H., W. J. Griebstein and R. J. Neal: Structure of Natural Human Dental Enamel as Observed by Electron Microscopy, Arch. Oral. Biol., *10*, 775–783, 1965.)

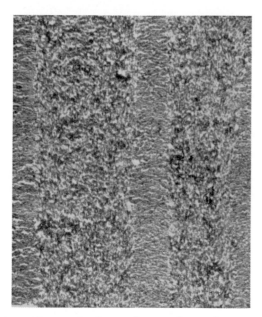

FIG. 6–9. Electron micrograph of a section cut from a human permanent incisor. The plane of sectioning was parallel to the long axis of the enamel prisms and passed across the head and tail regions of adjacent prisms. × 5000. (Meckel, A. H., W. J. Griebstein and R. J. Neal: Structure of Natural Human Dental Enamel as Observed by Electron Microscopy, Arch. Oral. Biol., *10*, 775–783, 1965.)

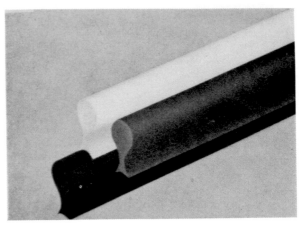

FIG. 6–10.  Model of human dental enamel prepared by cementing together individual model prisms as shown above.  Note the variety of patterns formed by milling the surfaces of the model at different angles to the prism axes.  (Meckel, Griebstein and Neal: Enamel Structure, Arch. Oral. Biol., *42*, 775, 1965.)

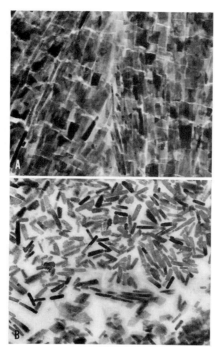

Fig. 6–11A. Electron micrograph of longitudinally sectioned prisms from hypomineralized human enamel depicting the relationship between 2 prisms from adjoining layers. The orientation of the longitudinally cut crystals differs between the 2 prisms so that a more continuous space, identified as the prism sheath, results where the 2 crystal groups abut. × 25,000.

Fig. 6–11B. A portion of a prism sheath separating 2 enamel prisms in a transverse section. The large coherent spaces characteristic of the interface between prisms in this hypomineralized enamel are much more evident in a cross than in a longitudinal section. The hexagonal shape of the crosscut crystals and their relative orientation to each other are also revealed in this type of section. × 50,000. (Nylen: Int. Dent. Journal, 17, 719, 1967.)

crystallites grow at right angles to the surface of the mineralizing front wherever possible, but (2) where there is a relative movement between the surface of the ameloblast and the surface of the mineralizing front, the crystallites tend to be oriented in the direction of this movement. Thus, in the head of the keyhole, the crystallites are oriented in the direction of the prism long axis and perpendicular to the Tomes' process of the ameloblast. On the cervical side of the prism the crystallites are oriented essentially perpendicular to the prism long axis and also perpendicular to the plane of slippage between the Tomes' process surface and the mineralizing front.

## DENTINE

### Mineral Phase

Dentine is always less mineralized than enamel but has a higher mineral content than either bone or cementum. The mineral fraction of dentine ranges from approximately 68 to 79% by weight as contrasted with approximately 97% by weight in enamel. The crystallites of dentine are considerably smaller than those in enamel. The average thickness is approximately 20 to 35 Å and lengths are usually 200 to 300 Å, although crystallites up to 1000 Å have been measured. The volume of an individual enamel crystallite is approximately 200 times that of a dentine crystallite. Since chemical reactions are confined to the surface of the apatite crystals, the smaller size of the dentinal crystal associated with a correspondingly larger surface area makes dentine less stable than enamel. The Ca/P ration in dentine usually, but not always, has been found to be lower than that in enamel from the same tooth, and exhibits more variability. As mentioned earlier, amorphous calcium phosphate (ACP) has been reported in dentine. Approximately 35% of the dentinal mineral phase was found to be ACP, about the same fraction as in compact bone.

### Dentinal Structure

Dentine, unlike inert enamel, retains a vital cellular component, the odontoblast, as it matures. However, dentine, like other connective tissues, consists primarily of extracellular substance and only a small amount of cellular material. The extracellular component occurs primarily in the form of a densely mineralized collagenous matrix enclosing tubular structures. This mineralized dentinal matrix forms the body of the tooth, protects the dental pulp, and provides attachment and underlying support for the protective enamel covering and the cementum. In mature dentine in the transverse section (Fig. 6–12) it is possible to demonstrate the following structures:
1. Intertubular dentine
2. Outer hypomineralized layer
3. Peritubular dentine

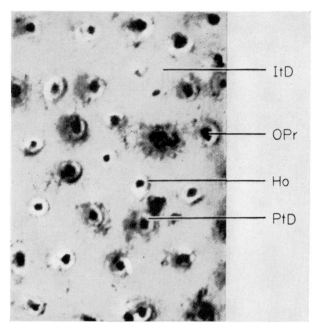

Fig. 6–12. Ground transverse section of human dentine stained with silver nitrate and reduced in sunlight. *OPr*, Odontoblast process; *Ho*, outer hypomineralized layer; *PtD*, peritubular dentine; *ItD*, intertubular dentine. × 1500. (From Bradford, 1951.)

4. Inner hypomineralized layer
5. Dental process of the odontoblast.

Not all these structures can be easily demonstrated in a single section. It will be noted that the innerhypomineralized layer cannot be seen in this particular section.

The intertubular dentine consists of a mineralized collagenous framework extending among the dentinal tubules. The collagenous fibers, exhibit a typical 640 Å cross banding. The arrangement and distribution of the collagenous fibrils can be seen in a section from the matrix of demineralized dentine (Fig. 6–13). This photograph shows that the collagenous fibrils of the matrix are arranged in a trellis-like framework, while some of the fibers appear to be running tangentially to the dentinal tubules. The presence of oblique longitudinal and cross-sectional views of fibrils indicates that they follow a random course relative to the tubules.

The tubular portion of mature dentine consists of the inner odontoblastic process, which is separated from the peritubular dentine by an inner hypomineralized layer. The peritubular dentine likewise is separated from the intertubular dentine by the outer hypomineralized layer.

The odontoblastic process is the cytoplasmic extension from the odontoblast through the tubule. Near the vicinity of the predentine-pulp border, the odontoblast process has been clearly shown to be an extension of the

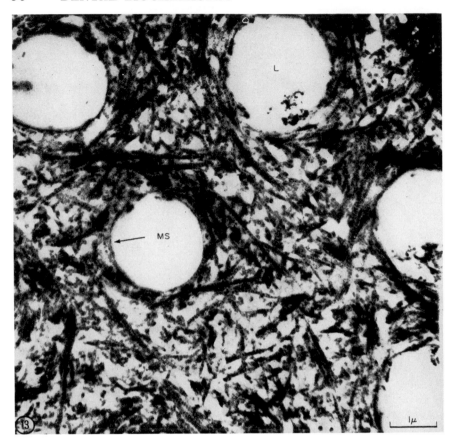

Fig. 6–13. The collagenous fibrils appear in longitudinal, oblique and cross-sectional views in matrix obtained from the vicinity of the predentine—dentine border. A membranous structure (MS) surrounds the lumen (L) of the canal, stained with phosphotungstic acid (approx. × 17,800). (Johansen, E., courtesy John Wright & Sons.)

odontoblast cytoplasm with continuity of the plasma membrane extending into the dentinal tubule. At this level the odontoblast process still retains some cytoplasmic organelles, including the endoplasmic reticulum and mitochondria. In progressing from the predentine-dentine border into the more mature dentine, the fine structure of the odontoblast process has proven difficult to study because of the high mineral content of mature dentine. In the predentine region, the diameter of the odontoblast process is approximately 5 microns. In the mineralized dentine the odontoblastic process is reduced to about 2 microns and continuity of the cytoplasm cannot always be demonstrated. In studies employing demineralization and fixation of the mature dentine, some dentinal tubules display collagenous fibrils. Others were empty or showed aggregates of granular material in the tubule lumen.

Peritubular dentine is a hypermineralized material laid down between the intertubular dentine and the odontoblast process. This tissue is presumed to be laid down or secreted by the odontoblast itself. With maturation of the tubule there is a reduction in the diameter of the odontoblast process from 5 microns to approximately 1 to 2 microns at the intermediate dentine level with a corresponding increase in the thickness of peritubular dentine. The peritubular dentine appears to be the most densely mineralized phase of dentine, having a specific gravity of 2.4 as compared with a specific gravity of 2.1 to 2.2 for dentine overall. The collagenous fibrils in the peritubular dentine are narrower than those in the inner tubular dentinal areas. Peritubular fibrils have diameters in the range of 250 to 500 Å, as compared with the 600 to 700 Å fibril width found in intertubular dentine.

Material is continually deposited on the walls of the tubules in the formation of the peritubular dentine until the lumen of the tubule is nearly or completely obliterated. Until complete closure occurs, the highly mineralized peritubular dentine is separated from the remainder of the odontoblast process by the hypomineralized layer. Because the intertubular dentine is formed prior to the peritubular dentine at any given plane, the two tissues are separated by a narrow zone of hypomineralized tissue. This zone is called the outer hypomineralized layer.

## SELECTED REFERENCES

BROWN, W. E.: Crystal growth of bone mineral, Clin. Orthop., *44*, 205–220, 1966.

CARLSTROM, DIEGO: X-ray crystallographic studies on apatites and calcified structures, Acta Radiol. Supp., *121*, 59, 1955.

JOHANSEN, E.: Comparison of the Ultrastructure and Chemical Composition of Sound and Carious Enamel from Human Permanent Teeth, in *Tooth Enamel*, Bristol, John Wright & Sons, 1965, pp. 177–181.

LEGEROS, RAGULL Z., TRAUTZ, OTTO R., LEGEROS, JOHN P., KLEIN, EDWARD and SHURA, W. PAUL: Apatite crystallites, effect of carbonate on morphology, Science, *155*, 1409–1411, 1967.

MILES, A. E. W.: *Structural and Chemical Organization of Teeth*, Vol. II, New York, Academic Press Inc., 1967.

NYLEN, M. V.: Recent electron microscopic and allied investigations into the normal structure of human enamel, Internat. Dent. J., *17*, 719–733, 1967.

STACK, M. V. and FEARNHEAD, R. W.: *Tooth Enamel*, Bristol, John Wright & Sons, Ltd., 1965.

TRAUTZ, O.: X-ray diffraction of biological and synthetic apatites, Ann. New York Acad. Science, *60*, 696–712, 1955

# Chapter 7

# The Periodontium

### Ernest Beerstecher Jr., Ph.D.

Structural Considerations
The Gingival Epithelium
The Connective Tissue Continuum
The Periodontal Fibers
The Mineralized Periodontium
Metabolism of the Periodontium

## STRUCTURAL CONSIDERATIONS

THE periodontium consists of that set of tissues which invest and support the teeth. These tissues are generally considered to include the gingiva, the periodontal membrane (or "ligament"), the cementum and the alveolar bone. Some of the biochemical aspects of the cementum and alveolar bone are discussed in earlier chapters. The soft tissues of the periodontium, however, require special consideration because of the frequency with which they become diseased in modern man. Periodontal disease occurs frequently in younger persons but is almost universally present to some degree in persons of middle age. It is a common cause for the loss of teeth which, aside from their supporting structures, are otherwise intact. This is partly due to the fact that the epithelial attachment to the tooth presents more or less of a cul-de-sac in which debris of an infectious nature may lodge and weaken the adjoining tissues. It is also apparent that the gingiva are exposed to extensive abrasive action from foods taken into the mouth and that the alveolar bone is the recipient of continuing stress during the process of mastication. These traumatic effects require a carefully balanced set of defense mechanisms to prevent permanent injury. It is generally believed that the relatively soft diet of modern man provides inadequate massage and stimulation to the gums for maintaining their proper state of health, and that inflammatory periodontal disorders are therefore, in one sense, nutritional diseases. However, *gingivitis* and periodontitis (depending on the extent of the injury) are but one kind of periodontal pathological condition. Excessive or inadequate pressures upon alveolar bone may bring about its dissolution; endocrine, nutritional, and other systemic factors bring about severe *periodontoses* in which inflammation is absent. Thus, just as one considers the biochemistry of the teeth in the investigation of dental caries, it is desirable to study the biochemistry of these tissues in order to obtain an insight into the dynamics of periodontal disease. The study of the periodontium is most appropriately initiated by considering certain structural details of the periodontal tissues upon which depends much of the biochemical activity.

## Gingiva

The gingiva consists of that part of the epithelium (mucous membrane) and its underlying connective tissue which covers the embedded portion of the teeth and their alveolar processes. Its stratified squamous epithelium consists of a variable number of cell layers, a fraction of a millimeter in thickness, which may be divided into four biochemically and morphologically distinct strata (Fig. 7–1).

*a.* An outer cornified layer which is sometimes keratinized.

*b.* A layer of flattened out basophilic cells with shrunken nuclei.

*c.* A polygonal spinous cell layer.

*d.* A cuboidal basal layer.

Fine protein filaments (tonofibrils) interconnect many of the cells of the latter layer. Most of these biochemically specialized cells serve the protective needs of the gingiva by forming keratin from these tonofibrils; however, a small number of cells are found to be melanocytes or pigment-forming cells.

The *gingival epithelium* is avascular, so that its nutriment must be obtained by diffusion from the underlying fibrous tissue or *lamina propria*. This factor in itself limits the thickness of the epithelium and doubtless contributes to the senescence of its surface layers. It would appear that massage of the gums is critical to the elimination both of stasis in this nutritive process and of wastes from the epithelium by the same type of pathway. Finger-like projections (papillae) of connective tissue invaginate into the basal layers of epithelium thereby greatly increasing the interface available for diffusion. There appears to be one patent capillary loop in each papilla; but the microcirculation of the gingiva has received limited study. The epithelium is separated from the connective tissue by a *basement membrane*, 300 to 700 Å in thickness, which appears to play a vital role in the maintenance of metabolite balance between the adjoining tissues.

The site at which the epithelium comes in contact with the neck of the tooth, the *epithelial attachment*, appears to be a point of weakness from the standpoint of defense against debris and infectious agents. The nature of this attachment has been vigorously debated for half a century with one group of investigators believing that the evidence indicates a structural attachment to the tooth, while the other group believes that the attachment is only by strong mucous adhesion and that an easily distensible pocket therefore *normally* exists (Fig. 7–2). Consequent upon the latter belief is the

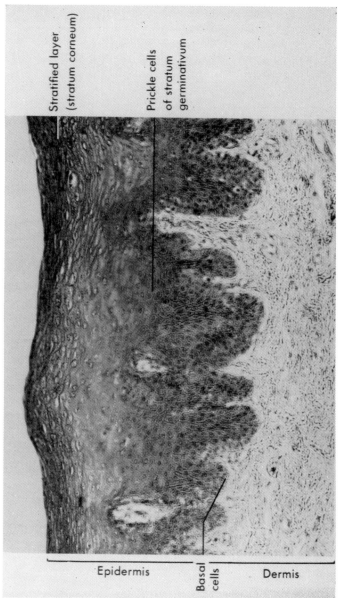

FIG. 7–1. Nonkeratinized gingival mucosa. × 400. The gingival mucosa consists of a layer of thick stratified squamous epithelium, the base of which is thrown into folds known as rete pegs. The epithelium rests upon a basement membrane and subjacent to this a loosely arranged lamina propria of collagenous and a few elastic fibers. The epithelium undergoes functional changes from time to time, especially in the character of the surface layers and in the number and depth of the pegs. Shown here is a portion of the gingival mucosa in which the surface layers are relatively unchanged. (Bevelander, *Atlas of Oral Histology and Embryology*, Lea & Febiger.)

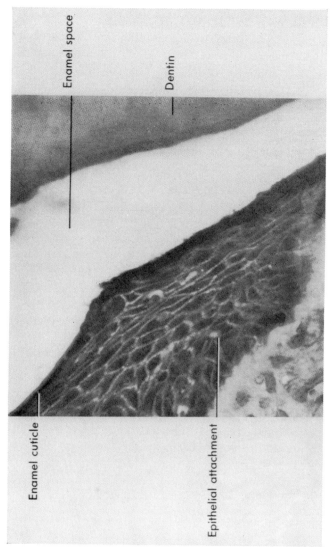

Fig. 7–2. Detail of epithelial attachment. × 640. A section of a portion of the epithelial attachment at relatively high magnification shows that this strip of epithelium may be quite extensive in nature. It normally terminates at the cemento-enamel junction and exhibits a cuticle on the surface adjacent to the enamel. (Bevelander, *Atlas of Oral Histology and Embryology*, Lea & Febiger.)

evidence that a fluid (crevicial fluid) normally emanates from this area into the gingival sulcus, cleansing the healthy pocket of cellular debris, but also, perhaps, nurturing the growth of calculus in the process. There is uniform agreement as to the existence of such a fluid emanation from diseased gingival tissues but not from the healthy periodontium.

The gingival *connective tissue* consists largely of an intercellular substance composed of tissue fluid, mucopolysaccharides, and various fibrous elements. The fibroblasts that account for nearly all of its metabolic activity are suspended in the intercellular substance, along with a variety of other cells in lesser number, vascular and neural elements. Vigorous leukocytic activity in the gingiva makes white blood cells indigenous components of this tissue. Aside from the nutritive and cushioning functions of the gingival connective tissue, its fibrous elements are of major concern in firmly anchoring the teeth and a site of biochemical weakness in gingival infections.

### Periodontal Membrane

The periodontal membrane (or ligament) is that portion of the gingival connective tissue that lies between the tooth and alveolar bone. It consists of all the elements of the lamina propria, therefore, with a greater variety of cell types and more dense bundles of fibers. As these fibers connect with the alveolus and cementum they are termed *Sharpey's* fibers (Fig. 7–3). The evolution of the periodontal membrane was a major advance in the development of the mammalian dental apparatus. It provides cushioning to seat teeth firmly and a conduction pathway to vascular and nerve elements. It acts as a type of periosteum to both alveolus and cementum since it contains cellular units involved in bone formation and resorption. To a considerable extent, masticatory function itself depends upon the sense of tooth contact derived from proprioceptive nerve receptors in the membrane. Destruction of the fibrous elements in this area through microbial enzymatic hydrolysis or faulty collagen synthesis for maintenance due to metabolic disease, results in a rapid increase in tooth mobility with subsequent frequent loss.

### Cementum

The cementum is in one sense a continuation of the connective tissue of the gingiva, being rigid by virtue of its mineral content. It serves as an anchor for the fibers that bind the teeth to the alveolar bone (Fig. 7–3). Only its apical portion is cellular, which cellularity increases with age. Its interlinking cementocytes account for the major portion of its considerable permeability (Fig. 7–4). The cementum functions as a sort of "nutritional organ" for the remainder of the tooth, and in advanced age as the tooth pulp diminishes in size, the cementum pathway may account for as much as 50% of the phosphate turnover in the tooth. The biochemical processes involved in cemental resorption are of major importance in deep periodontal pocket formation.

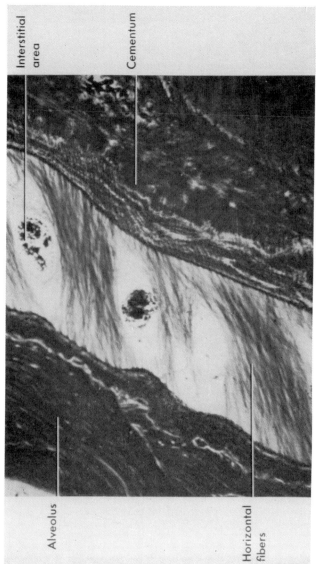

Fig. 7–3. Periodontal membrane. × 420. (Courtesy Dr. M. Cattoni.) Proceeding rootward in a study of the periodontal space one encounters another group of fibers which are arranged for the most part in a horizontal position
and are accordingly known as the *horizontal fibers*. Another group of fibers observed in a mesiodistal section of the
cervical region of two adjacent teeth arise in the region of the root apical to the cemento-enamel junction, pass over
the alveolar crest, and terminate in the same part of the adjacent tooth. These fibers are known as the transeptal
fibers. (Bevelander, *Atlas of Oral Histology and Embryology*, Lea & Febiger.)

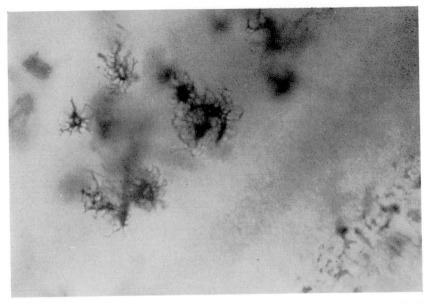

FIG. 7–4. Human cementocytes (protein stained with ninhydrin) showing complexity of interlinking processes which serve as nutritional channels. (Courtesy of Dr. R. W. Bell.)

## Alveolar Bone

The alveolar bone is the least stable of all the periodontal tissues. It is that part of the mandible and maxilla that forms the sockets of the teeth and it is a highly vascular material. It, too, may be regarded as a mineralized continuation of the gingival connective tissue and its osteocytes are hardly less active than the fibroblasts of the gingiva. Like the cementocytes, the osteocytes are interconnected by canaliculi which ultimately lead to the circulatory system so that these cells are highly responsive to systemic changes. This fact, coupled with their large protoplasmic mineral interface, makes it possible for alveolar bone to serve as a general systemic calcium reservoir, ready to contribute or receive calcium to meet the demands of transient homeostatic events. Of even greater dental significance, perhaps, is the manner in which this permits modification of the alveolus in response to occlusal stress and consequently leads to realignment of the teeth. Alveolar bone also resorbs in the absence of adequate tooth pressures upon it so that the metabolism of this tissue is of significance to virtually every branch of dental practice.

Until very recently, the metabolism of the mineralized periodontal tissues was considered quite independently of the soft tissues so that many of the metabolic interrelationships between the parts of the periodontium are, as yet, only poorly understood. An equally confusing situation exists in the older literature in that biochemical data were obtained from "gingival tissue," without any definition of just what type was meant. A small and variable amount of densely cellular epithelium connected to a fragment of sparsely cellular connective tissue could hardly be expected to be a reliable sample. In more recent years, studies tend to concentrate on the individual periodontal tissues with the knowledge that only when the characteristics of these have been defined can the biochemistry of the periodontium as a whole hope to provide a cogent picture. This approach has proven to be of considerable value in the measurement of metabolic activities in the gingival epithelium.

## THE GINGIVAL EPITHELIUM

### General Composition

Until quite recently most of the biochemical investigations of gingival epithelium were of a histochemical nature and the results were often vague and equivocal. This was most often due to the fact that the determination of results usually rested on subjective judgments and that the *in vitro* reactions of histochemical reagents with purified and identified chemical components of tissues have seldom been studied other than in a general manner. In 1965 the first systematic study of chemical methods for removing epithelium from gingiva without the losses entailed in dissection was reported. Agents such as acetic acid cause the epithelium to separate readily, but there is the obvious loss of enzymatic activity in the resulting sample. Solutions of thiocyanates are effective, but drastically change staining properties. Best results are attainable with specific enzyme preparations such as pepsin or collagenase, but the preservation of the specific substances to be studied in the epithelial sample can be insured only by carefully adjusting the conditions in each case. It is entirely practical to preserve most of the original tissue activity in an intact sheet of epithelium when adequate preliminary studies are made.

Studies on the *protein* content of gingival epithelium have largely centered around the formation of the keratinized layer on the outer surface and the nature of its progenitors in the filaments of the deeper epithelial regions. In this regard there appears to be little to distinguish the gingiva from other similar tissues. Rigid, simple criteria for defining *keratins* are not available; however, on the basis of the often used ratio of the basic amino acid residues histidine : lysine : arginine, oral epithelium closely resembles epidermis and other "pseudokeratins" in general, having a molar ratio of approximately 1 : 4 : 4.

*Enzymatic* studies on the gingival epithelium have been extensive. Virtually all of the recognized oxidative enzymes have been demonstrated to be present in the various cell layers generally, but not invariably, decreasing in their activity in the layers nearer the surface of the gingiva. A great many hydrolytic enzymes have also been identified in these tissues. In this regard it is supposed that many of these are lysozomal contents of the epithelial cells themselves. Because of large numbers of leukocytes in inflamed gingiva, the precise clinical condition of the sample studied may greatly influence the results obtained in studies of these hydrolases. Thus acid phosphatase is normally present in gingival epithelium and is known to be functionally involved in keratinization. Alkaline phosphatase, however, being derived from the leukocytes present, is apparently present only in inflamed gingiva.

Interest in epithelial *carbohydrates* has been concerned with the intercellular mucopolysaccharides, and despite conflicting data largely derived from histochemical studies, it appears that both sulfate and non-sulfate containing mucopolysaccharides are present (Chapter 3). Glycogen granules, particularly in the prickle cells, have also been extensively investigated with particular reference to keratinization and inflammation. There is some evidence that the basement membrane is at least partially carbohydrate in nature. Little is known regarding the *lipid* content of the gingival epithelium, a subject of considerable interest from the standpoint of the permeability of this tissue.

## Intercellular Components

Because of the bearing that the intercellular components of gingival epithelium might have on disease, these substances have been given extensive attention, largely through histochemical techniques. The presence of neutral, acidic non-sulfated and sulfated mucopolysaccharides have all been reported. Little or no attention has been directed toward other components of the interstitial fluid. Isotopic studies with $^{35}$S sodium sulfate suggest that sulfated mucopolysaccharides are present in the tonofibrillae of the stratified squamous epithelium. The concentration of radioactivity appears to increase from the basal layer through the stratum spinosum, paralleling the density of the tonofibrils. This suggests that the mucopolysaccharide binds together the tonofibrils into fibers much as it does in the case of collagen fibers. It further suggests a relationship of sulfated mucopolysaccharides with the sulfur-containing amino acids in the keratin molecule, particularly in view of the observation that keratin contains more sulfur than can be accounted for on the basis of the sulfur-containing amino acids.

## Keratinization

Keratinization may be defined as that process by which a horny material, keratin, is formed from living cells. Though much studied, the process remains poorly understood. It was once thought of as a degenerative process, but since connective tissue and adequate nutrition are essential for its success, it is, in fact, "the final stage in a process of intrinsic differentiation." It has been estimated that keratin production utilizes at least 2 to $3\frac{1}{2}\%$ of the total ATP produced by epithelial cells. The gingival epithelium of most animals is entirely keratinized, with the notable exception of the gingival crevicular epithelium in man and monkeys.

In the basal cells of the epithelium, fine tonofilaments may be observed passing from the nuclei of the cells to the cell walls. At points where neighboring cells adjoin, these filaments condense into larger *tonofibrils* which make up the cellular bridges or *desmosomes* that seem, along with the mucopolysaccharides, to hold the cells in proper relationship to each other. Reference has been made to the role of the mucopolysaccharides in binding these filaments together into larger fibers. Morphologically there is a gradual condensation of this fibrous material resulting in the occurrence of keratin in the final outer layers of the epithelium, as the cells of the basal layer gradually migrate toward the surface.

Biochemically the process is a complex one, involving basic changes in the precursor (tonofibrin). Fundamental among these changes are the intermolecular condensations of sulfhydryl groups which seems to parallel the sulfate mucopolysaccharide content of the epithelial layers. It is further paralleled by high reductase activity and by an *increase* in the glucose monophosphate shunt activity from the basal layer outward to the spinous cell area. Keratinization and the glycogen content of gingival epithelium have been shown to be inversely related, and even more markedly so in inflamed tissues. The presence of acid phosphatase in the sub-corneal layers and its absence from non-keratinizing gingiva, suggests that this enzyme also plays a special role in keratinization. Indeed it is apparent that with disintegration of the lysozomes of the cells in the outer layers, the acid phosphatase is ideally liberated to facilitate the desquamative process.

## Oxidative Enzyme Activity

While periodontal metabolism is discussed in greater detail in a later section of this chapter, a few special considerations relating to the gingival epithelium must be presented at this point. Virtually all of the enzymes of the glycolytic, citric acid, and phosphogluconate (pentose phosphate) systems have been shown to be present in gingival epithelium by histochemical techniques. There is reasonable agreement that while aerobic metabolism decreases from the basal layer outward, presumably with oxygen tension, the phosphogluconate (pentose phosphate) system *increases* at least as far as the spinous layer, presumably supplying a considerable portion of the energy for the active keratinization process in this anaerobic zone.

The metabolic rate of isolated gingival epithelial tissue is relatively low compared with many other tissues. Representative $Q_{O_2}$ values are in the range of 1.6, which are about the same as for skin and contrast with 0.2 to 0.6 for cornea, and 15.0 for kidney. Evidence has been presented for the presence in gingiva of endogenous inhibitors of respiration, which may account for the relatively low value reported above for epithelium. As a generalization, crevicular basal cells have greater activity than basal cells of the attached gingiva and these cells have a greater $Q_{O_2}$ value than the more superficial cell layers. The oxygen uptake of gingival epithelium is several times greater than that of the underlying connective tissue.

### Epithelial Dendritic Cells

Dendritic cells in the gingival epithelium and in epidermis are of two kinds:

*a.* Cells, found only in the basal layers, which produce melanin.

*b.* Cells, found *above* the basal layers, which do not produce melanin but give a positive reaction for adenosine triphosphatase.

Both are of interest because of the nature of their specialized biochemical function.

Melanocytes are believed to be a self-replicating system of cells which actively undergo mitosis to replicate those members lost by migration to the superficial epithelial layers. The only observable difference between the melanocytes from Caucasoid and Negroid gingivae is in the number and maturity of the melanin granules they contain rather than in the number of melanocytes. A fibrous framework upon which melanin is deposited is apparently derived from the Golgi vesicles; when partially melanized, the resultant striated particle is known as a *melanosome;* when mature, it becomes a melanin granule. Melanin is produced by the cell by oxidation of tyrosine to dihydroxyphenylalanine (DOPA), and the oxidation and condensation of this to the final pigmented substance (Fig. 7–5). The melanin granules formed in the melanocytes are finally transferred by a procedure known as *cytocrine activity* through the dendritic processes to adjacent epithelial cells which constitute the pigmented cells of the oral epithelium. As these cells then move superficially, they eventually lose their melanin content, probably through degradation of the granules in the later stages of keratinization. Histochemical tests for melanocytes depend on their oxidation of dihydroxy-

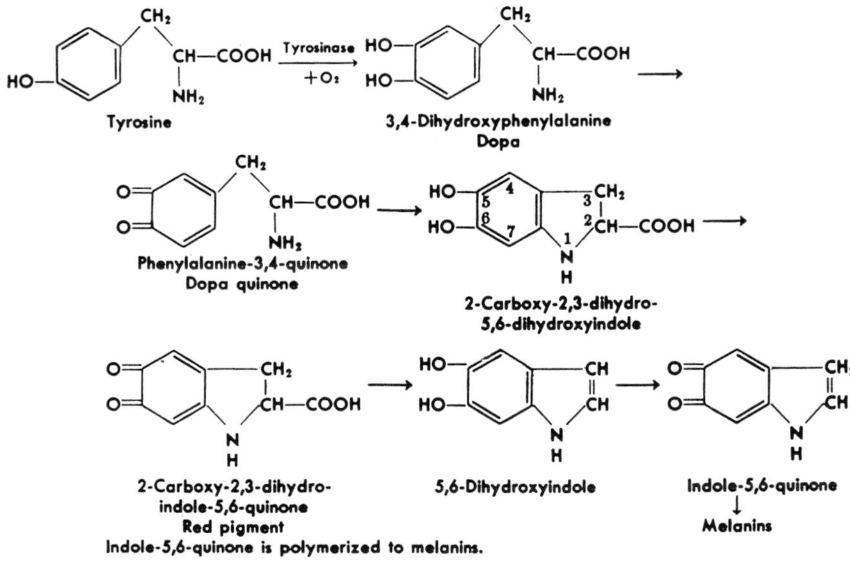

FIG. 7–5. Metabolism scheme. Conversion of tyrosine to melanin.

phenylalanine to melanin, and they are thus referred to as "DOPA positive" cells.

The DOPA negative dendritic cells in the upper layers of the gingival epithelium are, to some extent, sources of ATPase granules, and there is some evidence to suggest that the "basket-weave" appearance of the keratin over most of the body surface is the result of enzyme systems in which these granules play a specific role.

## THE CONNECTIVE TISSUE CONTINUUM

### Ground Substance

All parts of the periodontal system have many of the biochemical components of the gingival connective tissue ground substance in common, and for this reason the ground substance constitutes a continuum throughout the periodontium. This is true hydrostatically, mechanically, bioelectrically, chemically, pathologically, etc. This continuum may be visualized as a vast fluid/semi-fluid sea, which transmits the experience of one part of the periodontium to the other areas, and which, in its own way, is as changing and fickle as any sea on earth. The composition of the interstitial material of lamina propria is, like that of most connective tissue, the result of many variable contributions. Among these might be listed the tissue fluids derived from the blood, the metabolic products of parenchymal cells, and the mucopolysaccharides synthesized by the fibroblasts. While the present discussion is concerned primarily with these latter substances, it must be remembered that the blood provides the nutrients for periodontal maintenance and that its proteins include many of immunological significance in combating periodontal disease. Most of the neutral mucopolysaccharides also originate in the blood.

### Gingival Mucopolysaccharides

Since much of the knowledge concerning this subject is derived from the application of histochemical techniques, it is important that the polysaccharide components of human gingiva have been isolated and studied in regard to their staining abilities. It was found that the *PAS* staining technique, in the absence of glycogen, is specific for certain glycoproteins but does not react with hyaluronic or chondroitin sulfuric acids. *Toluidine blue* produces tissue metachromasia mainly due to the chondroitin sulfates, as does *alcian blue*. *Colloidal iron* stains both hyaluronic acid and chondroitin sulfate but is less specific than the other reagents. The structure and metabolism of the mucopolysaccharides are discussed in Chapter 3.

### Mucopolysaccharides and Collagen

From a clinical standpoint, one of the most significant properties of the mucopolysaccharides resides in their ability to bind collagen fibrils into

8

fibers, much in the manner of "sizing." This is achieved by salt type cross-linkages, which make the acid groups on the mucopolysaccharide moiety a contributor to the net charge on the collagen fiber. Other cross-linkages include hydrogen bonds, hydrophobic bonds and covalent bonds such as described in Chapter 2. Papain is able to cleave the cross-linkages without hydrolyzing the collagen, and when injected into a rabbit's ear causes it to become limp because of disaggregation of the collagen by removal of the protein from the mucopolysaccharide-protein complex.

Much evidence concerning this relationship of mucopolysaccharides to collagen has been obtained from a study of *Lathyrism*, a human disease occurring in some parts of the world due to the consumption of excessive amounts of certain legumes. The toxic principle in these legumes prevents the synthesis of adequate amounts of mucopolysaccharide to exert its sizing effect. This substance, $\gamma$-glutamyl-$\beta$-aminoproprionitrile, can conveniently be replaced in experimental studies by its simpler derivative, $\beta$-aminoproprionitrile (BAPN), or even aminoacetonitrile (AAN). Papain, when injected causes the collapse of a rabbit's ear in about 24 hours, but the defect is normally restored in 3 to 5 days. When AAN is also administered, this recovery does not occur but large amounts of soluble collagen and a low mucopolysaccharide content are shown to exist. Treatment of the periodontal membrane with BAPN results in the appearance of fine, disoriented collagen fibrils which fail to form fibrous bundles. The area so treated becomes edematous due to increased water retention brought about by the disaggregated mucopolysaccharide. This relationship is of particular importance because of the production of analogous conditions mediated by bacterial enzymes.

## Bioelectric Phenomena in Ground Substance

Because of the large and varying number of electric charges that may occur on protein and mucopolysaccharide molecules, countless opportunities exist for the generation of electric potentials that may have profound effects upon the organization of the micro-structure of the periodontium. Piezoelectric effects that have been observed in bone may well result from the slipping of collagen fibers past one another. In addition, "displacement potentials" have been obtained during the bending of rod-like polyelectrolytes of potassium hyaluronidate. These appear to result when a number of molecules are bent in the same way, displacing significant numbers of free charge carriers from the inside to the outside of the molecule. When bone is stressed, charges appear on its surface. It has been proposed that the local electrical fields resulting from them may influence the orientation of mucopolysaccharide, and thus collagen molecules and fibers, in a direction in the periodontium most calculated to resist the stress. The direction of bone growth in tissue culture is influenced by electric fields and it has been suggested that such forces may be of major importance both in orthodontic procedures and in explaining alveolar bone changes arising from traumatic occlusion and in edentulous patients. Thus the control of the adaptation of alveolar architectural arrangement and density to functional demands may reside almost entirely in this electrochemical aspect of macromolecular activity.

## Mucopolysaccharides and Water Binding

There is little doubt that one of the most clinically important properties of the mucopolysaccharides is their ability to retain water in the connective tissues of the gingiva and elsewhere in the body. While hydrogen bonding may account for some of this activity, it is now felt that most of the water held by these substances is actually trapped in the interstices of the molecules. The state of aggregation of the mucopolysaccharides and its metabolic control by the endocrines is at present poorly understood. The disastrous result to the gingiva when these carbohydrates are attacked by bacterial glucuronidases is readily apparent. Hyaluronic acid, and more particularly the chondroitin sulfates, obviously function as major reservoirs of cations, especially calcium. It has been pointed out that they tend to serve as ion exchange resins in regulating the ionic balance in various portions of the connective tissue.

## THE PERIODONTAL FIBERS

Suspended in the ground substance of the gingival connective tissue and the periodontal membrane are the periodontal fibers, which are responsible for transmitting all of the forces acting upon the teeth to the alveolar bone (Fig. 7–3). Although the fibrous elements of connective tissue may be of several different kinds (collagen, reticulin, elastin, oxytalan),* the circular, gingivo-dental and transseptal fibers with which the periodontist is primarily concerned are largely composed of collagen. Many of the chemical aspects of collagen are discussed in Chapter 2 and should be reviewed at this point. Collagen is the most abundant organic substance in the human body, accounting for about 6% of the body weight. Collagen disorders of one type or another are involved in most periodontal disease.

## Metabolism in Periodontal Tissues

Some indication of the normal metabolism of collagen in the periodontium may be obtained from studies on adolescent and adult mice, using tritium-labeled glycine or proline. Since these amino acids make up a major fraction

---

* Reticular fibers are fine, branched, and ramify throughout the lamina propria. They are most easily identifiable around blood vessels and may compose the basement membrane. They are said to contain more carbohydrate and lipid than collagen. Elastin fibers have a different amino acid composition from collagen or reticulin, contain some carbohydrate and are scarce in the gingiva. *Oxytalan* fibers are thought to be intermediate in many respects between collagen and elastin and may represent a peculiar reactive characteristic of certain of these fibers. Their existence is not as well established as the other types.

of the collagen molecule, it is presumed that areas of the periodontium in which these substances concentrate are sites of new collagen synthesis. (This is, in fact, true only in bone and dentinal matrix, other proteins also being formed in observable amounts elsewhere.) With this technique, fibroblasts of the periodontal membrane show heavy labeling (collagen synthesis) within a half hour following administration of the amino acids, with little labeled extracellular material. The situation was reversed, however, within about 4 hours. Collagen synthesis was most pronounced at the alveolar crest and root apex, presumably the points of greatest stress. The degree of labeling was much greater than in other dense connective tissue, such as tendon, ligament, or gingiva. The observation that the periodontal membrane is a site of highly active collagen metabolism is supported by its great sensitivity to nutritional deficiencies of protein or ascorbic acid.

In alveolar bone, labeled osteoblasts were also found after one half hour in adolescent, but not adult, mice, appeared later in the pre-bone of adult mice and in the calcified matrix of both, where it persisted for over 45 days with little change. It was apparent that calcification proceeded faster here than in cementum. The results support the earlier observation that there is a slow and continuous remodeling of alveolar bone tissue. Similar results were obtained with cementum but at a much slower rate with the greatest activity near the root apex. Only small areas of cementum were labeled, however, suggesting that not all cementoblasts were actively secreting collagen at the same time. A decrease in activity with time showed that in this tissue, too, there is some turnover of the collagen. The data supply ample reason for the great sensitivity of the periodontium as a whole to nutritional privation, as seen in all species studied.

## Collagen Levels in Gingival Disease

Collagen fibers in the periodontium, as elsewhere, are secreted by the fibroblast into the surrounding medium as a soluble precursor which is subsequently converted into collagen fibers. Collagen deficiencies in connective tissue may involve either a complete failure of the fibroblasts to synthesize collagen, a failure of the soluble collagen to form insoluble fibers, or accelerated collagen degeneration. By determination of the relative amounts of soluble and insoluble collagen in tissues, it would appear that information as to the fundamental nature of many periodontal disturbances might be obtained. In a study in which the soluble collagen was extracted with 0.1 M citrate buffer at pH 3.5,* it was found that distinct differences did occur. Thus in chronic periodontitis, normal amounts of soluble collagen were present, but insoluble collagen (and thus total collagen) was low, although not as low as histological appearances would suggest. This

---

* Somewhat different results may be obtained by extracting collagen with water, neutral salt solutions or dilute acids. It is believed that the material obtained by these different solvents represents arbitrary fractions from a continuous series of decreasing solubilities rather than distinct metabolic products.

led to the suggestion that a disorganization of fibers along with deficient precipitation of the soluble form may be involved rather than an increase in collagen breakdown. In one patient in which systemic factors were involved, the soluble collagen fraction was less than one-third of the normal value. On a dry weight basis, soluble collagen was normally present at about 1.7% and insoluble collagen at 30.8% but considerable variability existed.

The process by which collagen breaks down in inflamed tissues is still far from clear. Most studies involving collagenolytic activity have depended for their results on liquefaction of collagen gels without clearly indicating that *hydrolysis* of the collagen molecule is actually involved. With this in mind, it may be stated that collagen breakdown may occur as the result of the liberation of the lysozomal contents of leukocytes, which are present in inflamed but not in uninflamed gingiva. A second source of collagen "liquefying" enzyme is in the bacterium *Bacteroides melaninogenicus*, an anaerobic microorganism indigenous to the human gingival crevice. The enzyme in this instance appears inactive in other than anaerobic environments thus apparently differing from that of leukocytes. It is, however, of considerable significance in the anaerobic depths of periodontal pockets.

## THE MINERALIZED PERIODONTIUM

The alveolar bone and cementum provide rigidity to the periodontium but, as previously emphasized, they are tissues which are highly subject to change as a result of either local or general systemic factors. When one considers the millions of osteocytes buried deeply within the alveolus, a picture arises of their isolation from metabolizing tissues by tremendous spans of solid mineral material. But if one takes into account the tremendous cell surface area in relation to its mass, and multiplies this unit area for all of the osteocytes, it becomes apparent that a vast metabolizing surface is in contact with a mineral wall, and that minor changes in metabolism may affect a tremendous mineral surface. It is partially for this reason that the alveolar bone is capable of such rapid change. Cementum is less subject to change than alveolar bone, perhaps because of its less immediate access to the circulation. However, it should be mentioned that cementum is reported to have an exceedingly high fluoride content, probably because of its permeability, and this may have some stabilizing effect on its mineral organization.

Although metabolic studies of alveolar bone and cementum have not been extensive, there is adequate information to show that cementocytes and osteocytes, although generally described as "restive," have approximately the same metabolic activity as the fibroblasts in gingiva. Both cell types have been demonstrated to have virtually all of the enzymes essential to carbohydrate metabolism via glycolysis, the citric acid cycle and the phosphogluconate (pentose phosphate) system. In a quantitative sense, metabolic activity will appear low for mineralized tissue if reported on a tissue weight basis. However, on an extractable protein basis of reporting, very different results are obtained.

| Tissue | Per gm wet tissue | Per mg extractable protein |
|---|---|---|
| Alkaline phosphatase (units) | | |
| Alveolar bone | 125 | 56 |
| Gingiva | 316 | 9 |
| Malic dehydrogenase (units) | | |
| Alveolar bone | 3.9 | 1.8 |
| Gingiva | 66 | 2.0 |
| Liver | 215 | 2.1 |

(From publications by Nakamura *et al.*, 1965, 1966)

As would be anticipated, studies employing radioactive isotopes have uniformly confirmed this high activity. Using tritiated proline, it has been found that the growth rate of alveolar bone in mice is twice that of frontal bone. When $^{45}Ca$ and $^{32}P$ are injected into animals, the radioactivity in the alveolar septae reached a peak in less than half the time required by other bone studied. It is of the greatest importance to recognize that these rapid rates of organizational biochemical activity imply equally that the reverse activity will be of a proportional speed.

Because of the highly critical nature of the periodontal membrane in dental health, mention must be made of the role of alveolar bone in its maintenance and repair. The regeneration of periodontal membrane entails the production of a highly evolved tissue and newer portions always appear less developed and organized. Much of the repair derives from cells originating from perivascular locations within the alveolar bone and not from indigenous cells of the periodontal membrane itself. From this standpoint, then, metabolic activity in alveolar bone is highly interrelated with the sequence of physiological/pathological events that transpire in regions of the periodontium which may be considerably removed from it, and which do not directly involve it.

## METABOLISM OF THE PERIODONTIUM

Following the pioneering work of Alfonso Leng in Chili in 1942, a vast amount of research on the metabolism of the periodontium has appeared in the literature that can only be briefly summarized in an introductory treatise. Whether knowingly or not, this research has been directed largely toward studying the metabolism of the various versions of the fibroblast which occur in the periodontium. For the most part it has been concerned with the specialized functions of this cell in collagen and mucopolysaccharide synthesis. Some *general* aspects of the chemistry of the odontoblast may be found in Chapter 8 on the dental pulp, while the foregoing sections of the present chapter have considered many of the *special* metabolic activities of periodontal fibroblasts. With this material as a background, it now becomes possible to consider some of the over-all aspects of periodontal metabolism.

## Enzymatic Balance in Gingival Tissues

It has previously been pointed out that all of the enzymes necessary for glycolysis, the citric acid cycle, and the phosphogluconate system have been demonstrated to exist in the cells of all parts of the periodontium, but that in some areas of the gingival epithelium, at least, there is variability in the activity of the several systems to meet the relative degree of anaerobiosis which exists. Beyond this, several investigators have stated that the *relative* activities of the various enzyme components are not always compatible with the smooth operation of carbohydrate metabolism customarily seen in most other tissues. Thus it seems probable that considerably more lactate would be produced in the layers of the gingival epithelium than could be disposed of by existing mechanisms. The possibility has therefore been raised of the existence of intercellular metabolic reactions in which products of one phase of the epithelial respiration (*e.g.*, anaerobic lactate) may be transferred to the connective tissue for its complete oxidation. Since the effluent from the epithelium to the connective tissue must essentially equal in volume the nutritional influx of fluid, such a system is now considered highly probable. This concept further lends support to the consideration of endogenous respiratory inhibitors of epithelial respiration mentioned earlier in this chapter.

## Gingival Respiration

In addition to the reported data for the respiration of gingival epithelium, numerous investigations have been made on "gingival tissue" which have culminated in a wide variety of "normal" values. In general, however, studies of the $Q_{O_2}$ of mixed gingival tissue seem to arrive at normal values of about 1.5. In individual studies, where sampling techniques have been controlled, valuable data has often been obtained. Thus a normal $Q_{O_2}$ of 1.50 rose following gingivectomy in dogs to a value of 3.0 on the 5th day, perhaps largely due to the presence of inflammatory cells. It then increased to 5.0 by the 14th day and returned to normal in another week. Using similar techniques, inflamed gingiva is found to give $Q_{O_2}$ values of 1.8 to 3.0, depending on the degree of inflammation. In another study where intact and manually separated human gingival tissues were studied from both normal and inflamed samples, the following values were obtained:

| Tissue | $Q_{O_2}$ | |
| --- | --- | --- |
| | *Normal* | *Inflamed* |
| Intact gingiva | 1.90 | 3.46 |
| Epithelium | 4.80 | 8.50 |
| Subepithelium | 1.47 | 2.49 |

(After Schrader and Schrader, 1957)

The high epithelial values were believed due to release from endogenous respiratory inhibitors and to increased availability of oxygen. The respiratory quotient (RQ) of gingival tissue is usually about one, increasing several fold as a result of inflammation.

## Products of Periodontal Metabolism

From its very beginning, the study of periodontal biochemistry has been motivated by the belief that biochemical parameters would be discovered in the gingival tissues, blood or other body fluids that would provide an aid in the diagnosis and treatment of periodontal disease. It is apparent that the profound changes occurring in the tissues of many patients must be accompanied by abnormal products or quantities of products of metabolism, much as are disorders of other tissues. A further spur to such studies occurred with the early discovery of one such instance.

*Acatalasemia* is a rare, hereditary periodontal disease, transmitted by a single recessive gene and usually occurring in children before the age of 10 years. It is characterized by small gingival ulcers, with new ones following the old, and with eventual alveolar bone involvement and tooth loss. Healing is only followed by extraction or loss of the teeth, after which the patients remain symptom free. The basic biochemical defect in this disorder is the absence of blood and tissue catalase. Mastication in the normal fashion produces minute gingival injuries which, in these patients, become a suitable medium for bacteria that could otherwise not survive. While this disease is rare, there are numerous other periodontal disorders of equally obscure etiology. Indeed little is known about the reasonably common noninflammatory diseases of this tissue. The absence of catalase from the blood of acatalasemia patients, while not invariably accompanied by clinical symptoms, is sufficiently diagnostic that it has lent great hope to further studies of this nature. This concept was furthered by the recent discovery of the value of serum transaminase determinations in myocardial infarction patients and by the subsequent general resurgence of clinical chemistry.

In recent years, a number of promising observations have been made along these lines of investigation. Based on the observation that the enzymes of the citric acid cycle are relatively high in periodontal tissues, research has shown that in degenerative periodontal disease, blood levels of citric acid are abnormally high. In a series of 60 patients, an average value of $2.41 \pm 0.88$ mg % was obtained, as contrasted to $1.55 \pm 0.40$ mg % for a similar number of normals. Increased excretion of citrate following loading tests has also been reported. Elevation of plasma phosphatase in advanced periodontal cases has been observed by a number of investigators. Increased blood acetylase and choline esterase have also been reported. Blood pantothenic acid has been claimed to be low, a report apparently not in keeping with the elevated citrate and acetylase data. Changes in certain of the plasma globulin fractions have also been seen in many patients with periodontitis, presumably as a result of the inflammatory process. As against these successes, transaminase and a number of other enzymes existing in gingival tissue in high concentrations do not appear to be elevated in the blood in gingival disease. A variety of metabolites has been studied in parotid fluid, blood and urine without finding any significant correlation with periodontal disease. It is apparent, nevertheless, that the positive findings that have geen obtained offer considerable hope for the future of such investigations.

## Gingival Crevicular Fluid

Controversy has extended for over half a century concerning the nature of the space between the epithelial attachment of the gingiva and the tooth surface. For the greater portion of this time, it has been the consensus that the epithelium is structurally bound to the tooth and that only when this attachment is destroyed by the invagination of calculus, food debris, and bacteria, is the space patent and a clinical pocket formed. Under these circumstances, inflammatory exudate is to be expected and easily demonstrable. The work of Waerhaug in 1952, however, cast grave doubt on this concept, and presented instead the picture of an epithelial *cuff*, tightly adherent to the tooth, from which there emerged, from even the healthiest gingiva, a slight but constant flow of crevicular fluid into the gingival sulcus. Normally this fluid carries with it exfoliated epithelial cells and any other debris that may collect in the pocket, thus having a cleansing and protective effect for the epithelial attachment.

When very small strips of filter paper are gently inserted into the pocket area of healthy gingiva, a small amount of fluid is absorbed by the strip which can then be subjected to analysis. The amount of fluid increases with time, and it is considerably more copious when the gingivae are inflamed Micropipettes have also been employed for the collection of the serous material which is apparently the normal physiological secretion of the gingival crevice. Analytical studies have shown the fluid to contain the usual plasma proteins and a variety of fibrinolytic factors. The finding that fluid from normal pockets had a Na:K ratio of about 4:1 has in general led to the belief that it is a serumnal transudate modified by passage through the epithelial wall. Fluid from inflamed gingiva has a Na:K ratio of about 10:1, which is substantially that of inflammatory exudate. In view of the relationship of the flow rate, as measured by length of wetness on a paper strip, to severity of gingivitis and to pocket depth, the paper strip technique has been suggested as a diagnostic tool in the examination of patients with periodontal disease. The presence of a variety of antimicrobial substances in crevicial fluid further supports its value as a protecting cleansing fluid for the pocket area. On the other hand, it has been pointed out that the fluid would probably support the growth of subgingival calculus, most particularly when gingivitis stimulated a more copious outpouring.

Recently, a number of investigators have produced highly persuasive electron microscope photographs to show the connection of the epithelial attachment to the tooth surface by means of clearly visible hemi-desmosomes.

In addition, investigation of the subepithelial circulation in the pocket area shows that its capillaries are so remarkably close to the epithelial surface that even the insertion of the slightest trace of material (*e.g.*, paper strips) is prone to induce inflammation and edema. This is more understandable if it be considered that "micro-trauma" might well be caused by rupture of the hemi-desmosomes. Further, it is reported that continuous irrigation of the sulcus of patients with inflamed gingiva results in the accumulation of fluid like that described, but very little material whatsoever is obtained from healthy patients. As a consequence, it must be concluded that the true nature of crevicial fluid from patients with healthy gingiva and its relationship to the structure of the epithelial attachment has not, as yet, been conclusively established.

## SELECTED REFERENCES

CABRINI, R. L. and CARRANZA, F. A., JR.: Histochemistry of the Periodontal Tissues. A Review of the Literature. International Dental Journal, *16*, 466–479 (1966).

COCHRAN, G. V. B., PAWLUK, R. J. and BASSETT, C. A. L.: Stress Generated Electric Potentials in the Mandible and Teeth, Archives of Oral Biology, *12*, 917–920 (1967).

EICHEL, B. and SHAHRIK, H. A.: Cytochemical Aspects of Oxidative Enzyme Metabolism in Gingiva, in Advances in Oral Biology, *1*, 131–174 (1964).

LOE, H. and NUKI, K.: Oxidative Enzyme Activities in Keratinizing and Nonkeratinizing Epithelium of Normal and Inflamed Gingiva. Journal of Periodontal Research, *1*, 43–50 (1966).

SCHULTZ-HAUDT, S. D., FROM, S. J., and NORDBO, H.: Histochemical Staining Properties of Isolated Polysaccharide Components of Human Gingiva, Archives of Oral Biology, *9*, 17–25 (1964).

# Chapter 8

## Biochemistry of the Dental Pulp

### Ernest Beerstecher, Jr., Ph.D.

## INTRODUCTION

The first chemical studies of pulp by Wurtz in 1856 were unknown to the dental world until emphasized by Magitot in 1878. The first entire work on the chemistry of pulp by Whitslar in 1889 had only this single study on which to depend. Commendably, it pointed out the need for study of living rather than dead and decomposing material and the problems that the pulp's small size and inaccessibility presented to the chemist. Hodge's study in 1936 of pulpal lipids was perhaps the first dependable work on pulp chemistry. Hertz as early as 1866 had proposed that the intertubular substance of dentine was the chemically changed and calcified intercellular substance of the pulp cells, but this received little experimental verification before the histochemical studies on alkaline phosphatase in odontogenesis by Engel and Furuta (1942), Bevelander and Johnson (1945), and Greep, Fischer and Morse (1948). This, then, was the background to Bruckner's work on alkaline phosphatase in pulp (1949) and Pincus' study on pulp respiration (1950), which introduced the extensive literature which developed over the period of the past 15 years.

## HISTOLOGY AND FUNCTION

The dental pulp, although anatomically removed from the other soft tissues of the oral cavity, is inextricably related to them by considerations of structure, function, composition, pathology, and therapeutics, and its biochemical nature must therefore be considered in the light of this relationship. Histologically, the pulp is remarkably similar to the connective tissue of the gingiva, and this similarity is supported by all except a few biochemical considerations. Both tissues are concerned with the support of odontoblastic activity and the nutrition of adjacent mineralized connective tissue. The nutrition and innervation of the pulp is via channels that traverse the periodontium, which provide an inevitable common source of pathogenesis. The permeability of the dentine provides for appreciable nutritional interchange between these tissues and thus a certain degree of symbiosis and mutual responsiveness. Indeed, the aim of root canal therapy must, ideally, be directed toward stimulation of periodontal (cemental) closure of the apical foramina of the pulp chamber.

While the study of pulp chemistry evolved as an approach to odontogenesis, there can be little doubt that present emphasis is directed toward achieving more effective pulp therapy. The pulp is remarkably sensitive to its environment, and although it is seemingly well insulated, it is readily influenced and injured by a constant succession of both physical and chemical factors. Extremes of heat and pressure are easily transmitted to it and may bring about not only traumatic damage, but also chemical injury through ionic changes and changes in the molecular configuration of its macromolecules. Direct chemical injury may occur from filling materials either acting as enzyme poisons after diffusion to the pulp or electrochemically to modify its ionic balance. Other drugs used in cavity preparation and pulp therapy [*e.g.*, $AgNO_3$, $NaF$, $ZnO$-Eugenol, $Ca(OH)_2$] may act similarly or as outright protein precipitants. In addition, microorganisms may attack the pulp on all perimeters, creating biochemical damage in much the same manner as they do in other connective tissues (*i.e.*, by toxin production; by hydrolysis of macromolecules of cells, fibers and ground substance; by modification of low molecular weight organic substances to form noxious substances such as amines; and by changes in pH). The study of the biochemistry of the pulp is thus a prerequisite to the establishment of any system of dentistry or pulp therapy based upon "sound biological principles."

Histologically, the pulp has been described as "primitive connective tissue." Most of the chemical details of its structure may be deduced from a consideration of the biochemistry of the closely related gingival connective tissue so they will not be repeated in this chapter. The pulp is a loose or fluid tissue in a highly dynamic state. It contains relatively few cells: fibroblasts concerned with fiber production and odontogenesis, mesenchymal cells possibly concerned with mucopolysaccharide production, and histiocytes concerned with defense mechanisms. Dispersed among these are a few vascular elements, nerves, and lymphatic channels. Among the cells is a network of fibers, largely collagenous. All these formed elements are suspended in the ground substance composed of pulp fluid of vascular origin to which indigenous mucopolysaccharides have been added.

It is most remarkable that so simple a tissue serves so well the several functions for which it is responsible. These may conveniently be listed as:

1. Architectural—the elaboration of collagenous fibers and of dentine.
2. Nutritive—nourishes the nerve fibers and dentine (and in a more restricted sense, perhaps, even the enamel and periodontium).
3. Sensory—a source of pain receptors.
4. Protective—through inflammation and by secondary dentine formation.

In order to achieve this efficiency, each structural unit must serve at least one or more vital functions and these must be highly integrated. It is proposed, therefore, that the often cited defenselessness of the pulp rests in the fact that a disturbance in any one function is rapidly reflected in the whole organ, there being a conspicuous lack of relief mechanisms compared with other tissues.

These various considerations bring about a critical point with regard to the biochemistry of the dental pulp. The architectural, sensory, and protective functions of the pulp are performed by the cells, which are sparse in proportion to the great mass of ground substance. They contribute negligibly to the chemical composition, but virtually all to the pulp metabolism. The nutritive function of the pulp, and the preponderance of its mass, lies in its extensive extracellular material, which accounts for its chemical composition, but not for its metabolism, This is more true of pulp than almost any other tissue and bespeaks a significant need to cite quantitative metabolic data on the basis of some function of the total cellular mass. This varies greatly throughout the various histologically distinguishable zones of the pulp organ. It is for this reason that the discussion which follows concerns itself respectively with the pulp cells, the fibers, and the ground substance with its integrative functions.

## BIOCHEMISTRY OF THE ODONTOBLASTS

The biochemistry of the fibroblast and its modifications has been so extensively investigated that it is essential in this chapter to limit the discussion to those facets pertaining specifically to the pulp. These are primarily concerned with its respiration and its odontoblastic activity.

### Ribonucleic Acid (RNA)

One of the major functions of the odontoblast is the synthesis of collagen fibers. Whenever cells synthesize any protein, the pattern for that particular protein is transmitted from the chromosomal DNA in the nucleus to *ribosomes* in the endothelial reticulum of the cytoplasm in the form of templates consisting of ribonucleic acid (RNA). This material, which character-

izes actively synthesizing cells, is believed to give such cells their characteristic basophilia, and active odontoblasts tend to be more basophilic than
inactive ones for this reason. The RNA is at a maximum when collagen is
being synthesized and declines when the cells become quiescent, as after
secondary dentine formation. RNA increases as odontoblasts differentiate
from fibroblasts and is absent when collagen synthesis is impaired, as in
ascorbic acid deficiency (scurvy).

## Alkaline Phosphatase

Alkaline phosphatase is involved in the cleavage of phosphate ions from
organic ester linkage in the calcification process. Large amounts are found
in pulpal odontoblasts, particularly when active in calcification, but also
when the pulp is in the inflammatory state, presumably as a reflection of
secondary dentine depositing activities. Some acid phosphatase* also occurs
in the ground substance of the pulp along the collagen fibers.

Table 8–1.  The Cholesterol Content of Dental Pulp*

| Tissue sample | | Mean % cholesterol |
|---|---|---|
| BOVINE: | Embryonic pulp | 0.067 |
| | Young pulp | 0.069 |
| | Mature pulp | 0.078 |
| | Gingiva | 0.112 |
| HUMAN*: | Young and mature | 0.163 |
| | Most mature | 0.218 |
| | Mature | 0.245 |
| | Gingiva† | 0.200 |

* Modified from Fisher and Stickley.  Human samples pooled.
† Hodge (1933)

## Lipids

The peculiar carbohydrate metabolism of pulp cells is one that favors
fatty acid synthesis, and immense fat globules are seen in some more or less
isolated fibrocytes (e.g., chondrocytes). The material may function either
as a storage form of energy or in the synthesis of neural material. Hodge
found human pulp to contain (on a moist weight basis) 0.91% lipids,
0.70% phospholipids and 0.11% cholesterol. By comparison, he found
human *gingiva* to contain 0.20% cholesterol. In searching for some pulp
constituent that might show progressive changes during tooth maturation,

* Acid phosphatase also liberates phosphate ion from phosphate esters, but functions better
at a pH of about 6 than at the higher pH levels (9) at which the more common alkaline
phosphatase functions best.  Both function at normal tissue pH levels, but are distinguished clinically by the pH levels at which they are measured in the laboratory.

Fisher and Stickley studied the cholesterol content of both human and bovine pulp (Table 8-1). They found increases with age in both cases, with human somewhat higher than bovine material. It is of some interest that in comparing other human and bovine tissues, only liver and adrenal gland have higher cholesterol values. These tissues, like the pulp, are noted for their phosphogluconate metabolism and for their steroid synthesis and secretory activity. The increased sterol content with age, as in plasma and other tissues, is of unknown significance.

## Proteases and Peptidases

Pulp has been demonstrated to contain a variety of enzymes capable of hydrolyzing to utilizable fragments (amino acids) the ever accumulating debris of degenerate collagen fibers and other cell wastes, and of activating certain special cellular processes. The presence of such proteases have been demonstrated in the pulp by histochemical techniques. Preparations from pulp odontoblasts have been found to contain a variety of proteases and dipeptidases capable of digesting hemoglobin and reducing collagen to its free amino acids. Kroeger *et al.* found mouse, rat and dog pulp to contain a polypeptidase which hydrolyzes and inactivates the smooth muscle stimulating substance obtained from the pulp of stimulated teeth.

## Glycogen

Glycogen is generally found in high concentrations in those areas where calcification mechanisms exist, presumably serving as a source of glycolytic alcohols which may form phosphate esters and thus maintain high phosphate concentrations in solution. Glycogen granules have been demonstrated in pulp odontoblasts. They disappear during active calcification and appear again in the quiescent state as might be expected from their function.

## Carbohydrate Metabolism of the Pulp

Carbohydrate metabolism in the dental pulp must serve a number of major purposes other than that of the energy producing function common to all cells. Prominent among these is (1) the provision of materials for synthesis of the mucopolysaccharides which constitute the major portion of this organ, (2) the synthesis of carbon skeleton for the large amounts of glycine, proline, and hydroxyproline necessary for collagen synthesis, and (3) the provision of organic alcohols for the phosphate ester formation in the calcification process. While the synthesis of these carbohydrate derivatives has not been demonstrated to occur exclusively within the pulp (some may be supplied by the blood), it is most probable that a major fraction is endogenous in nature. In addition to the above considerations, the rapid production of collagen places a high demand upon the pulp for pentose used in RNA synthesis.

Studies on the respiration of the pulp contribute materially to explain how these manifold demands are met. These may be summarized as follows:

1. The sparse cellular population of the pulp accounts for the respiration of its entire mass so that, on a weight basis, its oxygen consumption at rest is low by comparison with other tissues.
2. Its respiratory quotient (RQ) ($CO_2/O_2$) is about 0.90 in most species studied.
3. The oxygen consumption is highest during dentinogenesis ($Qo_2 = 2.04$), falling to lower values (0.47) in the later quiescent state.
4. The oxygen consumption is higher in bovine pulp than in human pulp, perhaps because of continuing odontogenesis.

Certain observations suggest that the carbohydrate metabolism in pulp differs from that in most other tissues. In *in vitro* studies, despite the fact that carbohydrate reserves may be limited and rapidly depleted within the pulp, the tissue continues to respire for 8 to 12 hours without requiring added glucose or using cellular lipid or protein reserves (but possibly using reserves from the matrix). It has been demonstrated that some form of anaerobic glycolysis is more important in pulp than in most other tissues. Further, pulp produces a great deal of acid under aerobic conditions which may act as a controlling factor in its metabolism. These various data indicate the existence in pulp of a vigorous phosphogluconate (pentose phosphate) shunt type carbohydrate metabolism in addition to the usual glycolytic pathway and citric acid cycle. This shunt system provides for relative anaerobic function, supplies large amounts of ribose, leads to fat accumulation, and has been shown to parallel collagen synthesis in pulp.

Because of the manifold functions that pulp serves, inhibition of its respiratory system might well be expected to have dramatic results. Fisher *et al.* have shown that a great many materials frequently employed in clinical dental procedures do have the property of depressing the oxygen uptake of the pulp. Some of their results are summarized in Table 8–2.

Table 8–2.  Effect of Some Common Dental Material on the Oxygen Consumption of Pulp*

| Material | $Qo_2$ |
|---|---|
| Normal pulp . . . . . . | 0.55 |
| ZnO-Eugenol . . . . . . | 0.42 |
| Calcium hydroxide . . . . . | 0.42 |
| Eugenol . . . . . . . | 0.31 |
| Amalgam . . . . . . | 0.33 |
| Zn phosphate cement . . . . | 0.32 |
| Adrenalin . . . . . . | 0.34 |
| Procaine . . . . . . . | 0.16 |

* Bovine dental pulp, concentrations varied so as to simulate reasonably clinical exposure, Adapted from Fisher *et al.*, 1957.

The results reflect to some extent the water solubility of the various agents and the proximity to the pulp that they might achieve. A variety of similar observations suggest that data of this nature may be valuable criteria in the experimental evaluation of various new clinical therapeutic agents.

## BIOCHEMISTRY OF THE PULP FIBERS

Most of the known facts regarding the fibrous network of the dental pulp indicate that it is similar to that of gingival connective tissue. Therefore only a few salient points will require special attention. The fibers are synthe-sized by the odontoblasts and are of two main types. Collagen predominates in the matrix, and elastin is found predominantly in the walls of the larger afferent vascular channels. The two proteins are the onyl known source of hydroxyproline in living material and are further characterized by high concentration of proline and glycine. In the relative amounts of these three amino acids and of others, they differ greatly.

The collagenous fibers account for an integral portion of the nitrogen content of the pulp. The nitrogen content does not vary among different species, but it may increase slightly with age. In general, collagen synthesis (and therefore the fibrous content) does not appear to increase appreciably with age, but only as a response to irritation. Studies of collagen fiber synthesis by fibroblasts measured by [15]N labeled amino acid uptake show that both synthesis and breakdown proceed at a rate similar to that of liver and less than that of gingival mucosa.

## BIOCHEMISTRY OF PULP GROUND SUBSTANCE

The ground substance of pulp resembles in general that of gingival con-nective tissue. It is composed of dental pulp fluid (exudate) derived from the blood plasma and containing added colloidal mucopolysaccharides originating in the cellular elements of the pulp. A fluid portion of the ground substance also leaves the pulp by its lymphatic system and in lesser amounts via the dentine, cementum, and enamel. The ground substance has a higher calcium and phosphate content than plasma exudate due to the binding of these substances by the mucopolysaccharides. The calcium and fluoride content tends to increase with age, and the fluoride content is higher in geographical areas where the drinking water fluoride content is high. Parathormone administration tends to increase the citrate content of the pulp, which may account for some of the decalcification that occurs. It also increases the number of phagocytes present in the pulp, however, which may effect the same result.

In general, pulp contains the same amounts of glucose and other low molecular weight metabolites as does blood plasma. It contains only about one-fifth the protein content, however, as is characteristic of other filtrates. The protein is composed largely of albumin and $\alpha_1$, $\alpha_2$, $\beta$ and $\gamma$ globulins in proportions similar to those in blood plasma. Pulp fluid differs from dentinal and enamel fluid in having a much higher protein content than the latter two which are ultrafiltrates.

The colloidal mucopolysaccharides of the ground substance increase its viscosity while permitting it to remain readily diffusible to nutrients. They consist largely of two high molecular weight linear polymers.

1. Hyaluronic acid, composed of alternating units of glucuronic acid and N-acetylglucosamine.
2. Chondroitin sulfate B, composed of alternating units of iduronic acid and N-acetylgalactosamine sulfate. No other chondroitin derivative is known with certainty to be present in the pulp, although a sialic acid derivative may be present.

These substances are common to all connective tissue ground substance. It is still uncertain that fibroblasts play the entire role in their synthesis and subsequent destruction.

The precise functions of the mucopolysaccharides of the pulp are not all known with certainty but several are assured. It seems established that they stabilize collagen fibrils into fibers by chemically cross-linking the collagen molecules. In lathyrism, caused by consuming excessive amounts of certain peas or artificially by the administration of amino-acetonitrile, mucopolysaccharide synthesis is depressed, and collagen is not converted into insoluble collagen fibers. Mucopolysaccharides are also involved in calcium binding in mineralizable areas and in this manner, participate in the calcification mechanism. Finally, being hydrophilic colloids, they are involved in water binding and retention permitting sol-gel interconversions. This fact is believed to be associated with the observed effects of certain endocrine substances on connective tissue.

The dental pulp is a unique tissue from a biochemical standpoint in view of its remarkable adaptation of a few cell types to perform a variety of functions. In addition to a conventional glycolytic system, it contains a pentose phosphate shunt respiratory system permitting it to function under varying degrees of ischemia, to synthesize carbon skeletons for mucopolysaccharides and collagen synthesis, and to contribute large amount of ribose directly to RNA synthesis. The pulp has a highly organized structure but retains a permeable and fluid nature. Its respiratory enzymes and state of mucopolysaccharide aggregation are exceedingly sensitive to environmental influences.

## SELECTED REFERENCES

FISHER, A. K., SCHUMACHER, E. R., ROBINSON, N. P., and SHARBONDY, G. P.: Effects of dental drugs and materials on the rate of oxygen consumption in bovine dental pulp, J. Dental Res., *36*, 447–450, 1957.

FISHER, A. K. and SCHWABE, C.: Effects of procaine concentration and duration of contact on oxygen consumption in bovine dental pulp, J. Dental Res., *41*, 484–490, 1962.

————: The endogenous respiratory quotient of bovine dental pulp, J. Dental Res., *40*, 346–351, 1961.

FISHER, A. K. and STICKLEY, J. J.: The cholesterol content of some bovine and human oral tissues, J. Dent. Res., *39*, 1037–1040, 1960.

HALDI, J. and JOHN, K.: Sulfanilamide and penicillin in the pulp fluid of the dog, J. Dent. Res., *44*, 1386–1388, 1965.

HALDI, J., LAW, M. L., and JOHN, K.: Comparative concentration of various constituents of blood plasma and dental pulp fluid, J. Dent. Res., *44*, 427–430, 1965.

LEBLOND, C. P.: Elaboration of dental collagen in odontoblasts as shown by radio-autography after injection of labelled glycine and proline, Ann. Histochem., *8*, 43–50, 1963.

ROTBLAT, N. D. and YAEGER, J. A.: Dental pulp citrate during the development of abnormally mineralized dentine, Arch. Oral. Biol., *10*, 617–623, 1965.

SHAZER, D. O. DE: Glucose-6-phosphate and 6-phosphogluconic dehydrogenase in bovine dental pulp, J. Dental Res., *41*, 986–996, 1962.

STARK, M. M., MYERS, H. M., MORRIS, M., and GARDNER, R.: The localization of radioactive calcium$_{45}$ hydroxide over exposed pulps in rhesus monkey teeth, J. Oral Therap. & Pharmacol., *1*, 290–297, 1964.

TEN CATE, A. R.: Alkaline phosphatase activity and formation of human dentine, Arch. Oral. Biol., *11*, 267–268, 1966.

WHITSLAR, W. H.: A study of the chemical composition of the dental pulp, Dent. Regist., *43*, 581–586, 1889.

# Chapter 9

## Saliva

### James M. Klinkhamer, D.M.D.

Introduction
Anatomy of Salivary Glands
Stimulation of Salivary Glands
Functions of the Salivary Glands
Functions of Saliva
Inorganic Constituents of Saliva
Organic Constituents of Saliva
     Vitamins
Group Specific Substances
Salivary Enzymes
Hydrogen Ion Concentration
Bacteria
Surface Deposits
     The Mobile Mucus Phase of Saliva (MMP)
The Formation of Plaque
Calculus

## INTRODUCTION

Most thoughts about oral disease processes presuppose, either directly or indirectly, an influential role of saliva. The accumulation of accurate and reproducible data which supports or rejects many of these seemingly logical hypotheses is an important objective. For example, the bacterial contamination of saliva is often thought to be the cause of infections and inflammatory reactions. Just as often, however, saliva is believed to possess defensive properties against those same reactions.

The search for causal relationships by intensive study of humoral and cellular biochemistry is a valuable and necessary one.

## ANATOMY OF SALIVARY GLANDS

The parotid is the largest of the salivary glands and consists of encapsulated main and accessory components. It is a compound, branched, alveolar gland located around the mandibular ramus, anterior to the ear. The parotid (Stensen's) duct opens opposite the second upper molar. Secretory ducts are lined by conspicuously striated columnar cells. The intercalated ducts are long, narrow and branching and connect the secretory epithelium to the secretory ducts. Serous alveoli predominate; mucous alveoli are extremely rare. Histologically, the parotid gland is characterized by the large number of fat cells in the interstitial tissue. The nerve supply is autonomic. Both sympathetic and parasympathetic fibers end in varicose filaments and bud-like expansions between the secretory cells. Sympathetic fibers come from the superior cervical ganglion and the parasympathetic fibers from the otic ganglion.

The submaxillary gland is intermediate in size and fully encapsulated. It is a compound, branched, alveolar, partly tubular gland positioned beneath the mandible. Its duct (Wharton's) opens on either side of the frenulum of the tongue. The secretory ducts show conspicuously striated columnar cells. The intercalated ducts are much shorter than those of the parotid gland and the secretory epithelium consists largely of serous alveoli with relatively few mucous alveoli. Again, the sympathetic innervation comes from the superior cervical ganglion; the parasympathetic fibers come from the submaxillary ganglion.

The sublingual gland is the smallest and consists of a major gland and several minor ones. They are encapsulated, compound, branched, tubulo-aveolar glands situated in the floor of the mouth. The major (Bartholin's) ducts open near Wharton's duct. There are several minor sublingual (Rivinian) ducts, while secretory ducts are rare or absent. There are no intercalated ducts. The secretory epithelium of the major gland shows predominantly mucous alveoli, while the minor glands are pure mucous. The secretory nerve supply is the same as for the submaxillary gland.

For all three glands the sensory innervation is through the fifth cranial nerve. The sympathetic innervation controls vasoconstriction and the parasympathetic fibers control secretory activity.

The palatine, glossopalatine, minor buccal and labial glands are buried in the submucosal layer and are not encapsulated. The secretory portions may contain both serous and mucous cells with mucous cells in the majority. The glands of the tongue are serous, mucous, and mixed, the mucous being the most numerous.

The chemical composition and physical appearance of saliva depends on the method of collection and the type of stimulus. Mixed secretions can be collected in the "unstimulated" resting state by simple expectoration. "Stimulated" or actively secreted saliva can be collected by chewing paraffin. Pure secretions from the individual glands may be collected by applying Curby's double cup to the mucous membrane surrounding the papillae of the parotid ducts, or by direct cannulation of the submaxillary or sublingual ducts. Saliva obtained in this manner is clear and colorless, while stimulated or unstimulated mixed saliva appears as a frothy, opalescent, slightly viscous fluid.

In laboratory animals glands can be exteriorized or ducts can be diverted to the outside of the oral cavity.

## STIMULATION OF SALIVARY GLANDS

It has been stated that in man the total volume of saliva produced in 24 hours is about 1500 cc and that approximately 400 cc of this daily production is secreted by the minor mucous glands of the mucous membrane. These estimates were derived from short time collections. The 24-hour totals were based on the assumption that the measured glandular activity remained constant. However, intermittent periods of near total glandular inactivity occur during the resting hours at night. The above values are too generous to serve as the mean 24-hour production of saliva. Standardization of procedures for the collection of salivary samples has proven difficult. The reason is that salivary glands are controlled by both the parasympathetic and sympathetic divisions of the autonomic nervous system. The sight or even thought of food increases the salivary flow to an unpredictable degree. An increased flow rate can also be provoked by chemical or physical irritation of the tongue.

A high salivary flow rate results from the presence of noxious, nausea-causing substances in the stomach. The silent opinion or feelings of embarrassment, aggravation or enjoyment during collection of saliva has great influence on the flow rate as well as on the composition. The effect and degree of stimulation is hard to control, especially the psychostimuli.

Unstimulated saliva is often preferred because its composition is less subject to extraneous fluctuation. Uncontrollable factors in paraffin-stimulated saliva are, for instance, the effect of mechanical stimulation, the number of chewing motions per minute and the chewing force per square inch.

Many of the stimulating factors are different not only for each person, but also for the same person at different times. Substances used experimentally for stimulation of salivary gland activity cause a release of acetylcholine by the parasympathetic nerve endings. The pharmacodynamic action on the gland and its blood supply is not always known, which makes it difficult to evaluate concentration changes of the secreted fluids.

Reduction of salivary flow rate is achieved by the application of substances which relax the smooth muscle of the vascular system. Changes in blood pressure allow the gland to extract more or less water from the blood so that the amount of water available becomes the limiting factor.

Table 9–1 shows the principal drugs and the type of response elicited by their action on the autonomic nervous system. Pilocarpine is often preferred for salivary flow rate stimulation and atropine for reduction of salivation. Both are parasympathetic drugs. This does not imply that there is no response from the sympathetic division. For instance, besides pilo-

Table 9–1.  Principal Drugs, Type of Response and Action

|  | *Parasympathetics* | *Sympathetics* |
|---|---|---|
| STIMULANTS | Acetylcholine | Epinephrine |
|  | Mecholyl | Arterenol |
|  | Carbamylcholine | Ephedrine |
|  | Choline | Amphetamine |
|  | Muscarine | Synephrine |
|  | Pilocarpine | Neo-synephrine |
|  | Physostigmine |  |
|  | Prostigmin |  |
|  | Arecoline |  |
| DEPRESSANTS | Atropine | Ergotoxine |
|  | Hyoscine | Ergotamine |
|  | Hyoscyamine | Dihydroergotamine |
|  | Homatropine | Dibenzyl-$\beta$-chlor-ethylamine |

carpine's direct action as a stimulant for the parasympathetic system, it produces a reflex release of epinephrine from the medulla of the adrenal gland. Epinephrine is also a stimulant, but a sympathomimetic one.  Therefore, indirectly, pilocarpine stimulates the sympathetic fibers to the salivary glands as well.  Some believe that this is the reason for changes in the salivary potassium and sodium concentrations.

A more direct, but difficult, approach is the use of electrical nerve stimulation of the cervical sympathetic nerve trunks or of specific centers in the lower brain stem.  Obviously, laboratory animals are used for locating the activating center in the brain for stimulation and for collecting the secretory outflow for biochemical analysis.  It is often, but not always, possible to design the kind of experiment from which to deduce that the mechanisms under study operate the same or differently in humans.

The foregoing demonstrates the difficulties in establishing the "normal range" of salivary constituents.

## FUNCTIONS OF THE SALIVARY GLANDS

The primary function is to transform and secrete materials from the blood.  Therefore the gland can manufacture and discharge complex substances such as enzymes, mucopolysaccharides, and glycoproteins.

A second function is to excrete substances normally not present in the blood, such as drugs, metals, and alcohol.

## FUNCTIONS OF SALIVA

Swallowing of food would be practically impossible without the presence of saliva. With its moistening and lubricating qualities saliva dissolves many food substances thus aiding in food appreciation and stimulation of the taste buds, which in turn results in additional reflex secretion. Saliva and its mucus components keep the teeth moist and covered and may aid in their preservation by virtue of the presence of calcium and phosphorus ions, protecting enamel from acid dissolution.

Saliva functions in the regulation of water balance by arousing a sensation of thirst, resulting from a decreased salivary output and drying out of the oral mucous membrane. It also functions in conjunction with swallowing in removing food debris.

The mobile mucus phase of saliva serves as the medium in which the polymorphonuclear granulocytes live and function as active phagocytes. It contains substances responsible for antibacterial action, such as opsonins, antibodies, lysozymes and agents causing bacterial mutation. This leads to the indispensable quality of saliva in keeping the bacterial flora of the mouth practically constant throughout life.

## INORGANIC CONSTITUENTS OF SALIVA

By exposure to air, bacterial activity and enzymatic reactions, saliva changes upon standing and storing between collection and the time of analysis. Therefore the ranges of values given should be considered a guide and not strictly interpreted as standard values.

One liter of human saliva consists of 994 gm of water, 1 gm of suspended solids and 5 gm of dissolved substances of which 2 gm are inorganic and 3 gm organic material. The suspended solids consist of exfoliated cells of the epithelium, disintegrated leukocytes, oral bacteria, yeasts and a few protozoa. The specific gravity of saliva varies from 1.002 to 1.020 and the freezing point depression from $-0.2°$ to $-0.7°$ C.

The mean values in Table 9–2 are expressed as milligrams of the constituent per liter of saliva, unless stated otherwise. Range values are enclosed in brackets.

Sodium and potassium ions are the most abundant inorganic constituents of saliva. Sodium and chloride ion concentrations increase with the rate of salivary flow. The concentration of potassium ions remains relatively constant, regardless of the flow rate. The comparison of sodium and potassium concentrations in saliva with blood values is interesting. Sodium is about 10 times higher in blood serum than in saliva, potassium is approximately one-third the amount in serum and chloride close to one-seventh the concentration in saliva as in blood plasma.

Experimentally, steroids, such as deoxycorticosterone and adrenocorticotropic hormone have been shown to produce a decrease in sodium and chloride levels and a rise in potassium concentration.

Table 9–2.  Inorganic Composition of Stimulated and Unstimulated Saliva
(mg per liter unless indicated otherwise)

| Inorganic Constituents | Unstimulated Saliva | Stimulated Saliva |
|---|---|---|
| Sodium (mEq) | 14.8 (6.5—21.7) | 44.6 (43.0—46.1) |
| Potassium (mEq) | 22.1 (19.0—23.3) | 18.3 (17.9—18.7) |
| Calcium (mEq) | 3.1 (2.3—5.5) | 2.8 (1.8—4.6) |
| Magnesium | 0.6 (0.16—1.06) | —— |
| Copper ($\mu$g) | —— | 256  (100—470) |
| Cobalt ($\mu$g) | —— | 24  (0—125) |
| Chloride (mEq) | 10 | 43 |
| Phosphorus (total) | 193 | —— |
| Phosphorus (inorganic) | 149  (74—211) | —— |
| Phosphorus (lipid) | ——  (0.5—2.0) | —— |
| Sulfur | 76 | —— |
| Fluoride | —— | ——  (0.1—0.2) |
| Bromide | —— | ——  (1—7) |
| Iodide | ——  (0—3.5) | ——  (0.2—3.5) |
| Thiocyanate | ——  (26—270) | —— |
| Iron | —— | ——  (0.1—0.56) |
| Porphyrin | —— | 1.7 |
| Phenol | —— | ——  (0.28—0.37) |
| Oxygen (ml) | 10 | —— |
| Nitrogen (ml) | 25 | ——  (4.8—27.8) |
| Carbon dioxide (ml) | 150  (82—253) | ——  (190—500) |

The presence of phosphate and calcium ions in saliva has an important bearing on keeping the solubility of tooth enamel low.

Table 9–3 shows the effect of flow rate on calcium and phosphorus content of unstimulated human saliva.  Some people are slow and some are fast secretors of unstimulated saliva.  It demonstrates the difficulty in evaluating at what concentration a certain constituent of saliva is either optimally protective or optimally destructive for the condition being studied.  Table 9–3 shows that the concentration of calcium and phosphate is higher in the slow secretors.  The rapid secretors have a higher output per hour for both

Table 9–3.  Effect of Saliva Flow Rate on Calcium and Phosphorus Content

| | Slow Secretors | Rapid Secretors |
|---|---|---|
| Av. rate of flow (ml/hr) | 13.40 | 39.60 |
| Av. Ca conc. (mEq/l) | 3.00 | 2.83 |
| Av. rate Ca secr. (mEq/hr) | 0.40 | 1.13 |
| Av. P conc. (mg/l) | 17.00 | 11.80 |
| Av. rate P secr. (mg/hr) | 2.21 | 4.42 |

ions. Paraffin stimulated saliva has a lower concentration of both ions than resting saliva.

Inorganic phosphate accounts for 90% of the total P; the rest occurs as hexosephosphates, phospholipids, nucleoproteins and nucleic acids.

Citric acid has aroused much interest because of its possible role as a calcium solubilizing substance and as a factor in tooth erosion.

Thiocyanate has been used in the treatment of high blood pressure. It is passively excreted by the salivary glands and may play a role as an antibacterial agent. No correlation has been found with caries.

The small amounts of iron in saliva may contribute to the light brown staining of teeth due to the liberation of hemosiderin from red blood cell destruction.

The search for cobalt, molybdenum, zinc, vanadium, nickel, iron, copper, and magnesium stems from the fact that these metals, present in trace quantities are often active constituents of enzymes. Their importance is in the role they play in the exchange of molecules and ions between the cell and its environment; for instance, a copper ion inhibits the permeability of the cell membrane to dissolved substances. A deficiency in copper alters the integrity of the mitochondria so that they lose coenzymes and manganese ions rapidly. The result is a diminished ability to synthesize phosphatides which lowers the cytochrome oxidase activity of the cells.

Saliva contains variable amounts of $O_2$, $N_2$ and $CO_2$. Changes in the $CO_2$ concentration are closely related with shifts in the bicarbonate system and hence with changes in the buffer capacity of saliva.

## ORGANIC CONSTITUENTS OF SALIVA

A classification of salivary proteins has not yet been completed. The terminology used is often the investigator's choice and depends on the methods of isolation of the substances analyzed. Compounds isolated with different methods may carry identical names yet they may not be identical chemically. A large variety of results obtained by electrophoresis, immunoelectrophoresis, several methods of chromatography, ultracentrifugation and ultrafiltration has been reported in recent literature. Analyses have been carried out on fractions isolated from dialyzed and undialyzed saliva, from fractions of saliva obtained by centrifugation, from spontaneous precipitates, from precipitates obtained after the addition of chemicals or from water-, acid- or alkaline-soluble fractions. The results of these analyses assume significance only in light of the method used.

Analysis of the submaxillary secretion is technically more difficult because of its mucin content. Based on the nature and quantities of the carbohydrate moiety, more descriptive names have been proposed: mucopolysaccharides, mucoids, glycoproteins, mucoproteins and glycolipoproteins.

Mucin denotes a viscous solution, mucoid denotes a substance containing mucopolysaccharides in a firm chemical union with a peptide. The muco-

FIG. 9–1.  Scheme of the structure proposed for mucin.  Glutamic acid (GLUT); aspartic acid (ASP); amino acids (AA); N-acetylgalactosamine (Gal. Am.); sialic acid (SA).  (W. Pigman and Y. Hashimoto, Recent Studies of Mucins and Blood-Group Substances, Adv. Oral Biology, 7, p. 121, 127 and 128, 1964.)

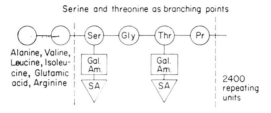

FIG. 9–2.  Scheme for the possible repeating units of the bovine submaxillary mucin bases on the molar ratio of serine and threonine to galactosamine and sialic acid.  Serine (Ser); threonine (Thr); glycine (Gly); proline (Pr); N-acetylgalactosamine (Cal. Am.); sialic acid (SA).  (W. Pigman and Y. Hashimoto, Recent Studies of Mucins and Blood-Group Substances, Adv. Oral Biology, 7, p. 121, 127 and 128, 1964.)

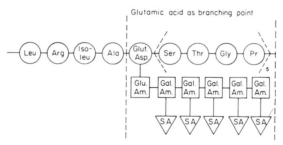

FIG. 9–3.  Scheme for the possible repeating units of the bovine submaxillary mucin based on the molar ratio of aspartic acid and glutamic acid to galactosamine and sialic acid.  Glutamic acid (Glut.); aspartic acid (Asp).  (W. Pigman and Y. Hashimoto, Recent Studies of Mucins and Blood-Group Substances, Adv. Oral Biology, 7, p. 121, 127 and 128, 1964.)

polysaccharide moiety is composed of hexoses, hexosamine (acetylated at the amino group) and uronic acids (Figs. 9–1 to 9–3).  A mucinous substance containing more than 4.0% hexosamine is a mucoid; less than 4.0%, a glycoprotein (Meyer).

Table 9–4 lists a group of organic substances detected in stimulated and unstimulated saliva.

Under normal conditions there is little reducing substance in the form of glucose in saliva.  The carbohydrate moiety of the mucoid substance in saliva consists of more than one protein carbohydrate conjugate: d-mannose,

Table 9–4.  Organic Composition of Stimulated and Unstimulated Saliva
(mg per liter)

| Organic Constituents | Unstimulated Saliva | | Stimulated Saliva | |
|---|---|---|---|---|
| Glucose . . . . | 200 | (110–300) | 200 | (140–300) |
| Citrate . . . . . | —— | | 100 | (20–300) |
| Lactate . . . . . | —— | | —— | (10–50) |
| Cholesterol . . . | 80 | (25–500) | —— | |
| Ammonia . . . . | —— | (10–250) | 60 | (10–120) |
| Creatine . . . . | 10 | (5–20) | —— | |
| Urea . . . . . | 200 | (140–750) | —— | (0–140) |
| Uric acid . . . . | 15 | (5–29) | 30 | (10–210) |
| Choline . . . . | —— | (6.2–36.4) | —— | (4.7–14.4) |
| Histamine . . . . | —— | (0.16–0.50) | —— | |
| Glutathione . . . | 154 | | —— | |
| Nitrogen total . . . | —— | (444–990) | —— | (259–750) |
| Protein nitrogen . . | —— | (340–2270) | —— | |
| Non-protein nitrogen . | —— | (60–560) | —— | (223–882) |
| Mucoid . . . . . | —— | | 270 | (80–600) |
| α-globulin . . . . | 33.3* | | —— | |
| β-globulin . . . . | 129.9* | | —— | |
| γ-globulin . . . . | 55.5* | | —— | |
| Lysozyme . . . . | 54.3* | | —— | |
| Albumin . . . . | 22.8* | | —— | |
| Sialic acid . . . . | 50.4† | | | |
| Hexose . . . . . | 415.8† | | | |
| Fucose . . . . . | 142.5† | | | |
| Glucosamine . . . | 130.68† | | | |
| Galactosamine . . | 22.86† | | | |

* Calculated from non-mucoid protein fraction percentages.
† Calculated from parotid saliva glycoprotein fraction percentages.

d-galactose, hexuronic acid, and n-acetyl amino acids are the main constituents. Hydrolysis of mucoid substances is rapid. Saliva loses much of its viscosity upon standing. It is believed that this is brought about by the action of mucinase or by mucolytic bacteria. The precipitation of mucoid substances on tooth surfaces is of importance in studies of dental plaque and calculus formation.

The iso-electric point of mucoid is approximately 3.5 and acidities below pH 5.0 are necessary for precipitation.

Which salivary glands contribute the most nitrogen is not known. The nitrogen content is higher in unstimulated saliva than in stimulated saliva. Prolonged stimulation reduces the concentration considerably.

Rapid breakdown of mucoids and urea leads to the liberation of ammonia. As a result the nitrogen concentration of the supernatant of centrifuged saliva is almost 3 times higher than that of the sediment.

Urea shows the characteristic of following the concentration present in blood. It is mainly secreted by the parotid gland. Ellison found, with the Folin method for nitrogen, 275 mg % protein from isolated secretion of the parotid gland and 122 mg % from isolated secretion of the submaxillary gland. However, the submaxillary secretion was richer in carbohydrates. The parotid secretion contained only 0.2 mg %, while the submaxillary secretion contained 50 times more dialyzable carbohydrates in the form of glucose, galactose, mannose, and fucose.

It was found that the dialyzable fractions increased in amount upon storage of submaxillary secretion samples. By adding potassium cyanide and simultaneously keeping the samples chilled, the increased carbohydrate yield could be halted. It was concluded that the unbound carbohydrates were derived in part from the enzymatic breakdown of the submaxillary glycoproteins. The composition of parotid saliva consists of serum albumin, $\alpha$- and $\beta$-globulin, amylase, sialic acid, hexoses, fucose, glucosamine, and galactosamine. Parotid saliva has been shown to contain traces of substances which are, in spite of the low concentrations, excellent intrinsic antigens.

Table 9–5.  Amino Acids Identified in Stimulated and Unstimulated Saliva
(mg per liter)

| Amino Acid Constituents | Unstimulated Saliva | Stimulated Saliva |
|---|---|---|
| Alanine | 12    (5–29) | —— |
| Arginine | —— | —— (33–100) |
| Aspartic acid | 1.5 (1.3–3.3) | —— |
| Cystine | —— | —— (1.6–4.5) |
| Glutamic acid | 12    (5–13) | —— |
| Glycine | 14    (5–36) | —— |
| Histidine | —— | —— (3.5–20) |
| Isoleucine | —— | —— (2–9) |
| Leucine | —— | —— (0.2–3) |
| Lysine | 7.7 (1.5–15) | —— |
| Methionine | —— | —— (0.05–0.1) |
| Phenylalanine | —— | —— (6–25) |
| Proline | —— | —— (3.5–15) |
| Serine | 6.6 (3.3–12) | —— |
| Threonine | —— | —— (4–56) |
| Tyrosine | —— | —— (2–10) |
| Tryptophan | —— | 0.14 (0–2.1) |
| Valine | —— | —— (7–22) |

Table 9–5 shows the amino acids that have been identified in saliva. Most investigators believe that they are a product of bacterial metabolism and breakdown of proteins. It is known that mixed saliva has an antibacterial capacity, but saliva also contains many amino acids, vitamins, and other nutrients essential for the life support of many species of microorganisms. Pure glandular saliva does not seem to be the source of the bulk of amino acids.

## Vitamins

It appears that saliva contains an unidentified inactivating substance for vitamin A. The concentration of vitamin C is slightly lower than in the blood and little affected by oral intake of ascorbic acid (Table 9–6).

Table 9–6.   Vitamins Found in Stimulated and Unstimulated Saliva (per liter)

| Vitamins | Unstimulated Saliva | Stimulated Saliva |
|---|---|---|
| Vit. C (mg)      .   .   . | —  (0.0–4.0) | — |
| Vit. A (mg)      .   .   . | — | — |
| Vit. K ($\mu$g)      .   .   . | 15 | — |
| Niacin ($\mu$g)      .   .   . | 30 | 115  (23–409) |
| Thiamine ($\mu$g)      .   . | 7 | —  (2–14) |
| Riboflavin ($\mu$g)      .   . | 50 | — |
| Pyridoxine ($\mu$g)      .   . | 600 | 6  (1–17) |
| Pantothenic acid ($\mu$g)      . | 80 | 88  (12–190) |
| Folic acid ($\mu$g)      .   . | 0.1 | 24  (3–75) |
| Biotin ($\mu$g) .   .   .   . | 0.8 | —  (0.1–0.26) |
| Erythrotin, $B_{12}$ ($\mu$g)      . | — | —  (0.02–0.40) |

Apoerythein is a protein that forms a complex with vitamin $B_{12}$. In this combined form it resists the destructive influence of digestion which would inactivate free vitamin $B_{12}$. The complex is called erythein, $B_{12}$ is erythrotin or the "extrinsic factor" and apoerythein the "intrinsic factor." Apoerythein is present in saliva at a concentration of approximately 55 milliunits per ml. Beerstecher has determined the thermal stability characteristics of apoerythein in saliva and also found a substance of high molecular weight named sapisin which can inactivate apoerythein in saliva.

## GROUP SPECIFIC SUBSTANCES

The agglutinogens A, B and O occur in the saliva of 80% of the population. The M, N and Rh factors are absent in saliva. The group specific substances have been detected in the mucus of saliva and correspond to polysaccharide-amino acid complexes containing d-glucosamine, d-mannose, d-galactose, and l-fucose.

## SALIVARY ENZYMES

Among the enzymes, amylase has been estimated to be about 12% of the total amount of organic matter. It is a combination of two enzymes, α- and β-amylase. α-amylase hydrolyses dextrins and lowers the viscosity of starch gels. β-amylase breaks down the larger molecules into smaller fractions, primarily into maltose. Amylase is derived mainly from the parotid gland. It is the only salivary enzyme which plays a significant part in digestion.

Alkaline phosphatase activity is found in all fractions of saliva. Acid phosphatase is derived mainly from cellular debris and to a smaller extent from microorganisms. Acid phosphatase has been identified in pure glandular saliva in small quantities.

Table 9-7 presents a list of enzymes found in saliva by Chauncey.

The aliesterases hydrolyze esters of short chain fatty acids. Lipases attack the glycerides of long chain fatty acids. Both are able to split esters of intermediate size.

It has been postulated that chondrosulfatase and arylsulfatase are able to attack the sulfated glycoproteins present in undemineralized dentine and enamel and thereby contribute to the formation of dental caries.

Transferring enzymes catalyze reactions in which a chemical group is transferred from one compound to another.

Catalase, peroxidase, phenyloxidase, and succinic dehydrogenase are oxidizing enzymes. Catalase and peroxidase contain iron and require hydrogen peroxide as their hydrogen acceptor.

Hexokinase is involved in the transference of a phosphate group. The activity of the proteolytic enzymes appears to be due to bacteria, leukocytes and epithelial cells in salivary suspensions.

Pyrophosphatase induces the hydrolysis of an acid anhydride. Hartles and Wasdell found that certain salivary microorganisms possess an intracellular beta-fructofuranosidase. It was absent from salivary secretions. Sreebny and Angle found a collagenase-like enzyme in the dialyzed fraction of stimulated whole saliva. There may be several enzymes in saliva which possess mucolytic properties.

Mucinase activity decreases the viscosity of saliva. Mucoid is hydrolyzed with the liberation of carbohydrate. Several promising leads have resulted from salivary enzyme research that deserves consideration for further work. For instance, the salivary lysozyme concentration has been found to be 8 times higher than in blood serum. This enzyme could be of glandular origin or derived from salivary leukocytic remnants. Hyaluronidase appears to be exclusively of microbial origin. Its titers were found to be elevated in the presence of periodontal disease. Chondrosulfatase and arylsulfatase may play a role in periodontal disease as well as in the process of caries. It was shown that these enzymes are produced by microorganisms isolated from carious lesions and that they are capable of attacking the

Table 9–7.  Enzymes Found in Saliva from Different Sources
(x indicates presence)

| Enzymes | Source | | |
|---|---|---|---|
| | Glands | Microorganisms | Leukocytes |
| CARBOHYDRASES | | | |
| Amylase | X | O | O |
| Maltase | O | X | X |
| Invertase | O | X | O |
| Beta-glucuronidase | X | X | X |
| Beta-D-galactosidase | O | X | X |
| Beta-D-glucosidase | O | X | O |
| Lysozyme | X | O | X |
| Hyaluronidase | O | X | O |
| Mucinase | O | X | O |
| ESTERASES | | | |
| Acid phosphatase | X | X | X |
| Alkaline phosphatase | X | X | X |
| Hexosediphosphatase | O | X | O |
| Aliesterase | X | X | X |
| Lipase | X | X | X |
| Acetylcholinesterase | X | O | X |
| Pseudo-cholinesterase | X | X | X |
| Chondrosulfatase | O | X | O |
| Arylsulfatase | O | X | O |
| TRANSFERRING ENZYMES | | | |
| Catalase | O | X | O |
| Peroxidase | X | O | X |
| Phenyloxidase | O | X | O |
| Succinic dehydrogenase | X | X | X |
| Hexokinase | O | X | X |
| PROTEOLYTIC ENZYMES | | | |
| Proteinase | O | X | X |
| Peptidase | O | X | X |
| Urease | O | X | O |
| OTHER ENZYMES | | | |
| Carbonic anhydrase | X | O | O |
| Pyrophosphatase | O | X | O |
| Aldolase | X | X | X |

sulfated glycoproteins of undemineralized tooth substance. Of particular interest is the theory of Lisanti, Chauncy, Rovelstadt and others stating that salivary proteases, with the possible aid of hyaluronidase, could be capable of penetrating through the oral epithelium and be accountable for the lysing of the collagen fibers and the ground substance of the underlying connective tissue. This would result in rendering oral tissues susceptible to bacterial invasion. This theory was supported by Lazarus who showed the presence of collagenase in the granule fraction of human polymorphonuclear leukocytes.

## HYDROGEN ION CONCENTRATION

The pH of saliva in all its collectable forms has been surveyed with respect to sex, age, effect of stimulation, rate of secretion, kinds of food and drink and state of health. Much effort has been spent trying to find a correlation with tooth decay. So far no conclusion has been reached. Unstimulated saliva varies from pH 5.6 to 7.6 with a mean of approximately 6.7. In children the mean is approximately 0.1 of a unit higher. Stimulated saliva ranges from pH 7.2 to 7.6.

Saliva has a pronounced buffer capacity in the region of pH 7.0, due to the presence of bicarbonate and phosphate ions. Stimulated saliva exceeds unstimulated saliva in buffer capacity as well as in sodium and potassium concentration. The secretion of the submaxillary gland with its higher protein content provides a high buffer capacity around pH 5.0 or lower. The same holds true for dental plaque, since plaque has a high mucoid content. Pure parotid saliva is more acid with a pH range from 5.5 to 6.0. It is generally agreed that saliva becomes more acid during sleep. Intra-orally the pH values vary from one area to the next as well as in the same region from time to time in the same person.

## BACTERIA

Bacteria in saliva and in oral surface deposits have been the focal point of interest every since Miller published his chemicoparasitic theory of the etiology of caries in 1892. In general Miller's theory is still accepted, notwithstanding all the objections that can be brought against it. Accepting the theory makes caries an infectious disease with all its consequences. Numerous microorganisms have been isolated from the oral cavity which are biochemically active in their fermentation of carbohydrates, including starch, and in the production of proteolytic enzymes.

The search for acid producing bacteria has been extensive. Streptococci, Lactobacilli, Cladothrix, Leptothrix, fusiforms and anaerobic bacteria are among the best acid producers. Although good acid producers themselves, Lactobacilli have been found to inhibit to some degree the acid production of others, particularly of the streptococci. Lactobacilli have, however, been found in statistically significant numbers in relation to caries frequency.

10

The more this phenomenon was pursued, the less convincing became the evidence.

It is believed that the presence of oral aciduric bacteria is not the only factor in dental decay. Equally acidogenic types were obtained from immune as from caries active individuals. Plaque has been investigated when removed from caries-free tooth surfaces, from the walls of open cavities, from the interproximal spaces, from carefully preserved surfaces of ground sections, from caries immune persons, from cavities showing a slow decay rate and, of course, from those showing a fast rate of decay. Always present in the plaques from caries areas is a short rod or coccobacillus, named by Bunting *B. acidophilus*. He observed their absence in plaque from caries-free elements. Much attention has been given to those microorganisms which are able to produce a mucinous polysaccharide when plated out on sucrose-tryptose agar. Antibiotics inhibit their growth. The organisms responsible were shown to be *Str. mitis* and *Str. salivarius*.

There are many pleomorphic filamentous forms in saliva and plaque. They are morphologically similar to the actinomycetes and may be identical with Leptothrix, Streptothrix, Cladothrix or Leptotrichiae, terms no longer used. They are among the best acid producers. Their filaments form an irregular grid to serve as a framework in which other microorganisms live. They have also been found able to produce a yellowish-brown pigment as do other species.

The quantitative distribution of microorganisms in plaque or saliva has not been established because no standard routine for the method of collection and for specimen treatment has been adopted. This lack of standardization has prevented the accumulation of quantitative biochemical data.

Immediately after birth the mouth is sterile but within 6 to 10 hours, staphylococci and other organisms are present. After 1 week streptococci, staphylococci and coli-form organisms predominate. Anaerobic organisms are rarely found. Only after the onset of dentition does the oral flora show actinomycetes, spirochetes, fibrios, masses of cocci, long and thick filaments, and bacilli of different kinds. In the adult mouth these are augmented by the *Str. salivarius*, *Str. spirillae*, *B. acidophilus*, *B. fusiforms*, several species of neisseria, candidae, and diphtheroid forms. In the edentulous mouth the bacterial flora resembles that found in infants before the onset of their dentition. Saliva contains specific antibacterial substances. The growth of many strains of bacteria can be prevented by adding human saliva, especially to organisms not isolated from the mouth. Some of these susbtances have been found to be bacteriostatic, bactericidal, agglutinative, transformative or mutative. Saliva also contains opsonins, substances that render bacteria susceptible to phagocytosis.

Hugenschmidt found that whole saliva enhances granulocytic locomotion; filtered saliva does not. Hammond and Weinmann found that 37% of the leukocytes phagocytize bacteria in the presence of saliva from caries-free persons and only 4% of the leukocytes engulfed bacteria in the presence of saliva from persons with rampant caries.

Lysozyme appears to be most effective against bacteria. The concentration of lysozyme in saliva is higher than in the blood and lower than in the tears.

There are also two distinct substances, specific to saliva, with a strong bacteriostatic effect, especially against host-microorganisms. The nature of these substances is unknown.

## SURFACE DEPOSITS

### The Mobile Mucus Phase of Saliva (MMP)

The mucus, covering the mucous membrane, is elaborated by the intrinsic secretory glands buried in the submucosal layer of the mucous membrane. Mucus removed from the surface is replenished from below. It is distributed over areas without intrinsic glands in the deeper layers, such as part of the alveolar mucosa, the gingiva and, of course, all free surfaces of the teeth.

Stagnation of mucus over areas containing mucous glands is prevented by elaboration of more mucus from below and by the production of new cells through mitotic activity in the stratum germinativum of the mucosal stratified epithelium, followed by exfoliation of the uppermost cell layers. The rate of desquamation equals the rate of mitotic activity. This shedding process prevents mucus stagnation on all mucous membrane areas with or without glands in the submucosa. Only tooth surfaces are not benefited by this physiological turnover process. There is nothing forthcoming from the deeper layers to prevent mucus stagnation on the teeth. This is the reason for having to brush our teeth and not the insides of our cheeks.

The MMP serves as the only medium in which polymorphonuclear granulocytes live and function as active phagocytes. All body fluids, including MMP, are isotonic except mixed saliva which is hypotonic, mainly because of the participation of the parotid secretion. All polymorphonuclear granulocytes swell and rupture in mixed saliva, except a few in their early second phase of cytomorphosis. Kölliker described these expanded cells in 1854 and called them salivary corpuscles. They have been called orogranulocytes in the MMP. The MMP is the fourth out of five environments for polymorphonuclear granulocytes: (1) in the bone marrow as myeloblasts or myelocytes, (2) in the blood as neutrophils, (3) in the tissues as microphages (Metchnikoff), (4) in the MMP as orogranulocytes (Klinkhamer), and (5) in mixed saliva as salivary corpuscles (Kölliker).

The MMP is a separate salivary entity. It can be collected without losing its identity and has the following functions: (1) The MMP catches and carries off all exfoliated epithelial cells, (2) the MMP receives the migrating orogranulocytes, distributes them over all free surfaces and carries them off, (3) the MMP catches all microorganisms and carries them off, (4) the MMP allows the microorganisms to be subjected to the action of orogranulocytic phagocytosis, especially during temporary stagnation. The matter of stagnation is extremely important. Temporary stagnation is unavoidable; permanent stagnation can be prevented through oral hygiene.

Mixed saliva contains exhaustible and inexhaustible components. The exhaustible are microorganisms, host-cell remnants and food debris. The inexhaustible are epithelial cells and orogranulocytes. This can be demonstrated in the sequential collection of twelve 30-second rinses. The counts of exhaustible and inexhaustible components in the first MMP sample are high. The second, third, fourth and fifth MMP samples show progressively lower counts for all components. From here on the exhaustible population continues to dwindle, while the inexhaustible population remains the same within very narrow limits from sample six through sample twelve. The steady level between sample six and twelve represents: (1) the number of epithelial cells exfoliated per 30 seconds, or "the epithelial cell exfoliative rate" (EER) and (2) the number of orogranulocytes migrating onto the surface into the MMP of saliva per 30 seconds or the "orogranulocytic migratory rate" (OMR). The OMR is in essence a non-subjective quantitative measure of leukopedesis. It determines the rate at which polymorphonuclear granulocytes pass through the walls of the capillaries, venules and lymph vessels adjacent to the gingival crevice and epithelial attachments. All first samples of a concatenated series of MMP collections show the unpredictable and perpetual change for any component that can be counted or any activity that can be measured, as is so often seen between different subjects or from the same subject at different times. This is in contradistinction to the OMR and EER showing different values from subject to subject, but the same values within narrow limits from the same subject at different times.

The pathway followed by the migrating orogranulocytes is from the vascular system, through the endothelial wall of the capillaries, through the connective tissues, through the basement membrane of the oral epithelium in the region of the epithelial attachments. If there are no teeth, there are no epithelial attachments. If there are no epithelial attachments, only very few orogranulocytes can be found in the MMP of saliva. However, by the absence of teeth, there are no caries, no periodontal disease, and no flourishing bacteriological population that presents itself as a threat to the edentulous person. This implicates the living orogranulocyte in the MMP of saliva as one of the factors in defense against oral disease. The accumulation of dead orogranulocytes in permanently stagnated MMP contributes to the aggravation of oral disease.

For the past 100 years we have been puzzled about the origin of "materia alba" (debris) and the formation of dental plaque. A contributing reason was that the MMP of saliva had not been recognized as a separate salivary entity with its own biological function. The formation of materia alba is caused by exposure of orogranulocytes to the hypotonic, serous part of saliva. The orogranulocytic cell membrane ruptures within 1/30 of a second upon losing its MMP protection. Each orogranulocyte contains between 80 to 120 specific granules and virtually all are released in mixed saliva after losing their mucus protection. Cohn and Hirsch determined that the specific granules of the polymorphonuclear granulocyte, derived from rabbit peritoneal exudates, contained acid phosphatase, ribonuclease, deoxyribonuclease, beta-glucuronidase, cathepsin, lysozyme, alkaline phosphatase, 5-nucleotidase, and the bacterial agent phagocytin. These biologically active substances have, indeed, been detected in human saliva. Both groups of exhaustible and inexhaustible populations carry their own biochemical activities. Left together for extended periods of time results in putrefaction with the enzymatic splitting of salivary proteins into foul-smelling components such as hydrogen sulfide, ammonia and mercaptans. The chemistry of putrefaction has been shown to be in correlation with oral disease of the soft tissues and with the state of oral hygiene.

Eichel and Lisanti have shown that the bulk of oxygen uptake and the total aerobic and anaerobic acid production activities of mixed saliva are principally associated with the metabolism of non-bacterial protoplasms of host-cellular origin. About 76 to 88% of the mixed saliva activities were recovered from the washed mammalian cell and granular mass fractions when they were resuspended in the supernatant. From 16 to 34% of the mixed saliva activities were recovered from the bacterial and mammalian sub-particle fractions.

## THE FORMATION OF PLAQUE

(1) The teeth, with all surface deposits removed or not, are covered with the MMP of saliva, (2) temporary stagnation of the MMP in the interdental spaces and other protected areas creates an environment containing trapped exfoliated epithelial cells, orogranulocytes and bacteria, (3) in the healthy mouth stagnation is temporary through the intermittent action of speech, mastication, drinking and swallowing, (4) "overdue" temporary stagnation must be prevented by regular and effective methods of personal oral hygiene, and (5) permanent stagnation of the MMP leads to the formation of materia alba, consisting of more than 95% orogranulocytic remnants and exfoliated epithelial cells, with the remainder consisting of food debris and bacteria. In time the formation of a non-transitional plaque results. During sleep all surfaces are potential stagnant areas due to the reduced mobility of the MMP for periods of time sufficient to lay the foundation of permanent plaque. During waking hours the reactivated MMP, augmented by the effect of routine oral activities, prevents stagnation of a permanent nature except in the protected areas where the interchange of MMP occurs at a slow rate. This happens, for instance, in all interdental spaces and may lead in time to the complete blocking of MMP interchange.

The self-cleansing power of the healthy mouth is excellent. This was concluded long ago from the surprisingly few food remnants found in the mouth within less than half an hour after a meal. It is also known that most people need additional support from effective methods of personal oral hygiene to prevent the formation of a non-transitional plaque.

The number of orogranulocytes in the MMP is proportional to the degree of marginal and crevicular damage of the gingiva and the epithelial attachments. The transitional plaque of the mucous membrane and gingiva, as well as the non-transitional plaque, do not contain viable orogranulocytes. If permanent stagnation is allowed to occur in a healthy mouth with a minimal degree of marginal and crevicular damage of gingiva and epithelial attachments, the non-transitional plaque will appear amorphous in its microscopic architecture. It contains few bacteria or structurally recognizable host-cell remnants. If there is marginal and crevicular damage of any consequence with permanent stagnation of the MMP, then the resulting plaque will appear to consist of fine granular material with an irregular interwoven pattern of actinomycetes, interspersed with many species of microorganisms and coarse granular material of host-cell origin.

Plaque material seems to consist of a highly insoluble, denatured protein and often shows brown to black pigmentation suggestive of a melanin-like substance. There are as yet undefined biochemical differences between one plaque and another. Some plaques seem to protect the tooth surface rather than harm it. Plaques are nearly insoluble in all solutions tolerable in the oral cavity. Chromatographically detectable quantities of amino acids have been found, most frequently arginine, alanine, aspartic acid, glutamic acid, glycine, valine, proline, and leucine. The study of pH values and buffer capacity of plaque still has to overcome many technical difficulties. Although data about acid production in the plaque are far from convincing much work is in progress to find means of inhibiting acid formation in plaque.

Urea has been tried to raise the pH of the plaque. The inhibition of acid production studies with the use of quaternary ammonium compounds and several other synthetic detergents like Zephiran and Phemerol, sodium-N-lauroyl sarcosinate and sodium dehydroacetate have extensively been tested in clinical trials. Of course, the use of antibiotics has been seriously considered but also seriously criticized on the grounds that its use may produce harmful side effects more serious than the loss of a tooth. No substance has been found yet of unquestionable practical value.

## CALCULUS

So far the mechanism of formation of calculus has evaded elucidation. In persons with calculus, saliva has a lower viscosity and a smaller concentration of proteins. Proteins may act as a protective colloid in preventing the precipitation of calcium phosphate. The ultra-filtrable calcium is about 90% of the total calcium. Paraffin stimulated saliva has an average concentration of 0.7 mg % calcium. There is no evidence that the concentration of calcium in saliva is of dominant importance in the formation of calculus. Unstimulated saliva contains 20.4 mg % phosphorus. *In vitro* a large amount of phosphate can be precipitated from saliva by removal of $CO_2$. In the mouth, however, there is little loss of $CO_2$ from saliva and excludes, therefore, $CO_2$ removal as an important factor in the precipitation of phosphates and the formation of calculus.

With respect to the binding capacity for calcium in mucoid substances it was found that there was no calculus formation with a mucoid nitrogen concentration of 21.48 mg %, a moderate deposition at 8.66 mg % and a heavy formation at 3.39 mg %. Jacobson studied the mixed salivas in calculus-free, calculus-present, and calculus-present periodontal-diseased subjects. He found a decrease in mucin nitrogen and an increase in non-mucin nitrogen and ammonia nitrogen. These findings may have bearing on the clinically known fact that subjects with periodontal disease and calculus formation accumulate an agent which prevents the formation of caries lesions. Possibly such an agent may account for the initiation of calculus in the periodontal-diseased subject.

Calculus generally forms on tooth surfaces nearest the orifices of salivary glands. This location suggests a free flow of saliva with minimum chance of $CO_2$ loss, bacterial action, and we may add, stagnation of the MMP of saliva.

Where do we stand today, what do we know at the end of the sixties and where are we going?

To the best of our knowledge a better oral health can be achieved by reducing the intake of refined carbohydrates, mainly in the form of sweets and candy, to a minimum and next by using effective methods of personal oral hygiene to aid in the removal of "overdue" temporary stagnation of the Mobile Mucus Phase of saliva.

There has been a great extension of our knowledge about proteins and glycoproteins of human saliva, which opens new areas for further study.

With the greatly improved analytical methods in biochemistry, an ever-increasing number of metabolic pathways has been detected and identified, not only with respect to cellular activity, but also for fluid media secreted by the cells and fluid media serving as cell substrates. As such, saliva is recognized as a provider, or carrier, or eliminator of cells, particles and substances of vital importance to the defense and attack mechanisms operative in the arena of metabolic events in the human oral cavity.

## SELECTED REFERENCES

Afonsky, D. (Ed.): *Saliva and Its Relation to Oral Health.* Birmingham, University of Alabama Press, 1961.

Brachet, J., and Mirsky, A. E. (Eds.): *The Cell—Biochemistry, Physiology, Morphology* Vol. II, *Cells and Their Component Parts.* New York, Academic Press, Inc., 1961.

Chauncy, H. H.: Salivary enzymes, J.A.D.A., *63*, 360–367, 1961.

Eichel, B., and Lisanti, V. F.: Leukocyte metabolism in human saliva, Arch. Oral Biol., *9*, 299–314, 1964.

Klinkhamer, J. M.: Human oral leukocytes, J. Am. Soc. Peridont., *1*, 109–117, 1963.

Lazarus, G. S., Brown, R. S., Daniels, J. E., and Fullmer, H. M.: Human granulocyte collagenase, Science, *159*, 1483, 1968.

Long, C. (Ed.): *Biochemists' Handbook.* Princeton, D. Van Nostrand Company, 1961.

Office of Naval Research, Department of the Navy, *Biography on Saliva.* Washington, D.C., Report ACR—48, 1960.

Orban, B. (Ed.): *Oral Histology and Embryology.* St. Louis, The C. V. Mosby Company, 1944.

Sreebny, L. M., and Meyer, Julia (Eds.): *Salivary Glands and Their Secretions.* International Series of Monographs on Oral Biology. New York, The Macmillan Company, 1964.

# Chapter 10

## Mechanisms of Dental Caries

### Samuel Dreizen, D.D.S., M.D.

### INTRODUCTION

ENAMEL, the primary site of the caries lesion, is the hardest of all human tissues. When fully formed it is acellular, avascular, aneural, and completely devoid of powers of self repair.

Dental caries is an anatomically specific and biochemically controversial disease of the calcified tissues of the teeth. Pathologically, caries begins as a subsurface demineralization of the enamel which progresses along the radial course of the enamel prisms to the dentino-enamel junction. At the junction, caries spreads laterally and centrally into the underlying dentine assuming a conical configuration with the apex toward the pulp. The dentinal tubules become infiltrated with bacteria and dilate at the expense of the intervening matrix. Liquefaction foci are formed by the coalescence and destruction of adjacent tubules. Softening of the dentine precedes disorganization and discoloration culminating in the formation of a cheese-like or leathery mass. Further disintegration undermines the cusps and sound tissue causing secondary fractures and enlargement of the cavity. If unchecked, caries will eventually involve the pulp and destroy the vitality of the tooth.

## THEORIES OF CARIES FORMATION

Numerous theories have been advanced to explain the mechanism of dental caries. All are tailored to fit the form created by the chemical and physical properties of enamel and dentine. Some maintain that caries arises from within the tooth; others that it originates from without. Some ascribe caries to structural or biochemical defects in the tooth; others to a propitious local environment. Some incriminate the organic matrix as the initial point of attack; others the inorganic prisms or rods. Some have gained wide acceptance; others are relegated to their avid and persistent progenitors. The most prominent are the chemicoparasitic, proteolytic and proteolysis-chelation concepts. The endogenous, glycogen, organotropic, and biophysical theories represent some of the currently held minority views.

### The Chemicoparasitic Theory

This theory was formulated by Miller, who in 1882 proclaimed that, "Dental decay is a chemico-parasitical disease consisting of two distinctly marked stages; decalcification or softening of the tissue and dissolution of the softened residue. In the case of enamel, however, the second stage is practically wanting, decalcification of the enamel practically signifying its total destruction." The cause was attributed to ". . . all microorganisms of the human mouth which possess the power of exciting an acid fermentation of foods may and do take part in producing the first stage of dental caries . . . all possessing a peptonizing or digestive action upon albuminous substances may take part in the second stage."

Recently Fosdick and Hutchinson updated the theory that the initiation and progress of a carious lesion requires the fermentation of sugars in or under a dental plaque and the production *in situ* of lactic acid and other weak acids. Caries was equated with a specialized series of reactions based on the diffusion of substances through the enamel. Caries penetration was attributed to changes in the physical and chemical characteristics of enamel during the life of the tooth and to the semipermeable nature of enamel in the living tooth.

Direction and rate of migration of substances through tooth structure appears to be influenced by the diffusion pressure. For uncharged particles, diffusion pressure depends mainly on molecular size and molecular concentration differential. The lines of diffusion are principally through the rod sheaths and inter-rod substance comprised of apatite crystals with comparatively little organic matter. Lines of Retzius and incremental lines may also serve as pathways for diffusion. During ionic migration from the saliva to

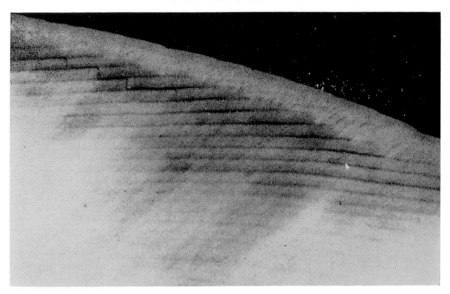

Fig. 10–1. Microradiograph of thin section of carious lesion showing parallel rods, inter-rod substance, lines of Retzius, Darling Layer, and incremental growth lines. (Fosdick and Hutchinson, courtesy of Ann. New York Acad. Sci.)

enamel, apatite crystals either react with or capture ions from the diffusant. Reaction or capture most probably occurs in the inter-rod substance through which the diffusant passes. The affected crystals become more or less stable and more or less soluble depending on the ions involved. Capture of calcium and phosphate ions tends to plug the diffusion pathways. Substitution of fluoride ions for hydroxyl ions in the apatite crystal forms a more stable and less soluble compound. Capture of hydrogen ions from acid diffusants, with the formation of water and soluble phosphates, destroys the enamel membrane (Eq. 10–1).

$$Ca_{10}(PO_4)_6(OH)_2 + 8H^+ \rightleftharpoons 10Ca^{2+} + 6HPO_4^{2-} + 2H_2O \qquad Eq. 10–1$$

If the surface of the tooth has been exposed to the oral environment long enough for maturation to occur, the diffusion pathways at or near the enamel surface contain salts which are more resistant to acids. When this layer of posteruptive maturation forms and is not too dense and impermeable it results in a "Darling Layer," if a lesion develops. Acids then have to penetrate to a considerable depth before encountering apatite crystals susceptible to dissolution. The surface may thus remain intact, while the deeper layers become water soluble producing the subsurface demineralization characteristic of initial enamel caries (Fig. 10–1). Figure 10–2 shows the same structures as Figure 10–1 with a more advanced carious lesion. Note that the Darling layer has suffered serious dissolution.

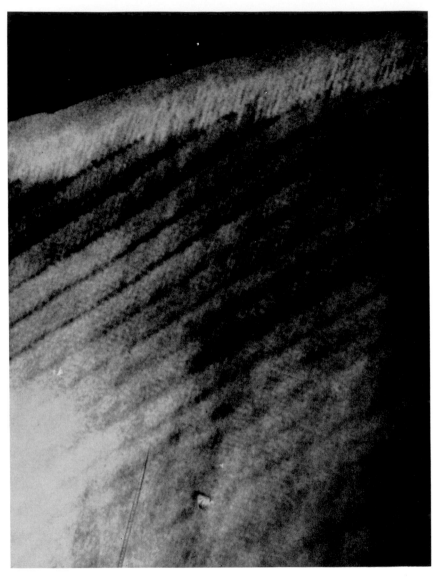

Fig. 10–2. Microradiograph of a thin section of a more advanced carious lesion than Figure 10–1. Note the parallel rods, inter-rod substance, lines of Retzius, partially dissolved Darling layer and incremental growth lines.

## The Proteolytic Theory

Proponents of the proteolytic theory and its various modifications regard the enamel matrix as the key to the initiation and penetration of dental caries. The mechanism is attributed to protein splitting microorganisms which invade and destroy the organic elements of enamel and dentine. The digestion of the organic matter is followed by a physical and/or acid dissolution of the inorganic salts.

Gottlieb maintained that caries begins in those enamel lamellae or uncalcified prism sheaths which lack a protective cuticular covering at the surface. The caries process spreads along these structural defects as the proteins are destroyed by enzymes liberated by the invading organisms. In time the calcified prisms are attacked and necrotized. The destruction is characterized by the elaboration of a yellow pigment which appears from the time the tooth structure is first involved. The pigment is presumed to be a metabolic product of the proteolytic organisms. In most instances the protein degradation is accompanied by limited acid production. In rare cases proteolysis alone may cause caries. Only yellow pigmentation, with or without acid formation, denotes "true caries"; acid action alone produces "chalky enamel" and not true caries. Acids not only fail to produce caries but are responsible for erecting a barrier against the spread of caries by contributing to the development of transparent enamel. Transparent enamel results from an internal shift of calcium salts. The salts at the site of acid action are dissolved with some going to the surface where they are washed out and some penetrating into the deeper layers where they are precipitated to form hypercalcified transparent enamel. The microbial invasion roads are obstructed by the increased calcification and further bacterial penetration is prevented. Fluoridation, whether by topical application or by ingestion of fluoridated water, protects the teeth against caries by fluoridizing the noncalcified organic pathways. This presumably attracts calcium from the adjacent prisms and obstructs the invasion roads.

Frisbie interpreted the microscopic phase of caries which occurs prior to a visible break in the enamel surface continuity as a process entailing a progressive alteration of the organic matrix and a projection of microorganisms into the tooth substance. The caries mechanism is identified as a depolymerization of the organic matrix of enamel and dentine by enzymes released by proteolytic bacteria. Both acid formed during the hydrolysis of dental proteins and mechanical trauma contribute to the loss of the calcified component and to the enlargement of the cavity.

Pincus related caries activity to the action of sulfatase producing bacteria on the mucoproteins of enamel and dentine. The polysaccharide portion of these mucoproteins contains sulfate ester groups. Following hydrolytic release of the polysaccharides, sulfatase liberates the bound sulfate as sulfuric acid. The acid dissolves enamel and then combines with calcium to form calcium sulfate. In this concept the teeth themselves contain the substances necessary for acid production by bacteria. An external source of carbo-hydrate is not required. The changes in the organic structure are primary; those in the mineral phase secondary.

The main support for the proteolytic theory is derived from histopatho-logical demonstrations that some regions of the enamel are relatively rich in protein and may serve as avenues for the spread of caries. The theory does not account for such clinical characteristics of dental caries as localization to specific tooth sites, relation to food habits, and dietary prevention. It does not explain the production of caries in experimental animals by high carbohydrate diets nor the prevention of experimental caries by glycolytic inhibitors. No mechanism has been demonstrated to show how proteolysis can destroy calcified tissue except through the formation of acid end products. It has been calculated that the total amount of acid potentially available from enamel protein is capable of dissolving only a small fraction of the total calcium salt content of enamel. Furthermore, there is no chemical evidence that there is an early loss of organic material in enamel caries nor have proteolytic forms been consistently isolated from early enamel lesions. In contrast, it has been found that before tooth protein in general and glyco-proteins in particular can be depolymerized and hydrolyzed, demineraliza-tion is necessary to expose the protein linkages bonded to the inorganic frac-tion. Electron microscope examinations demonstrate a filamentous organic framework interspersed in enamel mineral between and within the enamel prisms. The fibrils are about 50 millimicrons in thickness. Unless the adjacent inorganic substance is first demineralized, the spacing would hardly be sufficient for bacterial penetration.

## The Proteolysis-Chelation Theory

Schatz and co-workers extended the proteoyltic theory to include chela-tion as an explanation for the concomitant destruction of enamel mineral and matrix. The proteolysis-chelation theory affixes the etiology of caries to two interrelated and simultaneously occurring reactions; microbial de-struction of the largely proteinaceous organic matrix and loss of apatite through dissolution by organic chelators, some of which originate as matrix breakdown products.

The bacterial attack is initiated by keratinolytic microorganisms which decompose protein and other organic substances in the enamel. Enzymatic degradation of the protein and carbohydrate elements yields substances that chelate calcium and dissolve the insoluble calcium phosphate. Chelation can sometimes cause solubilization and transport of ordinarily insoluble mineral matter. It is accomplished through the formation of coordinate covalent bonds and electrostatic interactions between the metal and the chelating agent.

$$M^{++} + H_4EDTA \rightleftharpoons H_2MEDTA + 2H^+ \qquad \text{Eq. 10-2}$$

Calcium chelators including acid anions, amines, peptides, polyphosphates, and carbohydrates are present in food, saliva, and plaque material and may conceivably contribute to the caries process.

The theory also holds that since proteolytic organisms are generally more active in an alkaline environment, tooth destruction can take place at a neutral or alkaline pH. The acid producing oral microflora, instead of causing caries, actually protect the teeth by controlling and inhibiting the proteolytic forms. The chelating properties of organic compounds are sometimes altered by fluorine which can form covalent bonds with some metals. Fluorides may thus affect the linkages between enamel organic and mineral matter in a manner which confers resistance to caries.

There are serious questions as to the validity of some of the basic premises of the proteolysis-chelation theory. Although the solubilizing effect of chelating and complexing agents on insoluble calcium salts is well documented, it has not been shown that a similar phenomenon occurs in enamel *in vivo*. Keratinolytic organisms are not part of the oral flora except as occasional transients. Enamel protein is extremely resistant to microbial degradation. Bacteria which attack keratins have not been shown to destroy enamel organic matrix. A survey of the biochemical characteristics of 250 oral proteolytic bacteria uncovered none that could attack unaltered enamel. Jenkins maintains that the proportion of organic matter in enamel is so small that even if all was suddenly converted into active chelating agents, these products would not be capable of dissolving more than a tiny fraction of the enamel apatite. Also, there is no convincing evidence that plaque bacteria can, in the natural environment which is presumably saturated with calcium phosphate, attack the organic matter of enamel before decalcification has occurred. In contrast, Jenkins' data suggest that the chelators in plaque, far from causing decalcification of the tooth, may actually hold a reservoir of calcium which is released in ionic form under acid conditions to maintain saturation of calcium phosphate over a wide pH range. Like the proteolytic theory, the proteolysis-chelation theory fails to explain the relationship between diet and dental caries either in man or in experimental animals.

## The Endogenous Theory

The endogenous theory was promulgated by Csernyei, who claimed that caries results from a biochemical derangement beginning in the pulp and manifested clinically in the enamel and dentine. It is precipitated by an elective localized influence of the central nervous system or some of its nuclei on magnesium and fluorine metabolism of individual teeth. This accounts for caries affecting some teeth and sparing others. The caries process is pulpogenous in nature and emanates from a disturbance in the physiological balance between phosphatase activators (magnesium) and phosphatase inhibitors (fluorine) in the pulp. At equilibrium, pulp phosphatase acts on glycerophosphates and hexosephosphates to build calcium phosphate. When the equilibrium is disrupted, pulp phosphatase promotes the formation of phosphoric acid which dissolves the calcified tissues.

Eggers-Lura agreed that caries is caused by a disturbance of phosphorus metabolism and by an accumulation of phosphatase in the affected tissue but disagreed as to the source and mechansim of action of phosphatase. Since caries attacks teeth with either living or dead pulps, the origin of the enzyme must come not from within the pulp but from without the tooth, that is, the saliva or oral flora. Phosphatase dissolves tooth enamel by splitting the phosphate salts and not by acid decalcification. According to its proponents, the phosphatase hypothesis explains the individuality of caries and the caries inhibiting effects of fluorides and phosphates. The relationship between phosphatase and dental caries activity has not, however, been confirmed experimentally.

## The Glycogen Theory

Egyedi maintained that susceptibility to caries is related to a high carbohydrate intake during the period of tooth development which results in the deposition of excess glycogen and glycoprotein in tooth structure. The two substances are immobilized in the apatite of the enamel and dentine during the maturation of the matrix, thus increasing the vulnerability of the teeth to bacterial attack after eruption. Plaque acids convert the glycogen and glycoprotein into glucose and glucosamine. Caries begins when the plaque bacteria invade the organic tracts of the enamel and degrade the glucose and glucosamine into demineralizing acids. This theory has been criticized as being highly speculative and unsubstantiated.

## The Organotropic Theory

The organotropic theory of Leimgruber holds that caries is not a local destruction of the dental tissues, but a disease of the entire dental organ. The tooth is considered part of a biological system composed of pulp, hard tissues, and saliva. The hard tissues act as a membrane between the blood and saliva. Direction of exchange between the two depends on the biochemical and biophysical properties of the media and on the active or passive role of the membrane. Saliva contains a "maturation factor" which unites the submicroscopic protein and mineral constituents of the tooth and maintains a state of biodynamic equilibrium. At equilibrium the mineral and matrix of enamel and dentine are joined by homopolar valent linkages. Any agent capable of destroying the polar or valency linkages will disrupt the equilibrium and cause caries. These are to be distinguished from substances which destroy tooth structure once the linkages have been ruptured. The active molecules forming the linkages are water or the "saliva maturation factor" identified tentatively as 2-thio-S-imidazolon-5. This compound is biologically active in an acid medium and fluorine acts as a catalyst in its formation. Supportive evidence for the Leimgruber theory is extremely meager.

### The Biophysical Theory

Neumann and DiSalvo developed the load theory of caries immunity based on the response of fibrous proteins to compression stress. They postulate that high chewing loads produce a sclerosing effect on the teeth divorced from either attrition or detergent action. The sclerotic changes are presumably mediated through a steady loss of the water content of the teeth possibly connected with an uncoiling of polypeptide chains or a closer packing of fibrillary crystallites. The structural changes produced by compression are alleged to increase tooth resistance to the destructive agents in the mouth. The validity of this theory has not yet been proven due to technical difficulties which have prevented testing the concept of stress-sclerosis in human enamel.

## SOLUBILITY OF TOOTH ENAMEL

All of the foregoing theories of caries formation agree that the disease involves a dissolution of tooth enamel. The points of contention are the initial site and the method involved. Mechanisms have been proposed to explain the dissolution of enamel under acid, neutral, and alkaline conditions. Evidence derived from carefully controlled morphological, biophysical, and biochemical studies overwhelmingly supports the conclusion that in developing caries, enamel mineral is solubilized before the matrix is lost. Direct pH measurements indicate that carious dissolution takes place in an acid environment. Acid is present in detectable quantities in all stages and at all depths of the caries lesion. When measured *in situ* in the resting state with an antimony microelectrode, the pH averages 5.5. There is a return to the acid condition in the lesion even after repeated buffering. Either acid is formed continuously or there is a large reservoir of acid in the depths of the lesion which constantly diffuses to the surface.

Brudevold lists the evidence which suggests that enamel caries is primarily a process of demineralization as: (1) The morphological changes characteristic of the initial lesions can be reproduced in sound enamel by etching with weak acids. (2) Bacterial degradation of the organic matrix in intact enamel has not been demonstrated. (3) The matrix of demineralized enamel is so fragile that it is easily destroyed by slight mechanical trauma obviating the necessity of postulating degradation of the matrix.

The chemistry of tooth enamel solubility in acid solutions is complicated by changes in apatite composition induced by the interchange of ions between the crystal and liquid phases. Accordingly, enamel apatite does not have a constant solubility product. The solubility increases with a decrease in pH and is similar to that of secondary calcium phosphate at pH 6 and to that of primary calcium phosphate at pH 4. Carbonate tends to increase and

11

fluorides to decrease the solubility of enamel apatite. In acid solutions, the solubility of enamel apatite is also affected by the concentration and viscosity of available buffers, the volume ratio between mineral and buffer, and the interionic action occurring during the dissolution process.

Chemical kinetic studies show that the diffusion of hydrogen ions and molecules of undissociated acid into the enamel and the rate of reaction between acid and mineral are of utmost importance in controlling the speed and extent of acid attack. Diffusion barriers on the tooth surface or in the outer enamel layer reduce the rate of acid dissolution and retard surface demineralization. Once past the protected surface layer, the acidic ions and molecules are free to react with and to dissolve the tooth structure. As soon as local concentrations of dissolved calcium and phosphate become appreciable, the acid attack stops. It resumes again when the acids have diffused further into the enamel structure or when the released calcium and phosphate ions have passed out of the involved area. Cyclic repetition of these diffusion controlled processes leads to the ultimate decalcification of tooth structure in depth.

Microradiographical and electron microscope probes provide confirmatory evidence that demineralization antedates disintegration of the organic matrix in both enamel and dentinal caries. Zones of varying radiolucency manifested as alternating light and dark bands indicative of differences in mineral content are visible microradiographically in early enamel caries. Crystallites isolated from advanced lesions show perforations and surface erosions when examined under the electron microscope. Within the lesions, islands of organic matrix remain between the invading bacterial columns which contributed to the loss of rod substance. In dentinal caries, the collagenous fibers are remarkably intact even in regions of extensive demineralization.

The morphological changes are accompanied by alterations in the chemical composition of the affected tissues (See Chapter 1). Carious enamel and carious dentine contain more water, more organic matter and less mineral, when measured on a weight basis, than corresponding sound tissue in the same tooth. In the inorganic fraction, the most pronounced caries-associated changes are a diminution in carbonate and magnesium and an elevation in fluoride content. Decrease in total ash reflects the degree of tissue demineralization; changes in the inorganic component represent alterations in the remaining crystallites. The higher fluoride values connote that some fluorapatite remains in the lesion after the more soluble crystals have been dissolved. The increase in organic matter may be relative and/or absolute. A relative increase is associated with tissue demineralization without proteolysis; an absolute increase, with an influx of organic molecules from the salivary fluid and bacterial invasion of the involved tissues. The change in moisture content represents a replacement of the destroyed tissue elements by water.

The basic premise of the chemicoparasitic theory that the acids responsible for enamel demineralization are bacterial in origin is supported by an impressive array of experimental and clinical data. Proof that microorganisms are essential to the caries process is found in demonstrations that "germ free" animals do not develop decay when fed a caries-promoting diet under sterile conditions. Bacteriological analyses of the dental plaques covering the sites of enamel caries invariably show a predominance of acidogenic and aciduric organisms. In the presence of a suitable substrate, these organisms produce acids in amounts which penetrate the enamel and dissolve the mineral element. The dissolution is initially confined to the subsurface enamel as the outermost layer is protected by a high fluoride content and by an organic surface film derived from the saliva. Eventually, sufficiently large spaces are created in the surface enamel to permit invasion by bacteria. Inward progression of the lesion is followed by a gradual pulpward migration of the microorganisms.

A wealth of clinical data accords with the proposition that caries is caused by acids formed from the bacterial fermentation of foods retained in the oral cavity. In man, caries invariably begins at those anatomical sites on the tooth which are sheltered from the cleansing action of mastication and where food debris and plaque are most likely to accumulate. The plaque is comprised of a proteinaceous matrix incorporating finely divided food particles, residues of mucin and desquamated epithelial cells and various microorganisms and their metabolites. Plaque is permeable to glucose and sucrose but relatively impermeable to starch. It contains the enzyme systems required for the conversion of fermentable carbohydrates into acid end products. Direct intraoral determinations of human plaque pH reveal that plaque acidity reaches levels capable of dissolving tooth structure within 4 minutes after oral introduction of a glucose containing test solution. The demineralizing plaque pH is maintained for approximately 30 to 45 minutes before returning to the pretest values. The temporal sequence of acid production in the plaque corresponds closely to the oral glucose clearance time. These studies indicate that acid formation in the plaque is a discontinuous process with periods of activity directly related to the frequency with which fermentable carbohydrates are introduced into the oral cavity.

Numerous surveys show that the dental caries incidence in susceptible individuals exists in direct proportion to the quantity, form, and frequency of ingestion of fermentable carbohydrates. The carbohydrates are dietary in origin, since freshly secreted human saliva contains only negligible amounts of carbohydrate regardless of the blood sugar level. The salivary carbohydrates are bound to proteins chiefly as the glycoproteins sialomucin and fucomucin, which are resistant to degradation by the oral acidogens. Dietary regulation of carbohydrate intake, when carefully controlled and faithfully adhered to, has been reported effective in inhibiting caries formation.

Variations in caries susceptibility of teeth in different regions of the mouth have been explained, in part, by local variations in the chemical composition of the plaque. Reported differences include a high calcium concentration in lower incisor plaques, a high phosphate level in lingual plaques and a high fasting plaque pH in caries resistant areas. Fasting plaque pH values often exceed the pH of the surrounding saliva signifying that alkalies are actively produced within some plaques and may contribute to caries prevention.

## EFFECT ON THE ORGANIC MATRIX

As originally postulated by Miller, after caries enters the dentine, the process becomes one of both decalcification and proteolysis. Confirmation is derived from studies of the bacterial populations of carious lesions. In dentinal caries, the microbial composition differs significantly from that of enamel caries. There is a dichotomy of predominance associated with the depth of the dentinal lesion. The deepest penetration contains a preponderance of aciduric forms with a virtual absence of dentinolytic organisms. Bacteria capable of hydrolyzing the organic residues of decalcified dentine are concentrated in the superficial aspects of the lesion. The microbial distribution suggests that in dentinal caries, as in enamel caries, decalcification precedes proteolysis.

Histological studies demonstrate further that proteolysis of the insoluble organic matrix occurs only after demineralization is well established. According to Darling, lysis of the organic component does not occur until there has been a breakdown of the enamel surface. Microradiographical and polarized light studies show that there is a differential demineralization of the enamel in caries. The earliest evidence of demineralization in the surface zone is found, most often, along the striae of Retzius. The underlying enamel already shows marked salt loss. From the striae of Retzius, demineralization spreads to the interprismatic areas and thence to the prism cores. The sequence is precipitated primarily by the loss of soluble organic matter which facilitates differential demineralization. It has been duplicated experimentally by exposing teeth to the action of dilute lactic acid and to formic acid. Whether chelating agents produce a similar pattern of mineral loss remains to be determined.

Because of technical difficulties, studies of caries-associated changes in the properties and composition of the organic matrix have usually been confined to dentine. Armstrong categorized these changes as: (1) Reduction in the concentrations of arginine, histidine, hydroxylysine, proline and hydroxyproline. (2) Increase in the quantities of phenylalanine, tyrosine and methionine. (3) Modification of the basic amino acid residues in the intact matrix. (4) Acquisition of resistance to collagenase attack. (5) Formation of a characteristic brown pigmentation. (6) Apparent loss of fluorescence activity. (7) Increased amounts of bound carbohydrate, particularly in the completely collagenase resistant fraction. These alterations are believed to result from a combination of proteolytic degradation of dentinal collagen by bacterial collagenases, formation of a dentine-carbohydrate complex between dentinal protein and carbohydrates or allied substances and contamination of the residual matrix by noncollagenous protein.

A yellow-brown discoloration is an integral part of the organic component of the lesion in advanced caries. The discoloration has been ascribed either to exogenous staining or to an endogenous pigmentation. The former denotes a physical deposition of microbial or food stains onto the involved tooth structure; the latter a chemical combination between the organic fraction of the tooth and chromogenic substances elaborated during the caries process. The pigment has been recovered from carious lesions and identified chemically as a melanoidin. There is now substantial evidence that the pigmentation represents a nonenzymatic browning reaction between exposed dental proteins and carbohydrate derivatives. Reactive carbonyl containing fermentation products of glucose, specifically, dihydroxyacetone and glyceric aldehyde and chemical decomposition products of pentoses and hexoses, notably, furfural and hydroxymethylfurfural have been found to interact with decalcified human coronal protein to yield a yellow-brown pigment. The pigment thus formed is identical in chemical and physical properties with that present in the carious lesion. Each of the 18 amino acids with a functional amino or imino group, which are common to both human enamel and dentine, brown nonenzymatically when exposed to carbonyl containing carbohydrate degradation products under conditions of temperature and pH which prevail in the oral cavity and in the caries lesion.

## EFFECT OF FLUORIDE AND OTHER IONS

It has become increasingly apparent that fluorides play a multiple and complex role in the prevention of dental caries. The effect of ingesting fluoridated water is related primarily to the fluoride deposited in enamel preeruptively and in the few years immediately following eruption. In the posteruptive state, accessible surfaces acquire fluoride to a greater extent than inaccessible areas, thus limiting the effectiveness of fluorides in the sites most susceptible to caries attack.

Ingested fluoride is deposited in enamel as fluorapatite which is more resistant to caries formation than hydroxyapatite. Fluoride also has the unique ability to induce apatite formation from solutions of calcium and phosphate. It favors the conversion of soluble acid phosphates to solid basic phosphate thereby maintaining the apatite structure even at low pH values. In the alternating process of demineralization and reprecipitation which characterizes the reaction between acid and tooth mineral, fluoride promotes the deposition of apatite. This effect is counteracted by carbonate, magnesium, and other ions that possess a tendency to disturb the apatite lattice and by agents such as pyrophosphate and other organic phosphates which alter the surface of the apatite crystal and prevent crystal growth. Since there are no detectable changes in the concentrations of other tooth components as a result of fluoride deposition, the caries resistant effect of fluoride appears to be mediated in part through the maintenance of the integrity of the apatite crystal.

## EFFECT OF AGE

Resistance of human teeth to carious attack appears to increase with age. Newly erupted teeth are considerably more susceptible to caries than are older teeth. The diminished propensity to decay has been ascribed usually to a posteruptive maturation process in the enamel. While the mechanism responsible for maturation and enhanced resistance is unknown, it is generally associated with exposure to saliva. Following eruption, teeth will undergo both physical and chemical alterations with time. Saliva contributes significantly to the change in ionic content and permeability of enamel. Thus, the bone seeking elements, fluorine, zinc, lead, and iron accumulate in the surface enamel in quantities related to the external environment of the tooth. With increasing age, there is also an increase in the fluoride and a decrease in the carbonate concentrations of surface enamel. In addition to affecting sound enamel, there is evidence that the organic and mineral constituents of saliva may deposit in areas of defective or demineralized enamel to decrease the rate of development of the carious lesion.

## BIOCHEMISTRY OF THE SHEATH SPACES IN CARIES

Polarization microscopy and impregnation techniques which have been used to investigate the biochemistry of the sheath spaces in caries provide additional evidence that the disease is essentially an acid induced, inorganic leaching process. The sheath spaces partially surround the enamel rods and separate them from the interprismatic substance. The spaces are completely enclosed in fully calcified enamel except in the regions of the enamel tufts. During calcification, the sheath spaces fill with crystals of the type present in the prisms and interprismatic substance. In caries, the sheath spaces reopen. The reopening has been attributed to the early dissolution of the rod crystals lining the sheath spaces. The position and greater solubility of these crystals, due to a high carbonate content, render them highly susceptible to acid action.

## REMINERALIZATION

Although human enamel is lacking in biological powers of regeneration, *in vitro* studies indicate that saliva has the capacity to remineralize slightly decalcified enamel surfaces. The ability varies between individuals but is fairly constant for samples obtained from the same subject. Saliva serves as a calcifying metastable solution with respect to enamel in this process. The oral fluids act as a source of minerals for the remineralization of submicroscopic spaces inaccessible to organic molecules and for nucleator organic molecules necessary for the repair of large spaces. Remineralization is accelerated in the presence of 1 ppm fluoride. The fluoride promotes nucleation of calcium phosphate and decreases the solvent power of the liquid phase. It is doubtful whether remineralization restores the continuity of the enamel surface in its entirety or is ever sufficient to produce complete healing of the carious lesion. It may be of considerable importance, however, in retarding or arresting caries.

## SELECTED REFERENCES

SOGNNAES, R. F. (Ed.): *Chemistry and Prevention of Dental Caries*, Springfield, Charles C Thomas, 1962.

STAPLE, P. H. (Ed.): *Advances in Oral Biology*, New York, Academic Press, Inc., vol. 1, 1964; vol. 2, 1966.

WHIPPLE, H. E., (Ed.): Mechanisms of dental caries, Ann. New York Acad. Sci., *131*, 685–930, 1965.

WOLSTENHOLME, G. E. W. and O'CONNOR, M. (Eds.): *Caries Resistant Teeth*, Boston, Little, Brown & Company, 1965.

## Chapter 11

# Nutritional Basis of Oral Health

### Kenneth O. Madsen, Ph.D.

Nutritional Standards
Composition of the Daily Diet
Summary of Gross Dietary Constituents
Nutritional Balance
Dietary Catalysts
Foods and Nutrients in Metabolism
Malnutrition
Further Applications of Nutrition to Dentistry

BELIEFS about foods and proper diets are ancient; however, nutrition and chemistry as sciences developed concurrently mostly during the 18th century emerging finally as biochemistry near the end of the 19th century. Biochemistry remained synonymous with nutrition until recently when there has been an increasing tendency to separate nutritional biochemistry into a separate discipline.

The nutritional aspects of biochemistry began with the study of calorimetry. It was established that carbohydrate, fat, and protein were the gross constituents of foods that upon oxidation in the body (respiration), released characteristic equivalents of energy. It was soon recognized, however, that protein probably played a more specific role than that of providing body heat. Today, a host of specific roles in body chemistry has been assigned to the amino acids and proteins, although the amino acid, threonine, was not recognized as being required in the diet until 1935.

About the same time it was realized that certain amino acids were necessary, it was also discovered that there existed other essential materials or "accessory food factors" besides the gross components of foods. That is, in addition to carbohydrate, fat, protein, and minerals, other factors were required for growth and health. The discovery of these factors, the vitamins, excited the interest of nutritional biochemists for several decades. Vitamin $B_{12}$, latest to be discovered, was not structurally defined in its coenzyme form until 1955. All the water soluble vitamins have now been assigned one or more specific roles in intermediary metabolism. The roles of ascorbic acid and the fat soluble vitamins still remain largely obscure.

The need for dietary minerals is now well known. By the beginning of the century, the requirements for the major mineral elements sodium, chlorine, calcium and phosphorus, and the trace element iron were fairly well recognized. The importance of other major elements such as potassium and magnesium, as well as other trace elements, was subsequently discovered. Presently, metabolic roles for the trace or catalytic mineral elements are quite well known. If any nutrients remain undiscovered, they are most likely to be found among the trace minerals of foods. For example, there is recent evidence that chromium may be nutritionally essential. Fluoride, long considered only beneficial for dental caries prevention, may stabilize bone, when ingested over the lifespan.

That our knowledge of man's nutritional needs is essentially complete is shown by the fact that mixtures of known chemical compounds have supported life and the apparent health of young adults for several weeks.

The essential elements and compounds and other significant food constituents that must be obtained from the external environment, usually diet, are listed in Table 11–1. Despite the occurrence of thousands of different compounds in food or synthesized from food by the body, relatively few are quantitatively significant. Even the food constituents that are nutritionally essential in small amounts (micronutrients) are relatively few in number. Moreover, the significant food substances can be broadly categorized into energy metabolism, body structures and homeostasis, and catalysts. These categories often overlap. For example, calcium is a skeletal building block, and has catalytic function. Notably, only protein, the major actor in the drama of life, defies classification. It routinely supplies calories. One-third of body protein is collagen; blood albumin and hemoglobin are major blood homeostatic proteins. Yet, active proteins like individual enzymes and hormones demonstrate their catalytic roles at very small concentrations.

Despite the vast accumulation of data, the complete function of each nutrient is only partly understood. Even where chemical mechanisms seem clear, factors regulating the mechanisms and their relationships to the cellular site of action or to other processes are often obscure. For example, although nutrition started with the study of energy metabolism, much about this subject is still unknown. The mechanisms of energy capture and transfer are still under active study at the subcellular level of the mitochondrion, while the control of this mechanism is being studied at the whole body level as well.

The status of our current nutritional knowlege and its application to oral health may be understood best in terms of what remains unknown. Frontiers of research are listed below. It is apparent that much remains to be learned and that we can expect the new knowledge to have an ever greater significance to dental practice.

## Table 11–1. Significant Constituents of Foods and Estimates of Daily Consumption by the Average American Adult (Essential Nutrients Capitalized)

### ENERGY METABOLISM

| Carbohydrates (gm) | | Lipids (gm) | | Proteins (Amino Acids) (gm) | |
|---|---|---|---|---|---|
| Starches, Dextrins | 200 | Fats & Oils† | 100 | 8 ESSENTIAL AMINO ACIDS | 30 |
| Sucrose | 100 | Phospholipids† | 5 | 10 Semi or Non-essential | |
| Other Sugars | 100 | Essential Free Fatty Acids† | 2 | Amino Acids | 50 |
| (Organic Acids | 2) | Cholesterol | 1 | | |
| Bulk (Indigestible) | 25 | | | | |

†TOTAL ESSENTIAL
FATTY ACIDS          30 of 10⁹

### BODY STRUCTURE AND HOMEOSTASIS

Major minerals (gm)

| SODIUM | 4. | CHLORIDE* | 5. | POTASSIUM* | 2.5 |
|---|---|---|---|---|---|
| CALCIUM* | 0.8 | PHOSPHATE* (as P) | 0.8 | MAGNESIUM* | 0.3 |

*Function as catalysts also

### CATALYSTS

Micronutrient Elements (mg)

| IRON | 10. | MANGANESE | 5. | Selenium | 0.5 |
|---|---|---|---|---|---|
| ZINC | 10. | MOLYB-DENUM | 0.5 | Chromium | 2. |
| COPPER | 2. | IODIDE | 0.1 | Fluoride | 2. |
| | | COBALT (in vitamin $B_{12}$) | 0.1 | | |

Vitamins (mg)

*Fat-Soluble*

| VITAMIN A (and active CAROTENES) Retinoic Acid or Retinal | 6. | VITAMIN E (TOCOPHEROLS) | 6. |
|---|---|---|---|
| VITAMIN D (CALCIFEROLS) | 0.04 | VITAMIN K (active forms) | 2. |

*Water-Soluble*

| THIAMINE ($B_1$) | 1.5 | PYRIDOXINE ($B_6$) | 3. | BIOTIN | 0.2 |
|---|---|---|---|---|---|
| RIBOFLA-VIN ($B_2$) | 1.8 | CYANOCOBALA-MINE ($B_{12}$) | 0.002 | CHOLINE | 1000. |
| NIACIN | 15. | PANTOTHENIC ACID | 10. | Inositol | 1000 |
| ASCORBIC ACID | 75. | FOLIC ACID (FOLACIN) | 1. | Vitamin P Complex | 25 |

(1) *Quantitative Requirements.* The most complete data have been established for average, normal young adults yet, even for these persons, the extent of individual variation has not been defined. The quantitative needs throughout the lifespan, under various physiological conditions and in disease or injury situations require further study. The best data measure only certain restricted ages during the lifespan, mostly under healthy non-stressed conditions. Further, these requirements need to be based on more sophisticated criteria than used in the past. For example, the importance of nutritional status to mental attitudes and performances in addition to effects on growth or susceptibility to disease is just now being measured.

(2) *Interrelationships of Nutrients.* It is now realized that the absolute daily requirement of a nutrient may be less critical than the relative amounts of other nutrients with which it interacts. For example, the calcium requirement is higher in the presence of a high caloric and protein diet. The correct balance of nutrients under various conditions requires much additional study.

(3) *Patterns of Eating.* Currently, nutritional requirements are expressed on a daily basis, but frequency of eating throughout the day can influence minimum requirements and may determine the optimal allowances for nutrients. Frequency and size of meals affect satiety and may also influence other factors such as the effectiveness of quick-acting metabolic feedback controls. The slower adjustments of hormonal balances may also be affected by food intake habits. The pattern of eating has only recently been shown to affect oral health.

(4) *Organoleptic Factors.* The effect of such physiological factors as taste, smell and salivation on satiety is important in designing calorie controlled diets and in the acceptability of new foods. The effect of dentures and dental materials on taste, palatability and food selection habits has received inadequate attention.

(5) *Inborn Errors of Metabolism.* Discoveries of these genetic deficiencies affecting metabolism are making it increasingly important to devise compensating diets. Genetic error may be suspected wherever the etiology of a disease is obscure and a nutritional component seems to be involved. The development of dietary regimens are expected to help those who are highly susceptible to such diseases.

(6) *The Practice of Proper Nutrition.* As social and physiological demands change and advances are made in science and dentistry, the role of the dental profession in patient counseling and community education will change and, predictably, will increase.

Development of new foods and food enrichment programs based on a growing understanding of nutrition will help to assure optimal nutrition for population groups, but will not replace the need of nutritional guidance and education to individuals, families, and communities.

## The Dentist and Nutrition

The dentist may become the professional person from whom an increasing number of persons will receive nutritional advice. Since a high incidence of oral ills exist, the dentist sees a broader cross section of the population more frequently, for longer visits and under less acute conditions of illness than the physician. These factors provide opportunity not only to determine nutritional status, but also for communicating nutritional advice. Although difficult, it is especially important to detect the symptoms of mild nutritional deficiency. Only repeated patient contact will establish whether nervousness, fatigue and associated vague symptoms are chronic and characteristic and therefore possibly related to nutritional status. Moreover, it is noteworthy that the head and neck areas and especially the oral cavity most readily show the outward symptoms of nutritional deficiency. As the practice of preventive dentistry becomes increasingly possible, nutritional guidance will become a greater part of "bread and butter" dentistry.

## NUTRITIONAL STANDARDS

### Recommended Daily Dietary Allowances

The development of nutritional standards is the first step in the application of nutritional knowledge. In 1941, the Food and Nutrition Board of the National Research Council of the National Academy of Sciences accumulated the available data on nutritional requirements. This Board, comprised of recognized nutritional authorities, estimated average physiological *requirements*. They then increased these requirements to levels that would compensate for average variations in individual requirements and for environmental variations encountered by normal persons in the United States. These levels were called *allowances* and termed the "Recommended Daily Dietary Allowances" (RDA). They include allowances for variations due to age, sex, and reproduction. Thus far, only a small percentage of the lifespan has been studied as the basis for making such assessments. The best data have been established with 22-year-old men and women represented in Table 11–2 as the 22 to 35-year-old groups. Much of the discussion of nutrition in this chapter will be in terms of these "standard" young adults.

### Other Nutrient Standards

In 1951, a governmental group, the Interdepartmental Committee on Nutrition for National Defense (ICNND), established a guide which helps to interpret the numbers found in the RDA table. It describes an acceptable range of nutrient intake for a standard man slightly smaller than the average man described in the RDA table. It defines high, acceptable, low, or deficient ranges (Table 11–3).

Neither the RDA nor the ICNND standards are directly applicable to small groups or to individuals. They are based on statistical averages and some persons may have greater or less than the average requirement for one or more nutrients. Nevertheless, in lieu of biochemical data or other measurements to judge individual nutritional status, a diet can be compared to these standards for detecting probable areas of nutritional improvement.

## Food Standards

For general public use and for the professional person giving nutritional guidance, it is desirable to have a standard based on foods rather than nutrients. First, the United States Department of Agriculture classified foods into seven groups in 1946. This was then simplified to a daily guide in which only four food groups were defined—milk, meat, vegetable-fruit and bread-cereal (Table 11–4). The minimum number of servings each food group should provide on a daily basis are 2, 2, 4 and 4, respectively. With a few exceptions in the meat group, two of the groups contain animal foods and two contain plant foods. A prime purpose of this chapter will be to describe the sound scientific basis for this food guide and to demonstrate its usefulness in the practice of dentistry.

## COMPOSITION OF THE DAILY DIET

### Nature and Sources of Nutrients

Since most foods contain a wide variety of nutrients, their relative contributions to the diet usually depend upon their containing significant concentrations of one or more nutrients. On the other hand, even low concentrations of nutrients in a food item become important when that food is eaten in large quantities or when the nutrients in it are of superior quality. For example, the low protein concentration in potatoes becomes significant when potatoes are eaten in large amounts. In addition, the potato protein has a higher biological value than most plant proteins. Another exception obtains when a low total nutrient content is readily available, that is, easily digested, absorbed, or utilized. Thus certain green vegetables high in calcium content may contain oxalate which forms insoluble calcium chelates which are unavailable for absorption.

### Dry Matter Composition

Understanding of the gross contents of the usual diet may readily be obtained by drying and weighing the several pounds of daily food. The dry matter in the usual adult diet will weigh about 1 to 1½ pounds or about 500 to 700 grams. Carbohydrate, fat and protein contribute most of the weight (Table 11–5).

Table 11–2.  Recommended Daily Dietary

| | Age[2] Years From / Up to | Weight Kg (lbs) | Height cm (in) | K calories | Protein gm | Fat Soluble Vitamins Vitamin A Activity I.U. | Vitamin D I.U. | Vitamin E Activity I.U. |
|---|---|---|---|---|---|---|---|---|
| Infants | 0 — 1/6 | 4  9 | 55  22 | kg×120 | kg×2.2[3] | 1500 | 400 | 5 |
| | 1/6 — 1/2 | 7  15 | 63  25 | kg×110 | kg×2.0[3] | 1500 | 400 | 5 |
| | 1/2 — 1 | 9  20 | 72  28 | kg×100 | kg×1.8[3] | 1500 | 400 | 5 |
| Children | 1 — 2 | 12  26 | 81  32 | 1100 | 25 | 2000 | 400 | 10 |
| | 2 — 3 | 14  31 | 91  36 | 1250 | 25 | 2000 | 400 | 10 |
| | 3 — 4 | 16  35 | 100  39 | 1400 | 30 | 2500 | 400 | 10 |
| | 4 — 6 | 19  42 | 110  43 | 1600 | 30 | 2500 | 400 | 10 |
| | 6 — 8 | 23  51 | 121  48 | 2000 | 35 | 3500 | 400 | 15 |
| | 8 — 10 | 28  62 | 131  52 | 2200 | 40 | 3500 | 400 | 15 |
| Males | 10 — 12 | 35  77 | 140  55 | 2500 | 45 | 4500 | 400 | 20 |
| | 12 — 14 | 43  95 | 151  59 | 2700 | 50 | 5000 | 400 | 20 |
| | 14 — 18 | 59  130 | 170  67 | 3000 | 60 | 5000 | 400 | 25 |
| | 18 — 22 | 67  147 | 175  69 | 2800 | 60 | 5000 | 400 | 30 |
| | 22 — 35 | 70  154 | 175  69 | 2800 | 65 | 5000 | — | 30 |
| | 35 — 55 | 70  154 | 173  68 | 2600 | 65 | 5000 | — | 30 |
| | 55 — 75+ | 70  154 | 171  67 | 2400 | 65 | 5000 | — | 30 |
| Females | 10 — 12 | 35  77 | 142  56 | 2250 | 50 | 4500 | 400 | 20 |
| | 12 — 14 | 44  97 | 154  61 | 2300 | 50 | 5000 | 400 | 20 |
| | 14 — 16 | 52  114 | 157  62 | 2400 | 55 | 5000 | 400 | 25 |
| | 16 — 18 | 54  119 | 160  63 | 2300 | 55 | 5000 | 400 | 25 |
| | 18 — 22 | 58  128 | 163  64 | 2000 | 55 | 5000 | 400 | 25 |
| | 22 — 35 | 58  128 | 163  64 | 2000 | 55 | 5000 | — | 25 |
| | 35 — 55 | 58  128 | 160  63 | 1850 | 55 | 5000 | — | 25 |
| | 55 — 75+ | 58  128 | 157  62 | 1700 | 55 | 5000 | — | 25 |
| Pregnancy | | | | +200 | 65 | 6000 | 400 | 30 |
| Lactation | | | | +1000 | 75 | 8000 | 400 | 30 |

[1] The allowance levels are intended to cover individual variations among most normal persons as they live in the United States under usual environmental stresses.  The recommended allowances can be attained with a variety of common foods, providing other nutrients for which human requirements have been less well defined.

[2] Entries on lines for age range 22–35 years represent the reference man and woman at age 22.  All other entries represent allowances for the mid-point of the specified age range.

[3] Assumes protein equivalent to human milk.  For proteins not 100 percent utilized factors should be increased proportionately.

[4] The folacin allowances refer to dietary sources as determined by *Lactobacillus casei* assay Pure forms of folacin may be effective in doses less than 1/4 of the RDA.

[5] Niacin equivalents include dietary sources of the vitamin itself plus 1 mg equivalent for each 60 mg of dietary tryptophan.

# Allowances[1] (Revised 1968)

| Water Soluble Vitamins | | | | | | | Minerals | | | | |
|---|---|---|---|---|---|---|---|---|---|---|---|
| Ascorbic Acid mg | Folacin[4] mg | Niacin mg equiv[5] | Riboflavin mg | Thiamine mg | Vitamin $B_6$ mg | Vitamin $B_{12}$ $\mu g$ | Calcium gm | Phosphorus gm | Iodine $\mu g$ | Iron mg | Magnesium mg |
| 35 | 0.05 | 5 | 0.4 | 0.2 | 0.2 | 1.0 | 0.4 | 0.2 | 25 | 6 | 40 |
| 35 | 0.05 | 7 | 0.5 | 0.4 | 0.3 | 1.5 | 0.5 | 0.4 | 40 | 10 | 60 |
| 35 | 0.1 | 8 | 0.6 | 0.5 | 0.4 | 2.0 | 0.6 | 0.5 | 45 | 15 | 70 |
| 40 | 0.1 | 8 | 0.6 | 0.6 | 0.5 | 2.0 | 0.7 | 0.7 | 55 | 15 | 100 |
| 40 | 0.2 | 8 | 0.7 | 0.6 | 0.6 | 2.5 | 0.8 | 0.8 | 60 | 15 | 150 |
| 40 | 0.2 | 9 | 0.8 | 0.7 | 0.7 | 3 | 0.8 | 0.8 | 70 | 10 | 200 |
| 40 | 0.2 | 11 | 0.9 | 0.8 | 0.9 | 4 | 0.8 | 0.8 | 80 | 10 | 200 |
| 40 | 0.2 | 13 | 1.1 | 1.0 | 1.0 | 4 | 0.9 | 0.9 | 100 | 10 | 250 |
| 40 | 0.3 | 15 | 1.2 | 1.1 | 1.2 | 5 | 1.0 | 1.0 | 110 | 10 | 250 |
| 40 | 0.4 | 17 | 1.3 | 1.3 | 1.4 | 5 | 1.2 | 1.2 | 125 | 10 | 300 |
| 45 | 0.4 | 18 | 1.4 | 1.4 | 1.6 | 5 | 1.4 | 1.4 | 135 | 18 | 350 |
| 55 | 0.4 | 20 | 1.5 | 1.5 | 1.8 | 5 | 1.4 | 1.4 | 150 | 18 | 400 |
| 60 | 0.4 | 18 | 1.6 | 1.4 | 2.0 | 5 | 0.8 | 0.8 | 140 | 10 | 400 |
| 60 | 0.4 | 18 | 1.7 | 1.4 | 2.0 | 5 | 0.8 | 0.8 | 140 | 10 | 350 |
| 60 | 0.4 | 17 | 1.7 | 1.3 | 2.0 | 5 | 0.8 | 0.8 | 125 | 10 | 350 |
| 60 | 0.4 | 14 | 1.7 | 1.2 | 2.0 | 6 | 0.8 | 0.8 | 110 | 10 | 350 |
| 40 | 0.4 | 15 | 1.3 | 1.1 | 1.4 | 5 | 1.2 | 1.2 | 110 | 18 | 300 |
| 45 | 0.4 | 15 | 1.4 | 1.2 | 1.6 | 5 | 1.3 | 1.3 | 115 | 18 | 350 |
| 50 | 0.4 | 16 | 1.4 | 1.2 | 1.8 | 5 | 1.3 | 1.3 | 120 | 18 | 350 |
| 50 | 0.4 | 15 | 1.5 | 1.2 | 2.0 | 5 | 1.3 | 1.3 | 115 | 18 | 350 |
| 55 | 0.4 | 13 | 1.5 | 1.0 | 2.0 | 5 | 0.8 | 0.8 | 100 | 18 | 350 |
| 55 | 0.4 | 13 | 1.5 | 1.0 | 2.0 | 5 | 0.8 | 0.8 | 100 | 18 | 300 |
| 55 | 0.4 | 12 | 1.5 | 0.9 | 2.0 | 5 | 0.8 | 0.8 | 90 | 18 | 300 |
| 55 | 0.4 | 10 | 1.5 | 0.9 | 2.0 | 6 | 0.8 | 0.8 | 80 | 10 | 300 |
| 60 | 0.8 | 15 | 1.8 | +0.1 | 2.5 | 8 | +0.4 | +0.4 | 125 | 18 | 450 |
| 60 | 0.5 | 20 | 2.0 | +0.5 | 2.5 | 6 | +0.5 | +0.5 | 150 | 18 | 450 |

Table 11–3.  Suggested Guide to Interpretation of Nutrient Intake Data*
(ICNND-Values)

| | Deficient | Low | Acceptable | High |
|---|---|---|---|---|
| Protein, gm/kg body weight | <0.5 | 0.5–0.9 | 1.0–1.4 | ≥1.5 |
| Calcium, gm/day | <.3 | 0.30–0.39 | 0.4–0.7 | ≥0.8 |
| Iron, mg/day | <6 | 6–8 | 9–11 | ≥12 |
| Vitamin A, I.U./day | <2,000 | 2,000–3,499 | 3,500–4,999 | ≥5,000 |
| Thiamine, mg/1000 Calories | <.2 | 0.20–0.29 | 0.3–0.4 | ≥.5 |
| Riboflavin, mg/day | <.7 | 0.7–1.1 | 1.2–1.4 | ≥1.5 |
| Niacin, mg/day | <5 | 5–9 | 10–14 | ≥15 |
| Ascorbic acid, mg/day | <10 | 10–29 | 30–49 | ≥50 |
| †Calories | .. | .. | .. | .. |

* This guide applies to a 25-year-old physically active male of 170 cm in height and 65 kg in weight living in a temperate climate and consuming a varied diet.
† The requirement for calories is so dependent upon both size, climate age and physical activity that no figures can be stated.

## Carbohydrate

*Calories.* Two-thirds of the daily intake of food, exclusive of water, is one nutrient, carbohydrate. Assuming 4 kilocalories per gram as a practical value for the energy level of carbohydrates, 420 grams of carbohydrate would supply 60% of the suggested 2800 kilocalories that are allowed for the standard man according to RDA values. This alone would supply nearly the entire 1800 calorie basal metabolism requirement for the standard man. This large intake of just one nutrient has important consequences to be discussed later in terms of vitamin requirements, body weight control, metabolism and oral health, especially with respect to dental caries.

*Starches.* Half of the more than 90% of the dietary carbohydrate is plant provided and is in polysaccharide form as plant starches largely from cereal grains. It is classified primarily in the bread-cereal food group. Processing and cooking may release sticky forms of starch and protein which increases oral retention and is detrimental to good oral health. Thus residues from breads, cereals and pastas such as macaroni and spaghetti are readily retained in the mouth. Newer commercial products attempt to limit sticky forms which are often the least acceptable from the standpoint of taste and texture. Further processing, toasting and baking, causes drying and hardening with subsequent reduction of stickiness. Partial hydrolysis also occurs, but the dextrins produced are probably no more soluble or fermentable than starches but less sticky so that the overall effect is beneficial. Starchy foods may increase in retention time in the following order: potatoes, pastas, whole wheat bread or toasted white bread, and white bread.

*Starches and Caries.* The effect of starchy foods on caries production has not been established. Such items should be eaten only during meals when saliva and other foods are available to aid in oral clearance and be avoided between meals when they enhance retention of sugars. Sugars are cariogenic and often are eaten between meals. Sugar coated cereals, especially, as well as regular dry cereals normally made with addition of some sugar should be restricted to the mealtime experience. Similarly, caramel-coated popcorn should be avoided between meals, but popcorn is not retentive and would seem to be ideal as a between meal snack from the caries preventive standpoint. Unfortunately, reliable rankings for food cariogenicities do not yet exist so caution is necessary when recommending between meal items.

*Sugars and Caries.* The remaining half of the daily carbohydrate intake is made up of sugars of which one-half, or about 75 to 100 grams, is sucrose. Sucrose, being readily fermented by oral microorganisms, is highly cariogenic. Recent studies have shown that sucrose more than other sugars promotes the type of dental caries associated with thick plaque deposits. These plaques, containing insoluble, highly-adhesive dextrans, which differ from food starches are alpha-1,6 linked chains with various branching configurations. They are produced extracellularly by certain strains of oral streptococci.

Oral enzymes offer possibilities for the control of oral carbohydrates, especially since food-borne enzymes after oral clearance would be digested as any other food protein. The normally-occurring enzyme, salivary amylase, does not demonstrably affect orally-retained starchy foods; however, dextranase, a bacterial enzyme that hydrolyzes bacterial dextrans, inhibits caries production when placed in the diet or drinking water of hamsters. Caries may occur readily without dextran or copious plaque residues and all sugars, even slowly-fermenting milk sugar, lactose, are cariogenic when tested in animal caries studies. The sweet sugar alcohols, sorbitol and mannitol, contained in some sugarless gums and pharmaceuticals are so slowly metabolized that they are considered noncariogenic. Therefore, these gums and some brands of "chewable" vitamins are not caries threats.

The consensus is that lactose consumed in milk, cheese, and other items of the milk food group is not cariogenic and can be consumed between meals. However, milk is retained on the oral mucosa so that, from the standpoint of caries prevention, it would be better to avoid sucrose-sweetened milk items such as malts, chocolate milk and ice cream between meals.

12

## Table 11–4. Daily Food Guide*

| Food Group | Foods Included | Daily Servings | Serving Sizes |
|---|---|---|---|
| Milk and Milk Equivalents | Milk: fluid whole; evaporated; skim; dry; buttermilk. Cheese: cottage; cream; cheddar-type —natural or processed. Ice cream. | Children . . . .3 to 4<br>Teen-agers . . . .4 or more<br>Adults . . . . . .2 or more<br>Pregnant women .4 or more<br>Nursing mothers .6 or more | When cheese or ice cream replace milk, calculate as calcium equivalents: a one-inch cube of cheddar cheese equal to $\frac{2}{3}$ cup milk; $\frac{1}{2}$ cup cottage cheese equal to $\frac{1}{3}$ cup milk; 1 cup ice cream equal to $\frac{1}{2}$ cup milk. |
| Meat and Meat Equivalents | Beef; veal; lamb; pork; variety meats, such as liver, heart, kidney.<br><br>Poultry and eggs.<br>Fish and shellfish.<br>As alternates.—Dry beans, dry peas, lentils, nuts, peanuts, peanut butter. | 2 or more servings. | Count as a serving: 2 to 3 ounces of lean cooked meat, poultry, or fish—all without bone; 2 eggs; 1 cup cooked dry beans, dry peas, lentils; 4 tablespoons peanut butter. |
| Vegetables and Fruits | *Sources of Vitamin C*<br>Good sources.—Grapefruit or grapefruit juice; orange or orange juice; cantaloup; strawberries; broccoli; brussels sprouts; green pepper; sweet red pepper. | 4 or more servings.<br>1 serving of a good source of vitamin C or 2 servings of a fair source.<br>1 serving, at least every other day, of a good source of vitamin A. If the food | Count as 1 serving:<br>$\frac{1}{2}$ cup of vegetable or fruit; or a portion as ordinarily served, such as 1 medium apple, banana, orange or potato, half a medium grapefruit or |

cantaloup, or the juice of 1 lemon.

Fair sources. — Lemon, tangerine; watermelon; raw cabbage; collards; mustard greens; potatoes and sweet-potatoes; spinach; tomatoes or tomato juice; turnip greens; pineapple.

*Sources of Vitamin A*

Dark-green and deep-yellow vege-tables and a few fruits, namely: Apricots, broccoli, cantaloup, carrots, chard, collards, pumpkin, spinach, sweet potatoes, turnip greens and other dark-green leaves, winter squash.

chosen for vitamin C is also a good source of vitamin A, the additional serving of a vitamin A food may be omitted.

The remaining 1 to 3 or more servings may be any vegetable or fruit, including those that are valuable for vitamin C and vitamin A.

## Breads and Cereals

Breads; cooked cereals; ready-to-eat cereals; cornmeal; crackers; flour; grits; macaroni and spaghetti; noodles; rolled oats; and quick breads and other baked goods if made with whole-grain or enriched flour. Par-boiled rice and wheat also may be included in this group.

4 servings daily of enriched, whole grain or restored breads and cereals.

Count as 1 serving: 1 slice of bread; 1 ounce ready-to-eat cereal; $\frac{1}{2}$ to $\frac{3}{4}$ cup cooked cereal, corn-meal, grits, macaroni, noodles, rice, or spaghetti.

## Other Foods

To complete meals and to provide additional food energy and other food values. Meals planned to include a variety of foods from each of the four food groups will provide most of the nutrients needed. To give interest and added flavor to meals, butter or margarine, other fats and oils, sugar and other sweets are often included. Amounts of these foods may be regulated to maintain desired body weight.

---

* If caloric intake must be controlled to achieve or maintain desirable weight, adjust the amount of food from each group—but keep selection balanced among all groups.

Table 11–5. Typical Estimates of Calories and Caloric Nutrients Provided by Minimum Number of Servings from the Daily Food Guide with Estimated Minimal Requirements and Suggested Allowances

| Food Group | Amount per day | Calories per Serving | Total Calories | Total Grams per Day[1] | | |
|---|---|---|---|---|---|---|
| | | | | Carbohydrate | Fat | Protein |
| Milk | 2 cups | 170 | 340 | 24 | 20 | 16 |
| Meat | 2 servings (3 oz. each) | 220 | 440 | — | 30 | 42 |
| Vegetable-Fruit | 4 servings[2] | 25 | 100 | 25 | — | — |
| Bread-Cereal | 4 servings | 70 | 270 | 60 | — | 8 |
| Total | | | 1150 | 109 | 50 | 66 |
| Estimated Minimal Requirements[3] | | | | | | |
| 22-year-old man | | | 1180[4] | 100 | 30 | 20 |
| 22–year–old woman | | | 1200[4] | 100 | 30 | 20 |
| Suggested Allowances[3] | | | | | | |
| 22-year-old man | | | 2800 | 420 | 95 | 70 |
| 22-year-old woman | | | 2000 | 300 | 65 | 55 |

[1] Estimates exclude amounts less than 1 gram.

[2] Assumes equal selections from: (1) vegetables providing essentially no calories (2) vegetables providing 36 calories per serving and (3) a typical estimate of 40 calories for fruit servings.

[3] See text for rationale upon which these requirements and allowances are based.

[4] Based on a B.M.R. of 1.85 and 1.35 kilocalories/square meter of body surface/hr. for standard man and woman, respectively.

Lactose comprises only 5 to 10% of the dietary carbohydrate and is the only common animal food source of carbohydrate. Glycogen, animal starch, is rapidly lost during meat processing and is ingested as such only through such pleasures as raw shell fish.

The remaining sugars are glucose and fructose from honey and vegetable-fruit food group items. This group also provides starches in the form of parenchymatous fruits and legumes, as do dry beans and peas which, however, are classified in the meat food group. The carbohydrates in most of these foods are usually not highly retentive.

## Carbohydrates of Vegetable-Fruit Food Group and Dental Health

Carbohydrate is the only quantitatively important constituent provided by the vegetable-fruit group which does not contain an orally fermentable form of carbohydrate. In fact if foods such as apples, carrots, celery or even potatoes or cauliflower are only gently processed to retain their firm texture or eaten raw, then they require chewing, stimulate salivation, and serve to promote oral clearance of food debris. Accordingly, such foods are termed "detergent" foods. It is unlikely that they aid in removal of much bacterial plaque; however, they ordinarily facilitate the oral clearance of sugar-containing food debris which may reduce caries. Preliminary studies suggest that the frequent presence of foods requiring chewing and elimination of the carbohydrate retention factor may promote periodontal health. Raw items are ideal in lunches as well as between meals. Care must be taken to assure acceptance of these foods by preserving crispness and freshness with appropriate hydrating, wrapping, and refrigeration.

Vegetable items are best if only blanched during cooking or cooked in minimum water until tender—a skill of Chinese cooking. This not only preserves their detergent qualities, but also prevents the extraction and loss of soluble vitamins and minerals. The destruction of heat and oxygen labile vitamins, especially thiamine by heat and ascorbic acid by oxygen, is also minimized. The flavor and color are also retained making these foods more attractive to many who otherwise may miss their nutritional benefits.

Since the effect of very sweet fruit on caries is largely unknown, oranges, pineapple, peaches, and sweet juices, although not highly retentive, probably should be used infrequently between meals. Citrus fruits may sufficiently stimulate salivation so as to be essentially noncariogenic. A beneficial effect was reported in a preliminary experiment where malic acid from apples was incorporated with sorbitol in a noncariogenic candy mint designed to stimulate salivation between meals as an anticaries measure. Dried fruits such as raisins are unquestionably retentive, contain sugar, and are to be avoided.

Table 11–5 summarizes the carbohydrate contributions from each food group when the recommended minimum number of servings per day is consumed. Commonly, much more than 60 grams of starches from the bread-cereal group are in the daily diet. Note that honey and sucrose items such as syrups, jellies, candies, and sugar are high in caloric value and contain essentially no other nutrients. They are not included in any food group and are often termed "empty-calorie" foods.

In summary, refined, processed starchy foods present the problem of oral retention. They may be cariogenic, per se, or under certain conditions and in the presence of sugars in particular caries-promoting. The clinical evidence relating to the cariogenicity of sucrose-containing items will be discussed in connection with the control of dental caries.

### Indigestible Bulk

All of the carbohydrates mentioned thus far are completely digestible by the adult. The indigestible material is termed "bulk" and comprises about 5% of the daily intake of dry matter. It is mostly "crude fiber" or plant polysaccharides such as celluloses, pectins or gums. A small portion of the bulk represents fibrous proteins such as skin keratin. The bulk materials bind water and stimulate intestinal movements promoting proper fecal elimination. In excess they can cause diarrhea.

Formerly, many persons were overly worried concerning constipation. Excessive use of cereal brans and certain cathartic fruits and vegetables seems less popular now. Even in older persons, good peristalsis may best be obtained by assuring good nutrition for healthy gastrointestinal tract musculature with a reasonable amount of exercise rather than by the persistent use of cathartic foods.

## Fat

*Caloric Considerations.* If the dry matter from an ideal diet were extracted with a fat solvent, 95 grams of fat equivalent to 30% of the total caloric intake would be obtained (Table 11–5). This is based on the 2800 calorie allowance for the standard man and a caloric equivalent of 9 kilocalories per gram for most food fats and oils.

The average person is aware of only about one-fourth of this fat, the so-called "visible" fat as butter, margarine, salad dressings, and fried foods. Another one-fourth includes in addition the shortenings and oils used in cooking which are hidden, except from the cook. Except for butter and lard, these fats are largely derived from plant sources and are rich in unsaturated fats. Note in Table 11–5 that plant foods included in the four food groups for their nutritional value do not contain appreciable fat. Therefore, plant fats and oils as well as butter and lard are regarded primarily for their caloric contribution. While they contain some fat-soluble vitamins and essential fatty acids, they are often considered as "empty-calorie" foods.

Avocadoes and olives which are rich in fat content are among the noticeable exceptions in the vegetable-fruit food group. Nuts, which range in fat content from 48% in peanut butter to 73% in pecans are listed in the meat food group.

Although the meat food group is commonly thought of in terms of its protein content, this group provides a rich source of fat (Table 11–5). For example, most meat items and eggs which are in this food group will contribute even more calories from fat than from protein because of their high fat content and the high caloric equivalent of fat. The same is true of whole milk or ordinary cheese in the milk food group. Skim milk and low-fat milks are often fortified with 5000 and 400 units of vitamins A and D respectively to be equivalent, except in fat calories, to a quart of fortified whole milk. They are excellent substitutes for those concerned with control of caloric intake but should be checked to be sure of both caloric and vitamin contents. Note, however, that even the 2 cups of *whole* milk suggested by the food group guide need not be inconsistent with a calorie-controlled regimen.

*Metabolic Considerations.* Both the carbohydrate and fat portions of the diet are primarily important for their caloric contributions. Although there are no nutritionally essential carbohydrate molecules, there are qualitative requirements for either di-, tri-, or tetra- (poly) unsaturated fatty acids. These essential fatty acids are linoleic, linolenic and arachidonic acids respectively. The word "essential" is commonly used in nutrition to describe compounds or chemical elements which cannot be synthesized by the body and must be provided by an outside source—usually the diet. The essential fatty acids are most abundant in plant oils, but even the 50 grams of animal fat provided in the recommended servings from the four food groups (Table 11–4) is sufficient to meet the essential fatty acid needs. Considering all food fats in the average mixed diet, 30 grams or about 1 ounce is sufficient to provide essential fatty acids equivalent to the 3 to 9 grams of linoleic acid estimated to meet the daily adult need.

Food fats also contain vitamins A, D, E and K which, like fat, accumulate and are stored in plant and animal foods. However, the vegetable-fruit food group which contributes negligible dietary fat provides important amounts of vitamins E, K and also carotenes, which the body can convert into vitamin A. Many meat food group items, especially organ meats and eggs, are rich in another fat-soluble but non-essential nutrient, cholesterol.

About 5% of the fat intake may be non-essential phospholipids some of which, lecithins, contain choline. An additional supply of choline enhances fat mobilization by the liver. Even more important perhaps to fat mobilization and transport and to metabolism is the level of unsaturated fatty acids —not because they are essential but for their more emulsifiable nature. This physical property may yet prove important in determining the oral effects of different food fats and oils.

## Fat and Caries

To date it appears that at a certain concentration of fat, cariogenicity is lessened. For this reason, it appears that high fat, non-sweetened, starchy foods such as potato chips or corn, rice and other cereal grain snacks, peanuts and even peanut butter may be acceptable between meals. However, they probably would not overcome the effect of sugar when combined with them in items like candy-coated peanuts or peanut butter and jelly sandwiches.

## Protein

*Comparison of Animal and Plant Sources.* The remaining large portion of the daily dry matter is protein. The ICNND and RDA rule of 1 gram of protein per kilogram of body weight states the standard man should receive 65 to 70 grams of protein per day or about 10% of his total calories. This recommendation includes the provision that at least 20 grams or about one-third of the recommended value be animal proteins. These are usually a rich source of the 8 essential amino acids: lysine, tryptophan, methionine, valine, phenylalanine, leucine, isoleucine, and threonine. Gelatin, a protein gel prepared from collagen, composed to a greater extent of non-essential amino acids, is a notable exception to the generality that all animal proteins are rich in essential amino acids. In general, proteins provided by the milk and meat food groups are rich in essential amino acids and are termed variously as "complete," or of "high biological value" or "balanced" or of "high quality." *

Animal protein is expensive and not easily available to many populations throughout the world or to lower income groups in this country. These populations depend on plant proteins which contain lower protein concentrations than do animal foods. Cereal grains are made into breads, cereals, pastas, biscuits, grits, and tortillas. Note the low amount of protein provided by the recommended minimum number of four servings from the bread-cereal food group (Table 11-4). Such foods must be eaten in large quantities to meet protein requirements when animal foods are not readily available. Dry beans, peas, and nuts, although plant foods, are placed in the meat food group because they are rich in protein and are often eaten in large amounts.

## SUMMARY OF GROSS DIETARY CONSTITUENTS

### Calories

Ideally the standard man will eat 420 grams of carbohydrate, 95 grams of fat and 65 grams of protein per day. This diet will give about 60, 30 and 10%, respectively, of the 2800 calorie daily requirement. Comparison with the diet that would be provided by the recommended number of servings from the four food groups is shown in Table 11-5. It is apparent that the food group plan of eating provides a low calorie basal diet because of low amounts of carbohydrate and fat. It thus serves as a base for upward adjustment to the caloric levels and food choices that meet individual needs. With this basal plan an adequate supply of high quality protein is assured. Both essential amino and fatty acid requirements would be met. Since other essential nutrients are also assured by this eating plan (Table 11-5), it provides the average person with a wide variety of calorically-wise and nutritionally-adequate diets. Additional food group items would be the foods of choice used to bring caloric intake to desired levels. The non-food group items, especially "visible" fat and "empty calorie" carbohydrates, may be added to enhance palatability and enjoyment of other food items.

* They may also be called "high ranking." It is convenient to use the mnemonic Lt. M. V. Plit (lysine, tryptophan, methionine, valine, phenylalanine, leucine, isoleucine, threonine) to remember the essential amino acids. The first two primarily are often low in vegetable proteins thus giving animal proteins higher rank. The last "t" is threonine, the last of the essential amino acids to be discovered.

Caution is necessary, however, since only 2 tablespoons of fat on salad or bread, or 5 tablespoons of sugar would add 200–250 calories.

## Minerals

Besides carbohydrate, fat and protein, the only other grossly significant portion of the daily intake of dry matter is the major minerals. An ashing procedure would reveal 10 to 20 grams of total inorganic matter. This amount would be highly variable because the salt component, NaCl, may vary from 5 to 15 grams in ordinary diets.

The pH of the ash predicts the urinary pH since the body also oxidizes and essentially ashes the daily diet and excretes excesses of minerals. $Na^+$, $K^+$, $Ca^{2+}$ and $Mg^{2+}$ predominate if the diet is higher in milk and vegetable-fruit food group items than in acidic ash foods from the meat and bread-cereal food group where the ions of $HPO_4^{2-}$, $SO_4^{2-}$ and $Cl^-$ predominate. A diet based on the four food group plan will provide a reasonable balance of metals and non-metals and a urinary pH near neutrality.

## NUTRITIONAL BALANCE

The word "balance" is very useful in the nutritional context. Having introduced it in the discussion of ash balance, it should be defined now in the two senses in which it is used. First, a balanced meal implies ideal proportions of various foods so that the nutrients will be in proper proportion to each other. Three such meals provide a balanced diet. Our knowledge of what constitutes proper balance is incomplete. Relative nutrient needs appear to vary for different tissues as well as for the body as a whole. In either case they are related to age, physiological and pathological status as well as to nutritional habits such as frequency of eating. The four food group concept is emphasized repeatedly since for this nation these food groupings and intake levels seem to be the most practical means of preparing balanced meals.

The idea of balance may also refer to foods such as milk which approaches nutritional balance in itself or to a single nutrient such as protein that contains a good distribution of amino acids, especially the essential ones. Balance also means the body's balance or balance within a body system. In this context then, good ash balance promotes acid-base balance in the body. In the case of protein, if the nitrogen (protein) intake equals nitrogen output, the body is in nitrogen balance. While useful, the determination and meaning of the state of balance is very difficult. Ideally, balanced nutrition may also depend upon many other factors besides total daily food intake. The habit of eating meals, the effects of meal size, the frequency of eating, and the influences of frequent unbalanced snacks all present questions that are only now being studied.

## DIETARY CATALYSTS

Although catalysts are not quantitatively important, they serve critical roles in facilitating the body chemistry. Accordingly, they are ideally provided in foods containing gross nutrients whose utilization they catalyze. Table 11–6 shows the distribution among the food groups of a number of these catalysts including the major mineral element calcium which serves both a catalytic and a structural role. Many essential nutrients are not in the table either because their quantitative requirement is still poorly defined or because of the thought behind the establishment of the list. The philosophy used in formulating the four food groups was to provide food patterns to meet the RDA standards with the assumption that adequate amounts of other nutrients would automatically be assured. This assumption seems well-founded to date. A corollary is that excessive deviation from the four food group concept such as the development of food idiosyncracies due to allergies, poor health, excessive dieting, or food faddism could exclude nutrients whose presence is normally assured. By choosing foods primarily to meet the needs for calcium, iron, vitamin A, ascorbic acid, B-vitamins (thiamine, riboflavin and niacin), and protein other nutrient requirements will almost necessarily be adequate.

### Vegetable-Fruit Food Group and Total Health Needs

The prime reason for listing the vegetable-fruit food group becomes apparent from Table 11–6. While these foods make only a minor caloric contribution, they supply 20% of the iron, thiamine, and niacin, more than 50% of the vitamin A and more than 90% of ascorbic acid. In fact it is nearly impossible to meet the RDA of the latter without this food group. Especially important are potatoes, tomatoes, other vegetables, and citrus fruits each supplying in the United States diet about 20% of the RDA for ascorbic acid. This food group is important to periodontal patients beyond the local or physical advantages noted during the discussion of carbohydrates since oral tissues are especially sensitive to ascorbic acid deficiency.

Vegetable-fruit foods may be more necessary than expected in some diets from high income groups where the intake of enriched bread-cereal is low. In low income families the enriched bread-cereal foods contribute a large portion of iron and the B-vitamins (Table 11–6). Lower income families must emphasize the vegetable-fruit group to provide vitamin A, riboflavin and calcium, whereas in higher income groups most of these nutrients are contributed by the more expensive milk and meat food group items. Thus, in lower income situations vegetable-fruit foods and the low cost enriched bread-cereal foods are especially important for healthy oral soft tissues. In fact, in such populations the symptoms of pellagra, ariboflavinosis, and other nutritional deficiency diseases were associated first of all with the head and neck area and especially with oral disease. Nutritional requirements for

Table 11–6. Average Quantity of Nutrients Provided by Minimum Number of Servings Specified from Each Food Group of the Daily Food Guide and Recommended Daily Allowances of These Nutrients for Young Adults

| Food Group | Amount | Calcium | Iron | Vitamin A Value | Thiamine | Riboflavin | Niacin | Ascorbic Acid |
|---|---|---|---|---|---|---|---|---|
| | | mg | mg | I.U. | mg | mg | mg | mg |
| Milk and Milk Equivalents | 2 cups | 514 | 0.3 | 870 | 0.13 | 0.69 | 0.4 | Trace |
| Meat and Meat Equivalents | 6 ounces | 70 | 6.9 | 1400 | 0.50 | 0.60 | 9.0 | 0 |
| Vegetables and fruits | | | | | | | | |
| Dark-green and deep-yellow vegetables | $\frac{1}{4}$ cup | 23 | 0.6 | 2,590 | 0.04 | 0.04 | 0.3 | 13 |
| Citrus fruits | $\frac{1}{2}$ cup | 27 | 0.4 | 140 | 0.08 | 0.03 | 0.3 | 53 |
| Other vegetables | $\frac{1}{2}$ cup | 22 | 0.8 | 80 | 0.07 | 0.05 | 0.9 | 13 |
| Other fruits | $\frac{1}{2}$ cup | 16 | 0.7 | 560 | 0.04 | 0.05 | 0.4 | 7 |
| Subtotal | | (88) | (2.5) | (3370) | (0.23) | (0.17) | (1.9) | (86) |
| Breads and cereals Whole grain, enriched, restored | 4 servings | 55 | 2.1 | 30 | 0.30 | 0.16 | 2.5 | 0 |
| Total | MDS | 730 | 12.0 | 5700 | 1.2 | 1.6 | 14.0 | 86 |
| Recommended Dietary Allowances | | | | | | | | |
| 22-year-old man | | 800 | 10.0 | 5,000 | 1.4 | 1.7 | 18.0* | 60 |
| 22-year-old woman | | 800 | 18.0 | 5,000 | 1.0 | 1.5 | 13.0* | 55 |

* Niacin equivalents

good general health are also required for good oral health. Deficiency symptoms, *e.g.* simple anemia from iron deficiency, which occur elsewhere than the oral cavity, would eventually affect especially anoxia-susceptible periodontal tissues. *It is academic and unnecessary to attempt to associate foods and their nutrients specifically with oral health effects in order to justify relevance when the health of the total individual is the real issue.*

## Other Food Groups

Both high and low income groups may use the four food group guide for oral health. Low income groups need economic counseling for wise food purchasing but both groups require education and guidance in food selection.

On the basis of only the low calorie basal diet provided by the four food group guide, it is apparent from Table 11–6 that all of the nutrients except niacin either approach or exceed the RDA values. Actually niacin is better supplied than indicated since the high quality protein from the animal food groups contains tryptophan from which the body can obtain 1 mg of niacin from each 60 mg of this essential amino acid. (The RDA table includes the conversion possibility along with the preformed niacin allowance and lists the total as a "niacin equivalent" allowance.)

It is obviously difficult to supply the calcium allowance without liquid milk or its use in foods. In U.S. diets, dairy foods supply 75% of the calcium, about one-half the riboflavin and an important portion of vitamin A. This otherwise nutrient-rich food is noticeably lacking in significant concentrations of iron and ascorbic acid.

The meat food group, like milk, provides a good balance of nutrients. Specifically, in the average U. S. diet it supplies not only 50% of the protein, but more than 40% of the iron and 25% each of the vitamin A, thiamine, and riboflavin.

Since most foods are incomplete in their nutritional balance and since some nutrients are found in relatively few food sources, the value of a variety of foods in the diet is apparent. Variety may provide balanced meals if as far as possible one item from each food group is selected for each meal. This allows the foods to complement each other.

## FOODS AND NUTRIENTS IN METABOLISM

### Biochemical Basis of Energy Nutrition

The best ratios of carbohydrate, fat and protein calories are generally unknown and may even differ with respect to age and sex. Total caloric requirements are based on the basal requirement with an additional portion of energy based on an estimate of activity. The basal requirement can be measured by the usual B.M.R. measurement which determines the overall rate of oxygen consumption. This value is highest at birth and decreases rapidly. After the "growth spurts" of adolescence, it begins to stabilize and nearly plateaus at about age 22 or when growth ceases. Actually it decreases slightly throughout adult life as does activity.

By age 45 the allowance is 7% less than at 22 and by age 65 it is reduced to 14% less than at 22. (Actually, these decreases would be about 10% and 20% if the current decreased activity with age persists. However, it is recognized that it is better for health to maintain activity rather than to further decrease the caloric allowance.) The greatest allowances are 3000 calories for 16-year-old boys and 2400 for 15-year-old girls who mature earlier than boys. At maturity these allowances are only 2800 and 2000, respectively. For the standard man 1800 calories is the basal requirement. The remaining 1000 calories represents the "activity" factor which is equal to 60% of the basal requirement as an estimate of normal activity. The basal caloric requirement is dependent upon body surface area as well as the age and sex of the individual.

*Energy Release from Foods.* It is not an accident of scientific discovery that the glycolysis scheme, the tricarboxylic acid cycle, and the capture of high energy phosphate occupy a central role in biology. Despite the great morphological and functional diversities manifested in living forms these strikingly similar metabolic schemes, at least in principle, represent an underlying biochemical simplicity and unity. In all organisms the *quantitatively* important metabolic pathways are associated with the release and capture of food energy. It is not surprising that most of the nutritional requirements are related quantitatively to energy metabolism. The gross carbohydrate, fat and protein constituents provide catalytic nutrients as well as caloric equivalents which make up nearly all of the daily intake of dry matter. This may be illustrated by a review of energy metabolism.

All the energy obtained from foods was originally captured from the sun by plants during photosynthesis as shown in the familiar equation:

$$6 \ CO_2 + 6 \ H_2O + Light \rightarrow C_6 H_{12} O_6 + 6 \ O_2$$

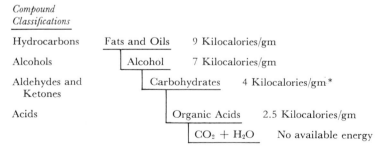

*Compound Classifications*

| | | |
|---|---|---|
| Hydrocarbons | Fats and Oils | 9 Kilocalories/gm |
| Alcohols | Alcohol | 7 Kilocalories/gm |
| Aldehydes and Ketones | Carbohydrates | 4 Kilocalories/gm* |
| Acids | Organic Acids | 2.5 Kilocalories/gm |
| | $CO_2 + H_2O$ | No available energy |

FIG. 11–1. Approximate energies available from organic food constituents during bodily oxidation

* Proteins average out at 4 kilocalories/gm—their amino acids being composed of hydrocarbons, alcohols and acids which are oxidizable and amino groups which are not.

Plants and animals which consume plants and/or other animals, utilize this stored energy by a process of oxidation. Photosynthesis is the reduction of carbon dioxide by hydrogen, and to the extent the oxygen is replaced more and more energy is stored. The caloric equivalents of carbohydrate, fat and protein are understandable in these terms. Fats contain very long hydrocarbon chains, alcohol is a slightly oxidized hydrocarbon, carbohydrates have a yet lower H to C ratio and organic acids are even less reduced. These generalities and the associated energy levels are summarized in Figure 11–1.

*Catalytic Nutrients and Energy Metabolism.* The over all metabolic pathways related to these energy transitions are summarized in Figure 11–2 with emphasis on the catalytic nutrients involved. Coenzymes containing vitamins are essential to nearly every aspect of the energy pathways. Oxidation is accompanied by the release of hydrogen. Niacin as niacinamide adenine dinucleotide (NAD) or its phosphate (NADP) captures this hydrogen and holds it at a high energy level as NADH or NADPH, respectively. This occurs once in glycolysis, four times in the citric acid cycle and twice in the hexose monophosphate pathway (HMP).

These hydrogens may then be used to reduce acetyl coenzyme A to cholesterol or to fatty acids. In the latter case, along with its use for glyceraldehyde reduction to glycerol, hydrogen facilitates energy storage as triglycerides (fats and oils). In oral microorganisms, it serves to reduce pyruvic acid, a ketone, to lactic acid, an alcohol. In both the formation of lactic acid in microorganisms and cholesterol in the human, these reduced energy stores are lost since the products are excreted. The hydrogen stored in fats, however, may reenter energy metabolism. In fat oxidation, hydrogen is removed with the formation, again, of the reduced coenzyme, NADH and the reduced riboflavin coenzyme, flavin adenine dinucleotide ($FADH_2$).

Cells are limited in their ability to utilize hydrogen directly in synthesis especially since metabolites other than those possible from the direct transfer of hydrogen must be produced. Therefore, the reduced coenzymes enter a hydrogen transport scheme conveniently located in the mitochondria along with the citric acid cycle that produces the greatest amount of reduced coenzymes. In the transport sequence, hydrogen or its electron is progressively lowered in its energy level. The energy lost is captured by adenosine diphosphate and inorganic phosphate to form the high energy compound ATP which the cell can use in a universal sense. ATP provides usable energy for synthesis, muscular work, active transport, and a host of other tasks. This scheme is diagrammed in Figure 11–3 which shows the involvement of several nutrients. From the coupled mechanisms, termed "oxidative phosphorylation," the body obtains 3 ATP molecules for every oxygen activated as the final receptor of the hydrogen, or if an $FADH_2$ is oxidized 2 ATP's are produced. Occasionally, oxidative phosphorylation is by-passed

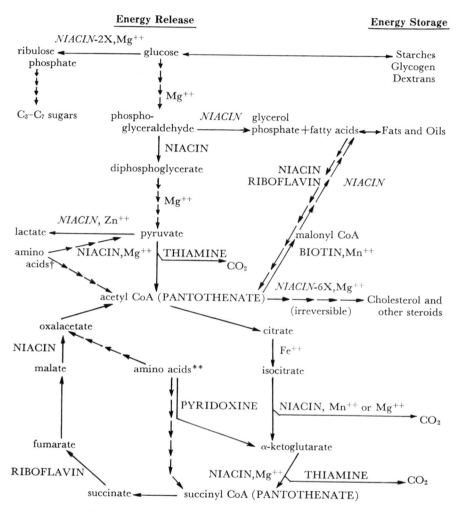

FIG. 11–2.   Energy Metabolism and Nutrient Catalysts.*

* All vitamins react in their coenzyme forms.  NIACIN = NAD⁺, *NIACIN* = NADP⁺
† Amino acid degradations require many nutritionally essential cofactors.

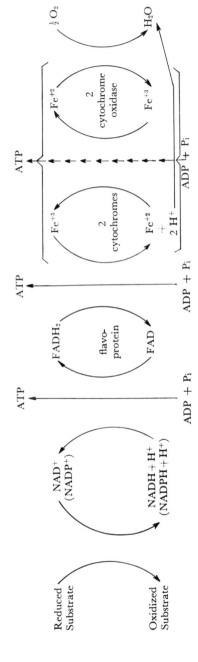

Fig. 11–3. Energy Capture During Oxidation-Reduction Reactions Involving Niacin, Riboflavin, and Iron.

and ATP is made directly in conjunction with substrate dephosphorylation and termed "substrate level phosphorylation."

### Energy—Nutrient Demands

It is easy to be sidetracked by the biochemistry of the energy pathways and miss their overall aspects and nutritional importance. Nearly all of the dry matter consumed daily by the average adult is processed by these pathways. Ninety-five % of the respiratory oxygen is utilized by the mito-chondria in the cytochrome oxidase reaction. This is essentially why we breathe. The moles of ATP made and utilized per day, assuming about a 40% efficiency of energy capture, roughly equal the body weight! This is, indeed, big biosynthetic business, and the critical role of the catalytic nutri-ents involved is apparent.

*B-Vitamins and Iron.* Niacin and riboflavin play key roles in energy transfer as hydrogen acceptors as does iron as an electron acceptor. More-over, another B-vitamin, thiamine, is required for decarboxylation in energy metabolism. The advantage of enriching the starchy glucose-providing foods of the bread-cereal group with these four nutrients to aid in glucose metabolism is obvious and assures a degree of nutritional balance for these foods.

Although the B-vitamins are utilized elsewhere, their quantitative require-ment is related to the degree of oxidative metabolism, *i.e.* caloric intake. The thiamine, riboflavin, and niacin requirements are 0.5, 0.6 and 6.6 mg per 1000 calories of food. In fact, the thiamine requirement is especially related to non-fat calories as expected since it permits glucose into the citric acid pathway as pyruvate.

*Growth.* Higher RDA values for caloric and B-vitamin requirements have been suggested for persons during growth especially in adolescence and also during pregnancy. Iron deficiency anemia is easily incurred at these times since growth entails increased hemoglobin formation. In energy metabolism iron is necessary for the cytochrome system and also oxygen transport. The high metabolic demands of growth require providing adequate iodine for thyroxine synthesis necessary for a proper basal metabolic rate, that is, a proper rate of oxygen utilization. Since the BMR decreases with age so does the RDA for iodine.

Because the need for calories continually decreases with age the RDA values for some B-vitamins, thiamine and niacin, have been decreased ac-cordingly (Table 11–2). On the other hand most other requirements are less directly related to caloric intake and the RDA values recommended for the young adult should be maintained throughout the lifespan. For example, the vitamin A requirement is related to the body weight, and, if the adult weight ideally remains relatively constant, the vitamin A requirement re-

13

mains constant.  The decreased RDA for the post-menopausal female is noteworthy.

*Other Energy-related Nutrients.*   Mention of other nutrients, some of which are not in the RDA tabulation, will further illustrate how the energy pathways set the demands.  They include phosphorus, for processing sugars as their phosphate esters, magnesium, for reactions involving ATP, and pantothenic acid which is part of the coenzyme A molecule, playing a key role in energy metabolism as acetyl coenzyme A and as succinyl coenzyme A in Krebs cycle.  Succinyl coenzyme A is also utilized for hemoglobin synthesis.  The transportation and elimination of carbon dioxide as an end product of oxidation depends upon the zinc-containing enzyme carbonic anhydrase.  The neutralization of carbonic acid and organic acids produced during metabolism is due to potassium intracellularly and sodium extracellularly with chloride as an important anion for maintaining electroneutrality.

In addition to iron for proper oxygen transport, copper, folic acid and vitamin $B_{12}$ (cobalt) are all necessary for proper hemoglobin formation.

Most amino acids from food proteins are oxidized in the body by entering the common energy pathways at various points to yield about 4 kilocalories per gram.  The transaminations of aspartic and glutamic acid requiring vitamin $B_6$ as pyridoxal phosphate coenzyme are quantitatively important.  These two amino acids together comprise about 25% of the protein in the usual diet and enter the citric acid cycle as the alpha-keto acids, oxalacetic and alpha-keto glutaric acids, respectively.  Thus, the RDA for vitamin $B_6$ is closely related to the RDA for protein.

While all of the nutrients mentioned in this brief review are involved elsewhere in the body chemistry, the amounts involved are determined primarily by the level of energy metabolism.  Unless the energy needs are met no other metabolism is possible.

## Carbohydrate Functions

*Metabolic.*   Although there are no nutritionally essential compounds, there is a minimal daily carbohydrate need for about 100 grams or about 400 to 500 kilocalories.  This amount assures functional carbohydrate metabolism so that the acetyl coenzyme A produced by fat oxidation can enter efficiently into an operative citric acid cycle.  Otherwise, ketone bodies accumulate as in diabetes where glucose metabolism is insufficient to allow the ready oxidation of fat.  These ketone bodies are acidic so that ketosis is followed by an acidosis leading to the excessive excretion of base, or sodium, and water.

An active carbohydrate metabolism also conserves the electrolyte potassium as well as sodium, both of which are necessary to neutralize organic acids.  The introduction of a low carbohydrate diet is followed by a decrease in body weight due to the loss of water caused by a decrease in organic acids and electrolytes maintaining normal osmotic pressure.

Without the minimal level of 100 grams of carbohydrate to maintain the minimum of 1800 kilocalories of adult glycogen stores, an excessive catabolism of body protein occurs to meet energy needs and for the obligatory maintenance of glycogen stores by the reversal of glycolytic pathways (glyconeogenesis).

*Physiologic.* Of more practical significance, a certain carbohydrate level decreases the need for calories from fat. Too high fat diets are currently highly suspect as factors in vascular and heart disease.

One practical dilemma should be mentioned. A sweet (cariogenic) snack containing highly soluble and readily absorbed sugar calories, can decrease fatigue and provide a "carbohydrate lift." How can this be utilized without interfering either with the appetite or with oral health? The disadvantages must be weighed against the advantage.

The minimum amount of carbohydrate recommended above is readily supplied by the servings specified in the four food group guide (Table 11–5).

## Fat Functions

About 30 grams of fat from mixed food sources assures the proper amounts of essential fatty acids, and fat-soluble vitamins, but fat also has practical value. Fat satisfies the appetite due to a slower rate of digestion and absorption and a higher caloric value than carbohydrate. It also decreases gastric motility which is associated with hunger. This high satiety value paradoxically makes it an ideal constituent of each meal of a *reducing* diet. The recommended servings in the four food group guide provide less than 1200 calories of which 40% is from fat (Table 11–5). This is certainly sufficiently low for weight reduction, and if this 50 grams of fat were distributed into each of three meals, it would aid greatly in satisfying appetite.

Fat is highly palatable since many food flavors are fat soluble. Persons choosing a low calorie diet often fail to take advantage of the appetite and taste satisfying values of fat. They further add to their appetite problem by eliminating breakfast which should be emphasized and should contain some fat. It has been suggested that on a regular diet all the advantages of dietary fat could be supplied by 30% of the daily calories as discussed previously. This provides about 900 kilocalories or 100 grams and is much lower than that currently eaten by the average person.

## Biochemical Basis of Protein (Amino Acid) Nutrition

*Functions.* Proteins play central roles in living processes. They function as enzymes and hormones; in blood clotting and immune reactions; muscular, connective, and skin tissues and calcifying matrices. They permit the transport and storage of materials and contribute to the maintenance of the proper osmotic pressure and pH. They even serve to meet energy needs and can be converted into either fat or glycogen.

*Amino Acid Pool.* The origin of the body proteins that perform these myriad functions is of course the food proteins. The nutritional aspects of protein metabolism are shown in Figure 11–4. Food proteins must first be hydrolyzed to amino acids before being reassembled into proteins characteristic of the host. The real requirement therefore is not for protein as such but for a balance of amino acids. Food protein contributes to the so-called amino acid pool which is defined as the total free amino acids distributed throughout the body at any one time. This pool contains the 20 or so common amino acids found in food and body proteins and weighs about 250 grams. The pool is fed by the digestion of proteins in the digestive secretions themselves (60 to 260 grams per day) as well as protein from desquamated cells (about 90 grams) sloughed into the GI tract. In addition, each day some body protein is degraded or catabolized by intracellular, lysosomal digestion and these amino acids are contributed to the pool.

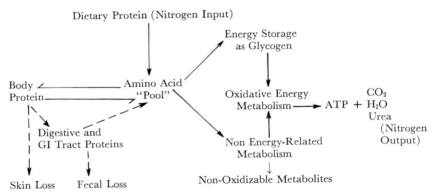

Fɪɢ. 11–4. Summary of amino acid and protein metabolism.

*Continual Need for Amino Acids.* All body constituents are maintained by a dynamic equilibrium which involves their continual synthesis and degradation or turnover. This balance of anabolism and catabolism and the associated maintenance of correct osmotic pressure, pH, temperature, etc. are all part of the condition termed "homeostasis" that characterizes all living things. Protein promotes and is itself maintained by homeostatic conditions. Such interdependence unites the body so that the body functions providing oral health are inseparable from those needed for total health.

As one criterion for the determination of dietary adequacy to maintain homeostasis, a balance study may be done. Nitrogen balance is used to measure the adequacy of protein nutrition by comparing nitrogen intake from food with nitrogen output as urinary urea. The usual situation for healthy adults eating adequate protein is a condition where nitrogen input and output are equal. For children, who are accumulating rather than merely maintaining existent body protein in dynamic equilibrium, the nitrogen input is greater than the output, and the balance is termed positive.

To meet requirements for new tissue synthesis in pregnancy, nitrogen balance is also positive as it is during recovery from any illness or injury associated with protein losses such as the fever of acute periodontitis or tissue loss from dental surgery.

For an individual to maintain nitrogen balance, a fixed quantity of protein is not necessarily involved in the dynamic equilibrium that maintains homeostasis. In fact, the body can adapt to a low protein intake and eventually drift into nitrogen balance, and it is very difficult to determine the point at which the adapted state becomes bad for health. Usually the intake low enough to produce negative nitrogen balance over a short time period is undesirable. The readily produced negative balance is undoubtedly due to the constant demands on the amino acid pool, not only for protein synthesis, but also for such purposes as glutamine for brain metabolism, maintenance of the urea cycle, synthesis of epinephrine, and formation of the amino sugars of ground substances as well as the nitrogen bases of DNA and RNA.

Also, amino acids are constantly being deaminated and transaminated and shunted into the energy pathways and thus lost from the pool. Although the functional requirement is primarily to maintain the possibility for continual protein synthesis, the constant caloric loss determines the minimal protein requirement. As the caloric intake is decreased amino acids will be used and body protein catabolized to meet the need. This is analogous to burning the furniture to keep the house warm. Moreover, if carbohydrate calories are limited, protein is catabolized to maintain an energy storage of glycogen even in starvation. As a corollary of this, it has been shown that recovery from protein loss, such as in wound healing, is dependent upon adequate caloric as well as protein intake. As discussed earlier, about 100 grams of carbohydrate in the daily diet has a protein catabolism-sparing action. It allows optimal dietary protein utilization from a low calorie diet.

A conclusion is that the amino acid pool is fairly small and easily depleted by the continual demands made upon it. It is generally stated that protein, *i.e.* amino acids, are like the water soluble vitamins and are not appreciably stored in the body.

*Simultaneous Amino Acid Needs.* The labile and small size of the amino acid pool is especially noteworthy because of the mechanism of protein synthesis. Each protein molecule has a unique amino acid sequence and its own relative proportions of amino acids. If each amino acid is not available almost simultaneously and in adequate amounts, the particular sequence of amino acids cannot be assembled on the RNA template at the ribosome and the protein is not synthesized. Since the cell will not normally synthesize incomplete protein, negative nitrogen balance can result if only one amino acid is limiting.

To assure adequate protein synthesis the pool must contain all the essential amino acids in adequate amounts. The most labile of amino acids may be lost from the pool and drop to a level that inhibits protein synthesis within a matter of hours. Enough total nitrogen from either essential or nonessential amino acids must be present to provide for the synthesis of nonessential amino acids.

### Provision of Adequate Protein

*Sources.* Because adequate protein nutrition is dictated by the continual and simultaneous need for maintaining a balanced amino acid pool and because of the lability and size of this pool, it is sound nutrition to distribute the RDA for protein in three protein-balanced meals per day. Inclusion of milk and meat food group items in each meal will accomplish this because of their balanced amino acid composition.

Recent evidence suggests that a balanced mixture of essential and non-essential amino acids is superior to the total nitrogen equivalent provided only by essential amino acids. Moreover, a natural balanced mixture of protein is superior to an equivalent mixture of amino acids. Thus, the presence of both high quality animal proteins and lower quality plant pro-teins as provided by the four food group guide has merit.

The lower the daily protein intake, the more critical it becomes to eat protein-balanced meals throughout the day. A person in nitrogen balance may go into a negative balance by eating his low ration of daily protein all at one meal. Nitrogen balance has been restored in such borderline situa-tions by adding as little as 6 grams of high quality protein, one egg, to one of the protein poor meals. Such is the delicate nature of protein nutrition.

About one-third of the RDA of protein should be provided by animal proteins to meet essential amino acid needs. Specifically, only about 20 grams of egg protein, which has the highest biological value of all food pro-tein, is required, whereas 24 grams of the major milk protein, casein, gives an equivalent of 5 to 7 grams of essential amino acids plus total nitrogen needs.

With plant proteins such as wheat and vegetable mixtures about 30 and 50 grams, respectively, will be required to meet essential amino acid and total nitrogen requirements. These quantities also represent the minimum requirements for maintaining nitrogen balance if no other proteins are ingested.

*General Needs.* Compared to minimum requirements for animal and plant protein diets, the RDA of 55 to 65 grams of proteins for adults appar-ently includes a large safety factor. However, even the ICNND guide (Table 11–3) which tends toward conservative allowances based on world needs where economy of expensive protein foods is a factor, suggests about 32 to 58 grams of protein from mixed food sources for a 65 kilogram standard man. Similarly, the World Health Organization (WHO) recommends 43 to 55 grams (0.66 to 0.84 grams per kilogram) of protein. The low values in these ranges would meet only minimal needs if the source was primarily from only one plant protein. Even U.S. Army emergency rations designed to meet survival needs for only 2 to 4 weeks specify a minimum allowance of 35 grams of protein per day.*

*Needs under Various Conditions.* On the basis of grams of protein per kilogram of desirable weight, the protein requirement, like that for calories, decreases from birth. The infant is allowed about 2.0 grams per kilogram of body weight. This value decreases to about 1.4 for prepubertal children prior to the sex-mediated growth differences occurring at age 10. Thereafter, even at the peak of adolescent growth and into adulthood, the allowance decreases to about 1.0, exclusive of reproductive demands. Actually, the progressive decrease with age is less dramatic than the figures indicate. Growth proceeds with the accumulation of an increasing percentage of body weight as skeleton and collagenous connective tissue in which protein metabolism is less active. Nevertheless, there is a progressive decrease in basal metabolic rate with age suggesting that the more vigorous cellular activities do slow. With a lower energy requirement, presumably, less protein would also be required. Lower RDA levels have not been suggested for protein intake by older persons because of the fundamental need for amino acids on a continual and simultaneous basis. The lability of the amino acid pool has been discussed and a depleted pool becomes a more serious health threat as one grows older and the circulation and other body functions decrease in efficiency. The progressive decrease in BMR itself implies decreased mobilization rates of antibodies, leukocytes and anti-infective processes as well as less efficient wound repair. To override such factors termed "conditioning factors" the RDA for protein has been maintained at the young adult level, which has the effect of providing a continually increasing allowance for protein. Even so, for old persons, an allowance of 2 grams per kilogram of weight is often suggested.

Negative nitrogen balance is almost always undesirable. However, under conditions of extreme fasting in very obese individuals hospitalized for weight reduction, negative nitrogen balance occurs as the excess musculature developed to support the overweight body is appropriately lost. For the average overweight individual, however, a weight control diet should be adequate in protein and high enough in calories to avoid negative nitrogen balance with its threat to health and normal performance. Even dissatisfaction with the caloric restriction itself should diminish if good protein nutrition is maintained. The four food group guide assures good protein nutrition along with a low calorie basal diet.

* A minimum requirement of 36 grams of protein is obtained if 3.2 mg of nitrogen per basal kilocalorie is taken as a minimum requirement. This nitrogen value is obtained from measurements of nitrogen losses per basal calorie as 2 mg in urea, 0.4 mg in feces and 0.8 mg as skin loss. The calculation for protein is then as follows: 3.2 mg nitrogen per basal kilocalorie $\times$ 1800 kilocalories $\times$ 6.25. The 1800 kilocalories represents the minimal requirement based on BMR measurements. The protein factor of 6.25 is based on an average of 16% of nitrogen in most proteins.

## Mineral Nutrition and Related Nonmineral Nutrients

Minerals accompany the gross constituents of foods. In the usual diet, metals and nonmetals usually balance each other to provide an excess of neutral ash when the diet is adequate in other respects. Excess minerals, if absorbed, are excreted primarily by the kidney and usually determine urinary pH. Sufficient sodium, potassium, chloride, and phosphate are retained to maintain normal pH, osmotic pressure, and membrane potentials for nerve and muscle excitability. Extracellular sodium and intracellular potassium are involved in the latter functions and seem to counterbalance each other in characteristic ratios maintained by normal hormonal and kidney function. Calcium and magnesium act similarly but in much lower concentrations.

Even in unbalanced or inadequate diets the only mineral elements of particular nutritional concern are calcium, iron, and iodine.

*Calcium.* Calcium is of great interest both metabolically and nutritionally. It is not only the nutrient for which the RDA is most difficult to establish, but one for which the present RDA levels are most difficult to achieve. Suggestions for daily calcium intake are described throughout the lifespan as follows:

|  | *Children* | *Adolescents* *(at Peak Growth)* | *Adults* |
|---|---|---|---|
| Calcium | 0.8 gm | 1.3 gm (girls) 1.4 gm (boys) | 0.8 gm |
| Milk (or equivalent) | 3 cups (0.9 gm) | 4 cups (1.2 gm) | 2 cups (0.6 gm) |

During pregnancy and lactation 0.4 and 0.5 grams of calcium are added respectively. The newborn infant is largely cartilaginous but contains 20 to 30 grams of calcium which must be obtained from the mother. This allowance is about three times greater than fetal needs, but it takes into account the inefficient absorption of calcium and the decreased efficiency with greater intake.

The dynamic state of calcium metabolism is described in Figure 11-5. In the diagram the net loss of endogenous body calcium is only about 320 mg which should be the daily requirement for maintaining calcium balance. In the typical adult where dietary and endogenous intestinal absorption are 40 and 75%, respectively, an 800 mg RDA provides 320 mg of calcium. During pubertal growth, where the skeletal accumulation of calcium may rise as high as 400 mg per day absorption efficiency is increased. Also, if calcium intake is decreased, the efficiency of absorption increases and calcium balance has been observed in adults with intakes of less than 300 mg. As

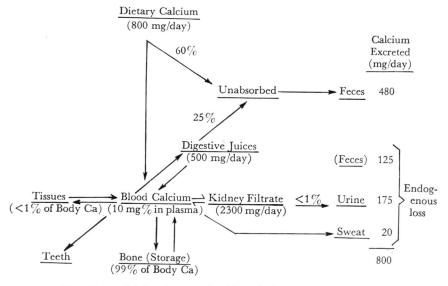

Fig. 11–5. Calcium homestasis with typical quantitative estimates.

with protein balance, it is impossible to state the point at which adaptation to low calcium intake is undesirable so the authorities differ about minimum requirements and RDA for different age groups.

In normal adults neither as little as 300 nor as much as 2000 mg of calcium is associated with demonstrable problems. Both national and international standards range from 400 to 1000 mg per day. The reasons for the caution reflected in the generous RDA values are the many known and unknown factors which inhibit calcium absoprtion. Dietary factors include excessive phytates in cereals and oxalates in green vegetables that form insoluble calcium salts. In fact some greens are so rich in oxalic acid that their calcium content is completely unavailable for absorption. Excessive phosphate also inhibits when the calcium to phosphate ratio is too low.

The many physiological factors involved in calcium metabolism also result in cautious estimates. Bone is continually reabsorbed and redeposited throughout adult life, especially in facilitating growth in the young. A study of the equilibrium indicates that there exists a constant threat of calcium loss via turnover of bone salt, the gastrointestinal secretions, primarily bile, saliva and pancreatic juice, and by urine and sweat. There are data indicating that in profuse sweating and even in severe tension calcium loss may increase to 1 gram a day: Obviously, calcium needs continue throughout life after the completion of bone and tooth growth.

*Milk Food Group.* The major dietary source of calcium in the United States is milk. Babies who are allergic to cow's milk must resort to other natural milks or simulated milks available as formulas containing the nutrient values of milk. A notable exception is that for infants the higher ratio of calcium to phosphorus found in human milk is favored and is reflected in the current RDA values. Adults, who do not care to drink milk, may obtain it from milks used in cooking, from cheeses, ice-cream, and other dairy foods.

Less rich but significant supplemental sources of calcium are greens, nuts, egg yolk, beans, and seafood, especially canned salmon. The eventual use of whole fish meal as human food is being seriously considered and would provide a good calcium source. Many of the virtues of milk may be reviewed within the context of calcium nutrition. Not only is the level of calcium high, but the calcium to phosphorus ratio is about ideal for their absorption and utilization together for bone formation. The fortification of milk with vitamin D is credited with the virtual elimination of rickets in this country. Vitamin D also facilitates calcium absorption and utilization. The high quality protein in milk contains the basic amino acids lysine and arginine which may enhance calcium absorption. The lactose of milk may also aid absorption. The relative importance and the mechanism of action of these milk factors are unknown but the preponderance of the evidence makes a strong case for milk as a calcium source.

Milk supplies calcium for the major task of bone formation, and for restoring mature bone lost in its function of maintaining a constant blood calcium level. Optimal protein metabolism and ascorbic acid is required to form a normal collagen matrix for calcification. Normal bone growth also depends upon the formation of the mucopolysaccharide, chondroitin sulfate, which requires adequate vitamin A. Moreover, adequate protein is required for absorption of either vitamin A or the carotenes, its plant precursors. Although notably lacking in ascorbic acid, milk is rich in both protein and vitamin A. The colostrum, the first milk produced, is especially rich in vitamin A, and human milk is several times richer than cows milk in vitamin A. This is especially important since the infant at birth is essentially deficient in vitamin A which does not cross the placental barrier.

The basis for eating protein frequently throughout the day has already been stated. Since calcium absorption is a major factor influencing calcium nutrition and since calcium like all nutrients must compete for absorption sites, it seems desirable to distribute milk, milk-containing foods or at least rich sources of protein and calcium throughout the day.

*Maintenance of Teeth and Bones.* It is intriguing that the teeth will calcify even when deficiencies in vitamin D or calcium are limiting bone formation or causing a net resorption of bone. Tooth formation occurs at a rapid rate and does not appear to be involved in the turnover equilibrium operative in bone. Therefore, teeth may retain within their structure a record of nutritional and other events which occurred during their formation. Someday we may be able to relate even short term nutritional deficiency that did not influence any other part of the body to effects on teeth. Dental caries does not appear to be increased by nutritional deficiencies common to man, since the least caries occurs in some of the most nutritionally deprived situations. Conversely caries is prevalent in the United States where gross undernutrition afflicts only a minority.

Fluoride is one nutrient that does influence tooth formation and subsequent susceptibility to caries. Recent findings suggest fluoride stabilizes bones against the osteoporosis manifested during aging and in the osteomalacia of pregnancy, possibly due to an excessive rate of bone resorption. It is probable that this bone loss is not replaced because adults tend to ingest insufficient calcium. Over many years the cumulative loss may become significant although on a daily basis there may be no detectable negative calcium balance. This explanation is more likely than systemic malfunction, because high calcium retention can occur in older persons provided with high calcium diets. While adults usually obtain sufficient vitamin D, maintenance of bone including alveolar bone so important in oral health is assured only with adequate calcium and protein nutrition and perhaps fluoride.

*Iron and Other "Trace" Nutrients.* In many respects iron metabolism presents the same nutritional problems as calcium. About 1 mg per day is lost by the adult man, but the RDA is set at 10 mg because iron absorption is only about 10% efficient. A larger RDA of 18 mg for the adult woman replaces iron lost through menstruation. An even greater allowance on a body weight basis is provided by the 15 to 18 mg RDA for adolescents where the actual iron growth requirement is estimated at 0.6 mg per day. Most of this is required for hemoglobin synthesis.

As with calcification, hemoglobin synthesis also depends upon a number of nutrients, and therefore a balanced diet. It is interesting that the roles of vitamins A, D, and C and the mechanism of calcification itself are poorly understood, while the mode of action of the nutrients in hemoglobin synthesis are fairly well known:

$$\text{glycine} + \text{succinyl coenzyme A} \xrightarrow{\text{pyridoxal-}PO_4} \longrightarrow \longrightarrow \xrightarrow[\text{(Cu)}]{\text{Fe}} \text{heme}$$

To assure synthesis of the heme portion of hemoglobin, two vitamins, pantothenic acid in coenzyme A and vitamin $B_6$ as pyridoxal phosphate, are required. A pyridoxine deficiency produces a microcytic anemia. Copper is required to incorporate iron into heme. Simple iron-deficiency anemia is frequent, especially during rapid growth. Red blood cells are synthesized at the estimated rate of 2.5 million per second to replace those lost due to their limited lifespan. Normally, most of the iron released from old cells is stored in bone marrow, spleen and liver in the iron-containing proteins ferritin and hemosiderin.

When iron stores are adequate, ferritin in the intestinal mucosa is saturated and iron is not absorbed. When needed, this protein transfers its iron to another ferritin in the blood for transport. The continual involvement of iron with protein suggests that in protein deficiency iron metabolism would be hindered.  Also, hemoglobin formation requires the globin or protein moiety as well as heme.  A frequent supply of iron and protein such as in meat food group items would assure efficient absorption and utilization of iron.

*Iodine.*  As discussed earlier iron is involved in cytochromes in all cellular oxidations.  Another trace nutrient, iodine, is also necessary for the proper rate of cellular oxidation.  Also like iron, its requirement is increased during puberty and pregnancy.  Just as the iron enrichment of bread-cereal food group items has alleviated some of the iron deficiency anemia, the fortification of table salt with iodine has lessened the simple goiter problem in the United States since it is due to iodine (thyroxine) deficiency.  The use of iodized salt by everyone is to be recommended as a prophylactic measure.  There is no problem of receiving excess iodine in this manner even if seafood, a good source of iodine, is eaten often and if local foods and water are rich in this element.  Persons on low salt diets may require iodine supplementation if they live in the so-called "goiter belt" in the central part of the United States.

## Considerations for Ideal Nutrition

*Ideal Eating.*  In summary, the ideal diet should contain three meals with each meal balanced on the following basis:

| *Appetite/* *Body Weight* *Control* | *Nutrients Not Stored* | *Nutrients* *Difficult* *to Absorb* |
|---|---|---|
| One-third of daily calories including fat and carbohydrate | One-third of daily protein including some animal protein.  Also continual and simultaneous need for balanced amino acid pool.  Water-soluble vitamins:  B-vitamins and ascorbic acid | One-third of all calcium and iron |

Not all meals can conveniently contain foods rich in all of the above nutrients nor will many persons eat three isocaloric meals; however, current nutritional knowledge indicates that such a plan is sound.  The satiety value of such eating will usually decrease between-meal appetite so that the frequency of snack eating may be reduced.  Between-meal eating usually produces three major problems by providing (1) undesirable excessive calories, (2) "empty calorie" foods that reduce appetite for meals especially in young children, and (3) highly cariogenic items.

Occasionally, suggestions are made that "nibbling," that is eating in small amounts continually, would solve many nutritional problems.  Besides the immense oral hygiene problem this would present, the probability of selecting or guiding people to select balanced diets in this manner seems very unlikely.

*Adaptation.* As previously stated, the body can adapt to low calcium and protein intakes and can achieve balance when output is not greater than input. This requires time, and the initiation of low intake levels results first in negative balances. At high intake levels excesses are excreted, but there may be some adaptation towards retention if high intakes are maintained. In the case of protein, the body can adapt to a higher maintenance level by developing greater muscle mass. Higher antibody levels may also result. On the other hand, to what extent do excesses unnecessarily overload body mechanisms?

Adaptation is essential to life. In fact, living organisms are first of all adaptive control systems. For each genetic and environmental situation there must be an ideal level for providing nutrition to facilitate adaptation. The question may well be, "adaptation for what?" For example, a higher muscle mass may be desirable for athletes but lower body weight may increase longevity. Animal husbandrymen can vary many characteristics of livestock by nutritional feeding procedures designed for particular objectives.

*Nutritional Goals.* RDA do not allow for tissue saturation with the vitamins since less than saturation supports apparent health. In the final analysis, balance studies or measurement of blood and urinary levels of nutrients must be correlated with the performance desired and this unfortunately must be tempered within the limitations of genetics, health status, and economics. Perhaps young persons wish most for optimal physical and psychological response, while older persons are concerned over longevity and response to illness. Fortunately, most aims do not seem mutually exclusive. Overnutrition or undernutrition are extremes to be avoided. These have to do more with the achievement of overall desirable health aims than the individual effects of each nutrient provided at an excess or deficient level. This means that for all recognized health aims there must be relative amounts of nutrients at which maximum adaptation can occur with a minimum of difficulty in maintaining homeostasis. *

From this discussion, it should be apparent that the prime function of optimal nutrition is to provide a maximum of freedom for the individual to express his genetic potential in response to environmental demands. Not only deficiencies, but excesses of nutrients also are threats to this freedom. If one meal or snack item is unbalanced either in quality or quantity of nutrients, the next food *may* or *may not* compensate but the body *must* compensate. The demand for some level of compensation to nutrition variables may offer a beneficial internal stimulus just as a variety of physical and mental experiences are stimulating. For example, fasting might have such stimulating benefits. This makes fine philosophy, but to date it seems that

* An analogy may be helpful. An ideal buffer is one that maintains the finest control of pH against both excess and deficiency of acid and is also of sufficient concentration never to be deficient—on the other hand, never so concentrated that it interferes with the system it is supposed to benefit.

the best adaptation requires the best nutrition—a continual supply of balanced food.

## MALNUTRITION

Present nutritional knowledge seems adequate for describing nutrient intake levels that will prevent gross nutritional deficiencies in populations. It is still inadequate to define the best body composition, body weight or functional levels of organs such as kidney, heart, liver and brain, etc. All these factors have been considered by nutritional scientists attempting to arrive at the compromise which determines the relative distribution or balance and the total quantity of nutrients of the meal. Within this context, having already defined the sources and functions of the more critical nutrients, the nature of malnutrition may be discussed.

### Overnutrition

*Patterns of Caloric Intake.* The major malnutritional problem in this country is probably excessive caloric intake. This includes not only too many calories, but also the habits of eating them. Also, the nature of carbohydrate and fat calories and their ratios may be important in determining if their intake is excessive. Trends in food consumption patterns during the past 50 to 60 years indicate a 10 to 20% decline in the percentage of calories supplied by carbohydrates. These are being replaced mostly by calories from fat and some protein. Fat calories may be most significant having increased from 25 to 30% up to 40 to 45%.

The following comparison by food experts of the caloric distribution in the average U. S. diet may be utilized to describe an ideal diet.

*Estimated Percentage of Calories*

| | Present | Recommended |
|---|---|---|
| Carbohydrate . . . . . . . | 47 | 50–60 |
| Fat . . . . . . . . . . | 41 | 30 |
| Protein . . . . . . . . . | 12 | 10–20 |

Surveys of dental students and hygienists at the University of Texas Dental Branch over the past 5 years suggest that the present data for the general U. S. population is true also for those in dental school.

The changes in diet have been qualitative as well. Less starch, 50% less potatoes and 60% less bread-cereal items, is eaten now, while the consumption of sugars and syrups has increased by 220% according to Department of Agriculture data. There has been about a 40% increase in unsaturated types of fat, largely vegetable oils. These qualitative changes were caused partly by food economics and partly by public preference for a host of sweets and fat-fried foods associated with convenience, availability, and taste. This is seen in the development of coffee-break snack habits and the replacement of adequate breakfast and lunch by sweet rolls, soft drinks, candy bars, french fried potatoes and pastries. These have been termed "pleasure foods" and are often empty calorie, highly unbalanced food items. Such eating habits often are associated with one overly-heavy evening meal. Alternatively, the convenience of satisfying appetite, but not nutritional needs, with such eating habits eliminates any semblance of meal-eating. Frequently the lack of a meal-eating pattern is directly related to the development of both overnutrition resulting in overweight or undernutrition leading to deficiency effects. Such unfortunate eating habits were less common at the turn of the century but are readily found today in the general population.

Recent surveys among students at the University of Texas Dental Branch indicate about 44% of the daily calories are eaten at evening meals and 9%, about 260 kilocalories, are eaten between meals. Sixty % of these between meal items were sugared soft drinks and pastries and 20% were candy and coffee with cream and/or sugar. These between meals items, based on a 2800 calorie diet, if in excess of caloric requirements, would cause a gain of about 1.5 pounds of fat per month.

Prior to age 22 the basal caloric requirement includes caloric requirements for growth. Thereafter only maintenance requirements are included in the BMR. Aside from the body surface area, sex and age which determine the BMR, estimates must be made for activity. Typically, activity slows at about the same time as growth ceases—at least in the U. S. population. However, the psychological aspect of hunger, the appetite, remains. (A similar situation occurs when the large energy demands of pregnancy and lactation are suddenly decreased at the time of partuition or weaning and the mother continues to maintain the same caloric intake.)

*Overweight.* Recent measurements of body composition indicate that with cessation of growth a progressive decline in the percentage of body muscle and bone begins. Accordingly, about age 22 the ideal adult body weight should be achieved and either maintained or decreased with age. Often the reverse is true and the spread between ideal and actual body weight increases. This results in "middle-aged spread." Many poor nutritional habits develop during teen age years and by the early twenties result in excessive body weight and associated health problems.

Ideal body weight is difficult to determine but to the extent that longevity is a goal then the population statistics favor the lean or slightly underweight. Life insurance companies in particular have found lower weights associated with longer life spans, and their actuarial tables indicate a 1% increase in death rate for every pound of body weight above these lean standards.

In recognition of the need to prevent excessive caloric intake and because average caloric expenditures are lower in our technological society, the 1958 RDA were decreased from 3200 and 2300 calories to 2800 and 2000 calories, respectively in the latest 1968 revision (Table 11-2).

Statistics also show that overweight persons are more susceptible to the health complications that are the main causes of death in our country. They are diabetes, hypertension, abnormal heart size, cerebral vascular accidents, and coronary artery disease or atherosclerosis. The blood vessel diseases are associated with increased tendencies for thrombosis and decreased fibrinolysis of those clots which do form. Although these diseases are emphasized in adults, they can also occur during the growing years. It should be mentioned that surgical complications are greater in the obese at any age. Burns, diarrhea, and other situations leading to dehydration are especially serious in obese children whose extracellular fluid volumes may be double that of lean children.

*Vascular Disease.* There has been an intense interest in the fat and cholesterol portion of the diet since atherosclerosis is associated with the deposition of cholesterol in the blood vessels. The elimination of high cholesterol foods such as egg yolks and organ meats is often recommended. To the degree that (poly) unsaturated oils replace saturated fat, cholesterolemia is lowered by the substitution of mostly saturated animal fats with plant oils.

Recently, sucrose, whose consumption has increased so dramatically during the past 50 to 60 years, has been associated with fat metabolism. The assumption had been that starches and sugars were nearly equivalent nutritional forms of carbohydrate. Now, it appears that sucrose is converted to fat much more rapidly than an equivalent amount of starch. Perhaps the greater solubility and minimal digestive action required causes a faster absorption rate. Fat formed from carbohydrate is saturated fat so not only is the free fatty acid level of the blood elevated by the rapid entry of sucrose, but also the ratio of saturated to unsaturated fatty acids is increased. Both of these increases in blood concentrations are associated with vascular diseases.

Much debate is possible and currently extant concerning dietary regimens for controlling weight and preventing atherosclerosis and other vascular problems. Atherosclerosis may be related to hormonal status, stress, smoking, race, and heredity and like dental caries is a multifactorial disease. One rational approach may be suggested by summarizing the major dietary excesses involved in many U. S. diets:

(1) Excessive caloric intake.
(2) Excessive fat intake.
(3) Excessive sucrose intake.
(4) High saturated : unsaturated fat intake.
(5) High cholesterol foods.

There is no mechanism to prevent absorption of excessive calories such as for iron and somewhat for calcium. Once absorbed, there is no mechanism for eliminating excess energy so it is stored as fat. The synthesis of cholesterol may represent such an elimination. Its synthesis requires a large amount of energy, and it is not catabolized in the body to release energy. When excessive calories are contributed by fat or sucrose which is quickly convertible to fat, the cholesterol level is often elevated. Normally cholesterol synthesis by the body is under feedback control and even depressed by cholesterol ingestion. The transport and metabolism of a surfeit of cholesterol or the control of its synthesis may both be more difficult under conditions where all energy pathways are flooded and the blood lipid level is high. Such conditions seem most likely whenever high levels of dietary fat and sucrose reinforce each other during any meal. Unknown factors, like stress from tension may also hamper circulation with a resultant increase in cholesterol accumulation, thrombus formation, or vascular disease. In this way the blood levels of saturated fats and cholesterol may act more as indicators rather than the cause of these health problems. Restricting saturated animal fats and food cholesterol seems warranted if the intake of fats and total calories is excessive either on a daily or a mealtime basis. On the other hand, it seems highly reasonable to suggest avoiding the overloading of the energy pathways with fats and sucrose and especially that total fat intake be reduced from the present high levels so that it represents only about 30% of the daily caloric intake.

*Conclusions for Ideal Caloric Intake.* The problems associated with energy malnutrition may be solved by using the standard suggestion of eating three balanced meals a day in order to satisfy appetite and cellular needs regularly. If the meals are planned according to the four food group guide, only about 15% of calories would be provided as fat. Each meal would contain ideally about one-third of the daily fat, carbohydrate, and protein. The tendency toward increased dietary protein has resulted in increased dietary fat. (A large portion of the increased fat intake in present diets exists as hidden fat in meat items.) This protein may be desirable provided the penalty is not an excessive fat intake. When the caloric nutrients are supplied by a balanced meal, not as empty calories or in overwhelming excesses, the probability of other nutrients being available for their proper utilization is increased. At least, the body is given an option for utilizing nutrients where needed rather than being forced to adapt to the stress of excessive calories alone. The fact that an overweight person gets hungry may indicate a time lag in the body control of energy metabolism during which it cannot adequately catabolize saturated fats.

The distribution of the daily fat and total caloric intake into three equivalent meals should aid in satisfying appetite without resorting to high calorie meals or to between meal eating. This should result in a more easily controlled caloric intake and therefore a lower body weight with a good possibility of reduction in the dietary factors promoting vascular disease.

Some of the calories may be used for protein synthesis which is most efficient when the mixture of amino acids consumed is balanced. When protein and calorie nutrition are optimal, the use of the ATP and proteins in calcification, erythropoesis, muscular work, kidney reabsorption and a host of other processes requires the other nutrients to be present. The quantities must be such that no system is either overwhelmed or deficient, but has the freedom to respond as best meets bodily needs. This response includes meeting nutritional needs such as the freedom to absorb calcium and iron without the competition imposed by excessive nutrients at any one meal.

No simpler more sound scheme for planning a balanced meal is available than the four food group guide. In light of the overnutrition and vascular disease problems, however, it would appear advisable to add the remaining 900 to 1200 kilocalories to the 1100 calories currently suggested in the guide by choosing more vegetable-fruit food group items and to avoid excesses of sweet and fatty foods.

The above plan for optimal nutrition would also tend to reduce between meal eating which is primal to oral health.

*Nutrient Excesses.* Excesses of water soluble vitamins are excreted as are the electrolytes and the nitrogen of amino acids. Fat is stored in the body, of course, and so are the fat-soluble vitamins. Vitamins A and D can accumulate to toxic levels. Poisoning can result from the over enthusiastic use of "therapeutic" pharmaceutical preparations which provide several times the RDA of these vitamins when used as directed. There is growing pressure for dispensing these preparations only on a prescription basis. Good nutrition is best assured by the use of good foods but if vitamins are supplemented, only those preparations providing maintenance dosages should be self-prescribed.

Excesses of calcium and iron can also occur since these elements are stored. Normally, an absorption barrier against excessive iron exists, but excessive use of pharmaceutical iron preparations has caused poisoning especially in children who have eaten candy-appearing coated iron tablets. Excessive calcium intake can produce ectopic calcification and calculi only when other etiological factors are present. The excess is usually excreted without event. The milk food group items play such a critical role in meeting nutritional needs that avoidance of the minimum suggestions made for milk consumption or concern over ingesting the RDA of calcium seems unwarranted except in unusual medical conditions.

There are, of course, many medical situations such as liver or kidney deficiencies where excesses of certain foods or nutrients should be avoided. The concern in many such cases would be better directed toward providing a sound dietary plan with counseling to assure that it is understood and followed rather than to single out specific foods as harmful because they contain a certain nutrient.

Food allergies cause a need to eliminate specific allergens but require appropriate provision made to maintain adequate nutrition. Milk, egg, wheat, fish, chocolate, nuts, strawberries, chicken, and pork are some of the common problem foods.

*Metabolite Excesses.*   Inborn errors of metabolism are being increasingly recognized.   When such exist, it is especially important not to overburden the enzyme deficient system with substrates it cannot metabolize.   Zeal here needs to be tempered also, however.   For example, the phenylketonuric infant should not be deprived of at least his minimal nutritional need for the essential amino acid phenylalanine.   Too much phenylalanine may cause mental deficiency in such individuals but so can the lack of adequate protein nutrition.

In deficient galactose metabolism, this sugar can be synthesized by the body and therefore can be eliminated from the diet if necessary.   These are mostly medical problems, but the dentist should be aware that some patients may be under dietary control because of allergies or metabolic deficiencies. The fact that a patient may be following dietary control measures should not inhibit inquiry into his nutrition, however, when his dental health shows any symptoms relating to nutritional causes.   Neither the physician nor the dentist should look at only one aspect of a patient's health and make suggestions (*e.g.* the elimination of milk or eggs from the diet) that ignore total nutritional needs having overall significance to systemic and oral health and to the conscious needs of the patient as a person.

## Undernutrition

*Deficiency Patterns.*   Undernutrition may be pictured as a series of levels of increasing nutritional deficiency of the tissues incurred at acute or chronic rates and accompanied by either specific or general symptoms (Table 11–7).

The reader can use this table along with medical, dental and dietary histories as an aid in assessing the nutritional status of patients.   For example, some acute deficiencies (*A*) may be expected to be reversed more quickly than chronic ones, (*B*) especially if the latter have become severe. The poor healing in case (C) may be the result of a developing chronic deficiency due to progressive loss of teeth and poor selection over many years and then suddenly appearing after an acute deprivation of nutrients due to influenza and high fever.   Case (D) could be the result of food deprivation due to multiple tooth extractions followed by chronic failure to obtain adequate good-fitting dentures.   Other cases may be drawn for nutritional changes associated with alcoholics, for those who have been on "fad" or "crash" diets and for those who have systemic ill health or psychological problems.

*Moderate-severe Deficiencies.*   The symptoms and confirmatory signs of nutritional deficiency are not specific.   Tissues have only a limited variety of possible responses and different nutrients or non-nutritional factors may cause the same effects.   It is important to recognize that tissues differ in their nutritional requirements and therefore in their susceptibility to deficiencies. For example, the tongue becomes painful and swollen early in a moderate-

**Table 11-7. Typical Patterns in Nutrient Deficiency**

| Nutritional Status | Patterns | | | | Associated Symptoms | Examples |
|---|---|---|---|---|---|---|
| | Acute | Chronic | Acute/Chronic | | | |
| Normal Tissue | | | | | Generalized (personality) defects | Irritable |
| Mild Deficiency | | | | | Biochemical changes ("lesions") | Decreased Hemoglobin |
| Moderate Deficiency | | | | | Improper physiological functions | Poor blood clotting |
| Severe Deficiency | | | | | Anatomical and physiological lesions | Glossitis |
| | A | B | C | D | | |

severe niacin deficiency yet thiamine deficiency is first indicated with neuritis effects in the lower limbs and probably never shows any typical effects in the tongue. There are many biochemical tests as well as physiological and anatomical observations used in determining nutritional status that are described in textbooks on clinical nutrition.

It is rare for the average dentist to encounter the classical symptoms such as the xerophthalmia of vitamin A deficiency, the stomatitis of pellagra, the angular cheilosis of ariboflavinosis, or the polyneuritis of beriberi, at least to the extent that he can classify them. It will suffice here to say that the dentist should develop skill at looking at the normal tissues with an eye toward detecting the abnormal. This is already being encouraged for detecting oral cancer. He can keep in mind that the head and neck region and especially the oral cavity are all prime areas for the manifestations of nutritional deficiency. He can be alert to the following effects:

stomatitis: generalized oral inflammation
glossitis: inflammation of the tongue (lingual swelling, papillary atrophy or hypertrophy, impaired taste, burning, pain, fissuring)
mucosa: pallor, reddening, ulceration
gingivae: hypertrophy, bleeding, secondary infection
salivation: xerostomia or ptyalism
cheilosis (cheilitis): inflammation of lips, secondary infection, especially at the angles of the mouth
osteoporosis: (not detectable even radiographically until about 25 to 30% of bone loss has occurred)
dermatitis: dry, itching, scaly, oily, secondary infection
eyes: dry, itching, reddened, secondary infection.

*Mild Deficiencies.* At the other end of the spectrum are the early, nearly subclinical mild symptoms familiar to every one. They resemble the effects produced when one has studied under nervous strain until late at night for several days. They were first used to describe early protein deficiency and may be classified as anorexia (loss of appetite), nervousness and fatigue. The general term neurasthenia best describes the condition. It is now generally agreed that most nutritional deficiencies first appear in this manner. Anorexia involves the gastrointestinal tract. The epithelial lining of this tract is replaced every 3 to 6 days so it has a very high nutrient demand. Two symptoms expected would be indigestion, due to lack of digestive enzymes and muscular tone for peristalsis, and abdominal discomfort followed perhaps by diarrhea. Poor appetite easily results in depressed growth and poor food selection habits. Infections are more common in the nutritionally deficient state and these often further inhibit proper food intake and compound the deficiency problem. Nervousness includes increased sensitivity to pain as well as paresthesia, headache, muscular pain, and psychic effects such as confusion, apprehension, depression, anxiety, and lack of concentration. Fatigue implies a generalized malaise or lassitude and weakness. The overall personality of such persons is affected and, as dental patients, they would be late for appointments, impatient with inconveniences, intolerant of dental procedures, difficult to accommodate, and disinterested in preventive programs including the nutritional guidance they need.

*Moderate Deficiencies.* In a moderate degree of deficiency, the problem of edema, especially prominent in protein and ascorbic acid deficiency, may make it difficult to fit dentures comfortably. A deficiency of either of these nutrients or niacin may make it difficult to prevent or cure gingival infection by periodontal therapy without treating the systemic deficiency also. Likewise, adequate wound-healing is especially dependent upon protein and ascorbic acid.

Prolonged inflammation and delayed wound healing may be the direct result of anoxia due to any of the nutritional anemias. Simple iron deficiency is most common in children, especially teen-agers, and during reproduction. It notably exhibits the generalized symptoms listed above, especially fatigue. Dental patients suffering from the forementioned moderate deficiencies and especially vitamin A deficiency would be expected to show high sensitivity to infection.

The blood-clotting phase of healing is inhibited by inadequate vitamin K. Vitamin K deficiency is not usually a problem except in the newborn where the intestinal flora are not yet developed for adequate synthesis of this vitamin. Because of the importance of intestinal synthesis of this vitamin and perhaps other vitamins, their lack may become critical in patients who have had extensive antibotic treatment or have suffered prolonged diarrhea sufficient to upset intestinal synthesis. Physicians may administer vitamins parenterally as a precaution when oral antibiotics are prescribed.

*Primary Deficiency.* Assuring the availability of an adequate diet is the first step in overcoming nutritional deficiency. The nutrients most likely to be lacking in the average diet have been tabulated as "critical nutrients" in Table 11–8 along with the factors that influence availability. Obviously, improper food selection may result in too little of any of these nutrients. Prejudices, idiosyncracies and, most often, ignorance of food values prevent proper selection. Selection is more difficult when there are few rich sources as with vitamins A and C and calcium. Selection is aided by specifically designating the vegetable-fruit and milk food groups as sources for these nutrients.

Enrichment also aids in the selection of quality foods. For example, diluted fruit juices such as grape juice enriched with ascorbic acid become valuable sources of this vitamin. In one study comparing breads from all over the world, white bread enriched with the three major B-vitamins and iron commonly sold in this country ranked very high nutritionally. More of

## Table 11–8. Availability of "Critical" Nutrients

*Factors Influencing Availability*†

| "Critical" Nutrient* | Per Cent Of U.S. Families Receiving <RDA | Primary Factors | | | | Secondary | Main Food Group Source‡ | Foods Commonly Fortified or Enriched |
| --- | --- | --- | --- | --- | --- | --- | --- | --- |
| | | Food Selection Habits | Limited Food Sources | Expense | Processing Loss | Problem of Absorption | | |
| Calcium | 30% | XX | XX | XX | | XX | DF | |
| Ascorbic Acid | 25% | XX | XX | X | XX | | VF | Fruit Drinks |
| Vitamin A | 20% | XX | X | X | | X | VF,DF,M | Margarine Milk |
| Thiamine | 10% | XX | | | X | | All four esp. M | (Flours, |
| Riboflavin | 10% | XX | | | | | All four esp. DF | Breads, Pastas, |
| Niacin | 10% | XX | | | | | All four esp. M | Cornmeal Cereals, |
| Iron | 10% | XX | | | | X | All except DF | Baby Foods) |
| Protein | 10% | XX | | XX | | | All except VF | Cereals Baby Foods |

* Critical nutrients are those that are most frequently unavailable in the average U.S. diet at recommended (RDA) levels.
† Number of X's indicates the probability of importance.
‡ DF = Dairy Foods (Milk Food Group); M = Meat Food Group; VF = Vegetable-Fruit Food Group.

such developments can be expected, *viz.* the baby food industry with formulas and cereals based directly on nutritional research. In addition to the nearly universal practice of fortifying milk with vitamin D, vitamin A fortification is also common. This provides an adequate supply of the vitamin to meet infant needs and modifies the large seasonal variations in the vitamin A content of milk. To compete with butter, margarine manufacturers have also added these vitamins to their product.

*Secondary Deficiency.* Conditioned malnutrition, due to secondary or conditioning factors originating with the patient, may result from failures *to ingest*, digest, absorb or utilize nutrients or factors that cause loss of nutrients. For these reasons, patients with acute or chronic infection or systemic diseases may also have nutritional problems. Fever, hyperthyroidism, drug treatments, and other stresses all may increase the turnover or destruction of nutrients and cause conditioned nutritional deficiency. Polyuria, diarrhea, excessive perspiration, loss of blood and exudate can also result in nutritional losses. Secondary malnutrition is more likely to occur than primary malnutrition in many dental patients, especially among older persons.

*Deficiency and Dentistry.* Preventing malnutrition, and specifically permitting proper food ingestion, is a prime biological purpose of dentistry. The ideal state of oral health allows for complete freedom in selecting foods for biting, mastication, and swallowing. Along with restorative work the patient needs guidance in choosing the foods necessary for good tissue tone, muscular strength, sensitive taste, and other physiological functions that make eating pleasurable. Without going the "second mile" to provide nutritional guidance, the primary value of oral rehabilitation may not be realized. Moreover, caries, gingival lesions, infections, and osteoporosis, all of which may involve nutritional considerations, can render useless even the finest of modern restorative therapy. Stomatitis may cause pain and discomfort with even the best dentures. Of practical interest are recent observations that protein supplements to denture patients decrease the amount of time required for additional appointments for adjustments by as much as one-half. Not only proteins but vitamins too may be associated with prosthetic patients. Patients select foods directly related to comfortable bite pressures, therefore firm foods such as salads and raw vegetables (high vitamin sources) are selected less often by denture wearers. This is true even for young, healthy individuals so the situation could be expected to worsen with age.

*Protein Deficiency.* In the United States the probability that diets will contain less than the RDA intake of protein is less likely than that they have insufficient calcium, ascorbic acid and vitamin A. However the protein requirement is so critical to dental health and so interrelated to the utilization of all other nutrients that special note should be made of the nature of protein deficiency beyond that already mentioned. Albumin, the most abundant plasma protein, contributes to the osmotic pressure of the blood and when its concentration is decreased by protein deficiency, water moves into the tissues. The resulting edema produces effects characteristic of the tissue. In the intestines, diarrhea results which enhances nutrient loss and compounds the deficient state; in the lungs this results in susceptibility to pneumonia; in the mouth inflammation of soft tissue is augmented due to decreased circulation caused by the edema and secondary infection then becomes a greater threat. In addition vitamin A transport is impaired in hypoproteinemia and since this vitamin is needed especially to prevent infection in mucosal linings, the resultant conditioned vitamin A deficiency further enhances the probability of infection and inflammation.

Moreover, the gamma globulin supplying antibodies will be limited by protein deficiency. Beyond this, it is known that infection increases the protein turnover and depletes the amino acid pool to a degree beyond that attributable to the lesion itself. In acute periodontal disease the total lesion size can be 6 square inches or greater and if accompanied by fever, many nutrients may be destroyed. For example, the ascorbic acid stores of the major endocrine glands may be depleted within hours. Protein depletion also causes vitamin loss in many cases, *viz.* the loss of riboflavin when flavoproteins are decreased.

In view of these critical roles for protein, periodontal patients, oral surgery candidates and those to be fitted with dentures, especially older persons, should be counseled prior to operative procedures involving blood loss or interference with food intake. They should be given appropriate food suggestions postoperatively to assure the best responses in decreasing inflammation and infection, while increasing blood clotting, wound healing, tissue metabolism, and underlying bone health. This also hastens a return to a normal diet. Acute needs can be readily provided by the commercially available liquid diets based on milk and fortified with ascorbic acid, iron, and other nutrients to make a balanced medium. However, once solid food is resumed most patients could profit in oral and general health from nutritional counseling in the four food group plan of eating which assures a high intake of complete proteins as well as other valuable nutrients.

## FURTHER APPLICATIONS OF NUTRITION TO DENTISTRY

### Caries Prevention

The simple plan that follows incorporates many general procedures that would apply in giving nutritional guidance for anyone.

*Etiological Factors.* Caries results when susceptible teeth are exposed to cariogenic diets. It is not currently feasible to decrease the population of cariogenic microorganisms significantly, but their effect of producing acid from fermentable carbohydrate can be reduced by eliminating these carbohydrates from the diet. Carbohydrate elimination is neither desirable nor possible on a long term basis. A youngster simply cannot "cut down on the carbohydrate" as is often suggested offhand and still meet energy demands— nor would this benefit him.

*Carbohydrate Factor.*  A number of studies, including the famous Vipeholm experiments by Gustafsson and co-workers in Sweden have indicated the quantity of sugar consumed per day is not the major factor.  As much as 300 grams of sugar added to liquids or 50 grams of sugar consumed in breads *at mealtime* did not appreciably affect caries.  Only two exposures between meals to smaller amounts of sweets, such as toffees or caramels, significantly increased caries.  Despite many variables  inherent in human caries studies and the resultant large experimental error, it was possible to show that four such exposures to sticky candy caused significantly more caries than two exposures.

Similarly, Weiss and Trithart in this country studied 783 children between 5 and 6½ years of age and found a correlation between frequency of exposure to sweet items between meals and DEF ratings (the number of teeth decayed, extracted, or filled due to caries).  As the number of exposures increased from zero to 1.75 to 4 or more, the DEF was 3.3, 5.9 and 9.8 respectively.

*Frequency.*  From these studies and others, it seems valid to conclude that one factor primarily needs to be controlled, namely, the *frequency of exposure* of the mouth to fermentable carbohydrates.  Since it is not feasible to control all such carbohydrate, it seems reasonable to allow it at mealtime only and advise that it be eaten at the table.  Perhaps a child would often prefer his candy or other sweets in place of the dessert being served.  He can then be instructed to practice immediate oral hygiene.

Similarly, the detrimental effects of sweet items in the lunch may be reduced by inclusion of a "detergent" food.  Even sufficient accessible water fountains in lunch rooms or near candy machines and the routine serving of water at the family table may be valuable in helping to remove oral residues of fermentable carbohydrates.

Oral hygiene, as usually practiced, is only partially effective even with guidance.  Some acid production can occur within minutes after sugar reaches areas of dental plaque so that oral hygiene can never be rapid enough to combat a high frequency of carbohydrates.  Also the average probability of practicing oral hygiene three times a day after meals is slight.  The patient should be counseled to plan non-cariogenic *meals* for times when routine brushing afterwards is impossible such as at lunchtime.  This seems simple enough but it is often overlooked.  As a practical compromise, such counseling can be made with full recognition that some meals must be cariogenic and that sometimes brushing will not be done.

*Retention.*  The Vipeholm studies showed that oral retention or stickiness was directly related to cariogenicity of carbohydrates.  Volker showed, on the basis of oral retention of reducing sugars, that in each of 3 items with the same amount of sugar, the effect of gum was retained twice as long as cake and a wafer was retained twice as long as gum. Obviously a less retentive sweet such as the cake would become more hazardous if consumed more frequently. Total cariogenicity of a food appears to be a function of both frequency and retention. Unfortunately, there is as yet no satisfactory ranking of foods based on their cariogenicity, and it seems impractical to attempt control of fermentable carbohydrate on only a partial basis. The best plan then is to eliminate all known and suspected carbohydrates from between meal eating whether they are highly retentive or not.

## Patient Counseling

Control of the frequency factor may be achieved in two ways. Ideally, the patient is counseled to avoid all between meal eating in favor of balanced meals. This will automatically limit frequency of exposures to fermentable carbohydrates. If this is impossible, the patient is instructed to replace all cariogenic between meal items with non-cariogenic foods.

*Initial Steps.* This approach, as does any nutritional guidance, demands knowledge of the patient's diet and eating habits. Inform the patient that eating habits may cause oral health problems and suggest the possibility that what he eats may have something to do with his oral health. Ask him to provide a complete and accurate 7-day record of his normal eating habits. It is best to give no dietary guidance at this time. He should understand that unless the record is pertinent to his normal habits, it would all be a waste of effort. The record is an educational experience in itself for the patient, and how well it is done informs the dentist of the patient's interest.

*Follow-up.* When the record is returned, the dentist can determine the general eating habits such as the presence of meals and frequency of eating. He may note all cariogenic items to educate the patient with regard to such items. The frequent occurrence of fermentable carbohydrate in meals shows the patient that these items, such as sugar on cereal, syrup on pancakes, sweet dessert items, chocolate milk, etc., often are unavoidable. One can then write the word "Brush" after each meal and also after each cariogenic between-meal exposure. The impracticality of such frequent brushing may lead him to conclude that he must either eliminate between meal eating or substitute noncariogenic items. It is usually desirable to make daily tallies, or even more impressively a weekly tally, of all between meal exposures to fermentable carbohydrates to introduce the discussion of the frequency factor.

If caries is even moderate, it is most likely that the frequency factor is involved, but this often is not apparent from the record. Careful questioning may bring out that gum is not listed, that candy is frequently or routinely kept in the house, that the children like sweets, etc. Often some omissions are due to the fact that the person did not consider the item a significant part of the diet so did not record it. Further questioning about certain exposures may also be necessary to find if, for example, the three cookies and soft drink listed as a snack were really eaten at one time or constituted two or even four exposures. Such questioning also allows emphasis of the frequency factor.

If the patient wishes to eliminate all between meal eating when he sees it as undesirable, it may be necessary to help him satisfy his caloric needs more efficiently at meal time. Additional milk and meat food group items may be useful because of their fat content. He may prefer, however, merely to transfer many of the cariogenic items into the mealtime, and this is the battle we are willing to lose in order to win the war against caries. The additional sugar at mealtime has not been shown to be a critical caries factor.

Although it is known that children may be weaned from their physiological desire for sweets, this may be undesirable. Mealtime exposures often fill this desire without between meal eating.

*Snack Lists.* Often single or multiple snacks throughout the day are part of the eating pattern and these cannot be successfully eliminated. In such cases the counselor should help the patient prepare an *individualized* snack list. This is more considerate, useful, and likely to succeed than handing out a pre-printed snack list.

Snack ideas may be obtained from the 7-day record which includes many of the patient's food preferences, if the patient considers the items suitable, is willing to buy them regularly, and keep them easily available. As a main principle, it should be at least as easy for the patient to use items from the snack list as to use cariogenic items. For a typical snack list see Table 11–9.

Table 11–9. Between Meal Snack Suggestions*

| Food Group | |
| --- | --- |
| Milk | milk (avoid sweetened drinks), buttermilk, cottage cheese, all cheeses, and cheese dip. |
| Meat | left-over meats (chicken, roast, etc.), peanuts, Vienna sausage, hard-boiled eggs, deviled eggs, bean dip, cold meats, assorted nuts, and smoked fish. |
| Vegetable-Fruit | carrot slices, raw cauliflowers, raw potatoes, green pepper, grapefruit, apple, tomato, salad, and orange. |
| Bread-Cereal | Buttered popcorn (avoid caramel). |
| Other | sugarless gum, dill pickle (avoid sweet), olives, artificially-sweetened soft drinks, unsweetened tea or coffee. |

* Many snack items may be combined.

Note that some of the items that could be eaten in sweet forms or with sweetened foods are qualified. Snack items need not necessarily be nutritionally important nor balanced foods. Caries patients commonly have adequate diets. Of course, if the diet is inadequate, the snack list can include foods to help meet nutritional needs. Milk is often a desirable between meal item in this respect. The inclusion of some items in the above list may be unpleasant to some persons, but the food prejudices of the counselor must not enter into his guidance.

*Technique.* Each counselor will ultimately develop his own technique. Diet is personal so that compliments on the good aspects of the patient's diet should not be overlooked. Suggestions are best given so as to lead a patient to an understanding rather than to administer rules, criticisms, and lectures.

There is evidence that dentists practicing personalized nutritional guidance and other preventive measures generally have the most successful practices. It could be that in this "computer age," the personal consideration is especially appreciated.

The guidance techniques given here for caries prevention would be generally the same for all dental patients except that different principles would be applied. Very similarly, periodontal patients would be counseled to include the frequency factor in terms of increasing the frequency with which he eats raw and chewy foods, especially from the vegetable-fruit food group. They, like caries patients, would be counseled to avoid between meal eating and, if not, to avoid retentive foods since periodontal disease as well as caries is alleviated by a clean mouth. For these patients, provision for adequate systemic nutrition should also be made. To achieve this, the dentist can confidently use the simple four food group guide. Suggestions based on careful observation of the 7-day dietary record can be made to bring at least the minimum number of servings from each food group into the diet. The suggestions should be specific, realistic and meaningful to the individual patient in terms of his likes, understanding, economic situation, food attitudes, and dietary habits. If desired, the dentist can analyze the nutrient content of the diet and compare the results with RDA and ICNND criteria. This procedure may be particularly needed when it is difficult to judge the diet by the four food group guide. Also, some patients may respond better to the counseling procedure when they are confronted with specific nutrient values.

## SELECTED REFERENCES

*Manual for Nutrition Surveys*, 2nd Ed., Inter-departmental Committee on Nutrition for National Defence, National Institute of Health, Bethesda, Md., U.S.G.P.O., Washington, D.C., 1963.

*Present Knowledge in Nutrition*, New York The Nutrition Foundation, Inc., 1967.

BEATON, G. H. and McHENRY, E. W. (Eds.): *Nutrition, a Comprehensive Treatment*, New York, Academic Press Inc., Vols. I and II, 1964, Vol. III, 1966.

212 · **DENTAL BIOCEHMISTRY**

CHURCH, C. F. and CHURCH, H. N.: *Food Values of Portions Commonly Used* (*Bowes and Church*) 9th Ed., Philadelphia, J. B. Lippincott Co., 1963.

NIZEL, A. E. (Ed.): *The Science of Nutrition and its Application to Clinical Dentistry*, 2nd Ed., Philadelphia, W. B. Saunders Co., 1966.

PIKE, R. L. and BROWN, M. L.: *Nutrition: An Integrated Approach*, New York, John Wiley & Sons, Inc., 1967.

WOHL, M. G. and GOODHART, R. S. (Eds): *Modern Nutrition in Health and Disease* (*Dietotherapy*), 4th Ed., Philadelphia, Lea & Febiger, 1968.

# Index